PLAYER'S GUIDE

Concept, Writing, Art Direction
Yuval Kordov

Art
Adrian Smith

Cartography
Ed Bourelle

Editing
Duane Wheatcroft

Graphic Design
Joe Millar

Layout
Kelly Thompson

Playtesting

Steven Allison, James Auton, Jennifur Auton, Christopher Batty, Troy Couch, Adam Cowen, Steven Cranford, Kevin Daggett, Steven Damon, Tim Daniels, Joel DeWall, Elizabeth Dwyer, Jason Furedy, Robert Garofalo, Theodore Greene, Scott Handley, Chris Hansen, Donald Hoyle, Bruno Kristensen, Mark Lawrence, Randy Lindsay, Michael Milligan, Henrik Noergaard, Andrew Nolen, Asger Normand, Wayne Pearson, Morten Pedersen, Anthony Perkins, Kristian Petersen, John Polack, Matthew Ruane, Eric Sack, Christa Savva, Buddy Simpson, James Sugrue, Allan Thomsen, Neil Van Duyne, Donald Wong, Myles Woods

Red Spire Press
www.redspirepress.com

Contents

List of Numbered Tables

Introduction

Dark Legacies is a gritty low-magic ruleset and campaign setting that is designed as a supplement to the d20 System core rules. As such, it requires the use of the Dungeons & Dragons® *Player's Handbook*, Third Edition, published by Wizards of the Coast. All Dark Legacies products utilize updated material from the v.3.5 revision. This book extends the d20 System by providing alternate rules for low-magic gaming and enough background material to get started on a Dark Legacies campaign. Wherever material in this book contradicts something found in the core rules, the rules in this book should take precedence, especially where magic is involved.

Setting Notes

Low-Magic Gaming

Magic is not as prevalent in Dark Legacies as it is in most fantasy settings. It is viewed by the general populace as the domain of demons, a position promoted by justifiably paranoid religious authorities. The mortal practice of magic, known as arcanism, is reviled due to its demonic origins and the dark alchemy required to invoke even simple spells, and is additionally limited by the slow proliferation of arcane knowledge throughout history.

Nearly all aspects of the game system have been affected in some way by the reduced power and frequency of magic. Though there is still a core spellcasting class – the arcanist – spells are oriented more toward ritual and non-combat effects, they take longer to cast, and spellcasting in general is extremely difficult. The spellcasting system has been modified so that skill checks are required every time a character wishes to cast a spell, with potentially catastrophic consequences in the event of a casting failure. A wide range of new spells is provided in the Magic chapter, along with guidelines for incorporating existing third party material into Dark Legacies. Magic items, categorized as demonic or holy items of power, are similarly rare. New feats and nonmagical equipment upgrades are provided so that characters can continue to be effective without relying on such items. Lastly, there is no concept of divine magic in Dark Legacies; instead, priests use a supernatural ability called the Voice to invoke miraculous effects.

Good and Evil

Alignments are not used in Dark Legacies, nor are there any rules, spells, or effects that are alignment-based or derived. Rather than relying on alignment as a moral compass, this campaign setting takes a mature and relative approach to dispositions, attitudes, and motivations. While some individuals, groups, or actions may seem "evil" on initial impression, there are no hard definitions or divisions along lines of alignment; rather there are an abundance of gray areas, some lighter or darker than others.

Welcome to Dark Legacies

From Pristine Eugenie Dupret
Master Librarian attending the Holy Mother
Office of the Under Matriarch
Nalterei, Sarlat

To: Servitor Librarian Silvie Lufesse

Re: Historical Primer

Let this document serve as official notice of your acceptance into the Beyella Divinity. Welcome servitor! Let it also serve as your necessary primer, describing the true world and how it has come to be, so that you may venture into it with the confidence and bearing befitting one of the Faithful. As a dedicated servant of the Under Matriarch and Deihass-On-Above, you have access to the wealth of knowledge that we maintain in the Divinity's historical archives, and by them this document. The text presented herein is sacrosanct, collected over centuries through information gathered by your predecessors, the confessions of enemies and traitors, and even from the lips of nonhuman insurgents who were compelled to reveal their heathen secrets.

This knowledge is our power, a means to control. You must control your parish through its careful dispensation, just as the Under Council controls you. Such is the proper way of things. For only through the knowledge of what has come before, can we hope to place our feet upon the righteous path Beyella set out for us.

Look around you, new servitor. Seek out your sisters, each a beacon of the Faith, a believer in Beyella's Dictates, and a vessel for the great knowledge held in the archives. Find comfort in the many righteous faces that surround you, for there will be few beyond our borders, and you will only find resistance and confrontation as you near the edges of the Earth where the black oceans separate the land from the Abyss and the ever-present Adversary, Azrae. Can you imagine them, child, the bleak storms that mark the edge of those waters and the beginning of her terrible plane? It sickens the heart to even contemplate the dark veil the demon goddess hides behind, but it also reminds us of our duty to keep the Abyss at bay lest it overwhelm the Earth once more.

Humanity may seem powerful today, but never assume we are invincible, for Azrae watches always. It was not so long ago that the Earth first fell into the skyless Abyss, taking with it, according to the fragmented legends and myths we have, a far more powerful human civilization that reached beyond the oceans. Billions of voices cried out in fear and despair before they were utterly silenced. And in that bleak, sulfurous plane did the remnants of humanity decline, descending into barbarism and madness. Our history begins thusly, with devastation. It is the responsibility of all Faithful to ensure it does not end in the same manner.

As our race fell, a new civilization rose up to usurp humanity's place on Earth. The assar – foul and haughty creatures all – dominated the land for untold years, their cities vast and sprawling, until a second cataclysm again changed the world. Once more all we have are legends, but they speak of a dark alliance between Azrae and the assar, which saw the latter prosper until they betrayed their vile goddess. A devastating war erupted between the assar and Azrae's demon legions that culminated with the Adversary's imprisonment in the core of the Earth, an act that shook its very firmament. Rivers were torn from their banks, mountains cracked and split and crashed into one another, forming new ranges. In this chaos of destruction, when the world finally seemed ready to shake it-

self apart, the sun suddenly returned. This was The Reversion: the lifting of the world halfway from the Abyss.

For their betrayal, the assar civilization was laid to waste in what is now the Deadlands. However, their original allegiance with the Adversary cannot be overlooked, nor their unwillingness to help humanity at its darkest hour. With their recent reappearance in the realms of humanity, the Beyella Divinity considers the assar old enemies rather than potential allies.

In the light of the new dawn, a figure emerged to greet the feral dregs of humanity. The First Priest, a paragon of order in a time of utter chaos, declared the Reversion was the doing of Deihass, his Lord and Commander, who wrought the miracle so that humanity could reclaim the world in His name. Our god had emerged. As the sun set on that first day, the Priest had his first converts to the Faith, and first dissidents. Those who resisted his teachings were destroyed, while those who followed were welcomed into a new ministry. The night also revealed that while the Earth did rise out of the Abyss, there were fewer stars left in the sky, and the moon was completely lost to us, leaving the night the color of pitch, and plagued by a surfeit of demons.

Even though suppressed, Azrae was not done with the Earth. Her demons continued to roam the world, more vicious and terrifying in the light of the new sun. The First Priest pledged to teach his followers the Voice, the Faith's most powerful force next to righteous conviction, with which they could battle demon and heretic alike. For Deihass's glory was the demonic host driven back to the fringes of the Abyss, and as the Priest's ministry spread, so too did fertility and abundance upon the land. Humanity's second age had begun.

As the fear of imminent destruction at Azrae's hand subsided, humanity once more built great cities and established nations, many of which still stand. The First Priest lived an extraordinarily long life, granted divine reprieve from death to build his ministry into the Church of Deihass: the first institution of human spirituality, and the betrayers of our Great Mother, Beyella. But even as humanity swelled, it had become clear that the world would never be as it once was. Demons still roamed the wilderness, forcing people to pile upon one another in overpopulated, heavily defended megacities. And humans discovered they were not alone upon the Earth.

Until our encounters with the novags, the small folk, we were ignorant of our nonhuman neighbors. They claimed to have suddenly washed ashore during the Reversion and brought news of other races that, it is assumed, also arrived on Earth in a similar manner. As they struggled to find their place on unfamiliar soil, the novags contended with these races: the savage briggs, whom they displaced in a brief and bloody territorial war; the hardy and suspicious dwerofs, entrenched in a vast and impenetrable nation beyond the Southwall; and further south, the arrogant and powerful eldrin who fully repelled the novag war machine. The novags attached a dire warning to this foe: treat them with suspicion and caution always, for the eldrin wield the vile power of demonry – what we now recognize as the abhorrent science of arcanism, which allows a mortal to harnesses demonic magic. The eldrin stole this knowledge from the dwerofs, who had themselves discovered it in a foul and ancient tomb in the bowels of the earth. The human ambassadors did not realize then that the novags were describing the stony prison of Azrae herself.

Only with humanity did the novags choose peace, feeling a sense of mutual respect for the tenacity with which each race had carved its place in the world, and due, no doubt, to a reluctance on the part of novags to enter into another war in light of their failed conquests against the dwerofs and eldrin. As humanity cautiously acquainted itself with its new neighbors, its own nations swelled and chafed against one another in the Corelands and the Eastern Ridge, surrounded by mountains, deserts, and death. Four territories made up the Corelands at that time: Ilfernac, Braile, Sarlat, and a northern region of small allied states. But where the civilizing hand of the Faith blessed and guided the Corelands, the godless city-states of the Eastern Ridge festered behind the protective walls of the Crimson Reach. To this day, the Ridge remains a safe haven for many of our enemies: heretics, arcanists, and demon-worshippers.

Still, the threat of renewed chaos lingered in the Corelands. The Synod, ruling body of the Church in Ilfernac, grew lax in its duties as it overextended itself, and its influence in the civilized nations waned. The namesake of our church, the blessed Beyella, was the first to speak out against this ambivalence. Initially, she was dismissed by the Church of Deihass as a petty dissident and given leave to do as she pleased, but her influence grew to surpass that of the Church's Synod, especially in the nation of Braile, and thus was born humanity's second religion. Our Beyella Divinity became a fertile institution of devotion to the Faith to replace an impotent predecessor. The Divinity thrived and its esteem was so great and threatening that war inevitably followed, forever changing the political landscape of the Corelands.

The Church of Deihass brought a violent reprisal against the ecclesiastic upstart. The Fist of Deihass, the Church's military branch, was originally tasked to combat Abyssal forces that resisted humanity's new dominance upon the Earth. What it became was a weapon against all enemies of the Synod. This blessed army was in turn pledged to the throne of Ilfernac, and The Fist waged war alongside legions of Ilfernac's soldiers, not only upon Beyella Divinity churches and lands, but on all nations beyond Ilfernac. Together, Church and state forged a great empire out of the Corelands during the Unification Wars, and in the three hundred years of concerted death and destruction that followed, the novag warnings of a threat from the south were completely forgotten.

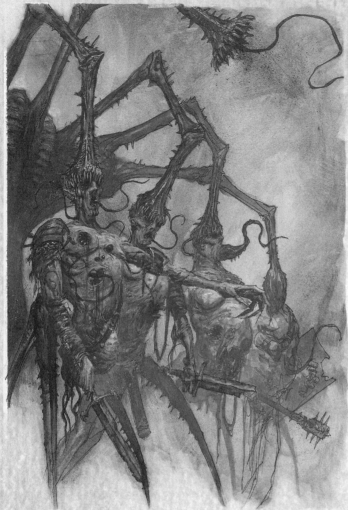

ness is hard to conceive of, but it is not uncommon amongst the Unbidden – those who reject the Faith. The mountains beneath the dwerof homeland quaked with the awesome and forbidding power, and the Abyssal storms on the horizon appeared to encroach upon Earth's shores once more. The Adversary was reborn and the world trembled as her legions gathered.

A great and terrible anxiety descended upon the Earth, though no one outside the borders of Illgoth could have known what had transpired. No one save the dwerofs. Hearing their imminent doom in the thunderous cracks of the mountain's stone, the entire race fled their homeland, knowing full well what had been unleashed. Miles-long convoys headed north to found a new nation. To reach their destination, the dwerofs were forced to skirt the border of Ilfernac, which set the Empire on alert for potential invasion. Massive armies were drafted and deployed to combat the perceived dwerof threat, but just as they prepared to engage the convoy, reports began to arrive of a substantial convergence of demons in Illgoth. Called to join the eldrin as allies against humanity, Azrae's demons instead turned on them. The eldrin had summoned their own executioners to their door. Black clouds choked the skies above Illgoth as the land was destroyed and its people murdered almost to the last. The Great War had begun.

Novdy Ottor, home of the novags, fell next. But rather than retreat like the dwerofs, the novag army fought long and hard so that their people could flee. Despite their best efforts, the majority of their race fell to the demon horde. However, not all the novags were lost as some managed a final retreat to the protection of human borders. On their heels came the army of Azrae, newly unleashed legions of demons upon chariots of fire, leading a half-breed army – hybrids born from an unholy union of demon and eldrin. The demons advanced from the south, moving both east and west, dividing the human army as they bypassed the Eastern Ridge for reasons that remain a mystery. Many cities fell to the horde and the churches of humanity destroyed many more to purify the land of heretics who pledged themselves to Azrae in the face of defeat.

At the Battle of Burnbridge, the combined military might of the Ilfernac Empire and the remnants of Novdy Ottor's armed forces met the horde head on. Our records put the size of the human army from one hundred thousand to one million soldiers and priests, bound together despite political and religious differences. The battle raged for days, scarring both land and soul – historical accounts speak of the foul atrocities of the horde, demons rending limbs from soldiers and biting the throats from priests so they might not use the Voice. But when the sun breached the horizon on the eighth day, it was humanity that stood victorious, though less than a thousand survived. Azrae's minions had been defeated and the Adversary herself was cast back into the Abyss. On your journeys, servitor, you

By the end of the Unification Wars, all human nations, save for the undesirable Eastern Ridge, were joined as the Ilfernac Empire. But the chaos of war further splintered the Church of Deihass despite Ilfernac's political triumphs. The Synod suffered a third and fourth schism. The first was in the form of Despinus Chapter: a heretical sect of delinquent priests altogether detached from proper worship, birthed amidst the Fifty Year Blight – a devastating pestilence that wiped out a third of mankind. To this day, priests of the Dark Church have yet to detach themselves from the foul association. The Church's fourth betrayal came at the hands of their very own Fist of Deihass. Emboldened by their conquest of the northern states, the Fist abandoned the Church and formed the reviled Prelacy of the Divine Adjudicator, claiming their new territory as Precaea.

In the centuries that followed, the hungry maw of the empire expanded further and further south, eventually violating the borders of Illgoth, the eldrin homeland. Incensed by the Empire's encroachment into their territory, the hateful eldrin set forth not only to repel the human invaders, but to wipe humanity entirely from the Earth. Their actions were as terrible as their ambitions, for a legion of eldrin arcanists combined their powers to summon forth Azrae herself, wrenching her out from her prison beneath Dwer Betha to do their bidding. Such mad-

will undoubtedly encounter the stains of that conflict: burnt-out cities, wide tracts of lifeless earth, even areas where strange magics seethe and flow upon the air.

However, the victory was tainted by scandal. The Supreme Emperor of the Ilfernac Empire, under the guard of an elite Prelacy war party, was killed while the entire escort escaped without injury. The facts of this event are still argued over by historians, but there is no doubt in our minds that it was a simple act of treachery by the arrogant, power-hungry Prelacy. Chaos reigned as the death of the emperor shook the very foundation of the Ilfernac Empire – each province made a claim for the throne as generations-old political and cultural loyalties resurfaced. The Great War was less than a year in the history books when the Kingdoms War erupted, pitting conflict-weary brothers and sisters against each other once more. By the time the dust settled, Ilfernac had regressed to much the same state it had been in before the Unification Wars, Braile had been absorbed into Sarlat, the Prelacy ruled in Precaea, and the Eastern Ridge remained lawless and oblivious. Stalemate came as each nation succumbed to exhaustion, their armies devastated, their resources depleted, and their populations on the brink of starvation. The Faith's divergent denominations isolated themselves behind these new borders, finally divorcing each from the other.

With the end of this most recent war came a wave of eldrin refugees from Illgoth, begging for sanctuary. Many were turned back and many more were slaughtered – as they should be for reviving the dread Adversary from her centuries of shackled slumber. However, some were forgiven their past wrongs and allowed entry, spirited into hiding by secret societies and guilds that recognized the eldrin's arcane legacy. The instability fostered by the Kingdoms War allowed arcanism to reach into the hearts of men and women with seductive promises of power and vitality. An unnatural longing grew in these human arcanists, a longing which holds sway even today, and they became insatiable, committing transgressions against decency and the tenets of the Faith to slake their thirst for more demonic knowledge. The very race that would have destroyed us now finds comfort in our cities, passing on their corruption so that we may destroy ourselves with it. Show them no mercy.

Before the governments of humanity could consider the repercussions of the eldrin arrival, a far more tangible threat arrived at their borders: the demon-eldrin hybrids. These remnants of Azrae's auxiliary legions emerged from the wastes and crept into the backwaters of human civilization. They were declared a second Blight: a new plague upon humanity, though they brought neither illness nor death, only fear. In an effort to wipe the pestilence from his lands, the arrogant Prelate Ascendant, high priest of The Prelacy of the Divine Adjudicator and enemy of the Divinity, initiated a Cleansing against both hybrid and heretic. It is perhaps fitting that priests of Despinus Chapter, bringers of the original Blight, were also targeted by this crusade. If you must feel pity for them, do so only because they suffered by the hand of our enemy, for these dark priests are just as culpable of corrupting the Faith as are agents of the Prelacy.

With the fervor of the Cleansing now faded and the threat of war absent for the time being, our denomination must finally turn our attention to the arcanist threat. Another dreadful abuse of the science might result in a rupture of the barrier between planes, offering Azrae an opportunity to devastate the Earth yet again. Compounding the possibility of a third coming, the assar have finally returned from their exile in the Burning Wastes, where they fled following the Reversion. Their presence serves as a reminder that Azrae is the true enemy of humanity, for who took up the mantle in humanity's absence? The assar. And even the vast libraries and truth-extracting techniques of the Beyella Divinity have not given us any insight into the extent of the dark secrets they carry, the arcane knowledge they have harbored since the fall of their kingdom, or the alliances in which they are willing to engage to return to their former glory.

Though she now lies behind the dark curtain of storms beyond the horizon, Azrae continues to exert her influence upon the Earth. Her demons prey upon us in the wilderness and wastelands, and arcansim spreads nearly unchecked through our cities. Be wary of the temptations of magic, child, and the exiles who brought it to our lands. Be wary of the unseen enemies who would see the Divinity fail. And be wary of your own sisters who would climb to power on the backs of fallen priestesses. But do not be so wary that you forget to spread the teachings of Beyella. Through this document and your training, you now know of our enemies and the temptations you will undoubtedly face as you journey through the world. An age of exploration is upon us as devastated lands, laden with precious secrets, are finally accessible. You must plunder these secrets before our enemies can – gain knowledge of the past so that we might use it to bolster our future. Knowledge is power. Never forget this.

May the Tenets of Beyella guide and protect you.

Transcribed by
Dilectate Fyona Galt
Red Spire Press
Nalterei, Sarlat

"It's all about perspective. Sure, you might say briggs hate novags, and I guess novags probably hate hybrids, and the eldrin… well, they hate everyone. But when you're running for your life through some god-forsaken ruin with a demon breathing down your neck, the neighbors suddenly don't seem so bad."

— Lucia, human mercenary

Humans number in the millions, crammed into sprawling megacities and diverse nations, divided by politics and religion. In the three thousand years since the Reversion lifted the Earth halfway out of the Abyss, they have repopulated the world. But humans are not alone – in that time they have been joined by alien races, most of these huddled within human borders. Only a handful of nonhuman nations linger, struggling to survive after Azrae's legions scoured the Earth during the Great War.

The origins of these alien races are a mystery. Of the fragmented legends that detail the state of the world prior to the Reversion, the most prevalent are those that claim that humans were Earth's sole children, spread out beyond the oceans before the sun fell, and before those oceans became a doorway to the Abyss. Conflicting treatises on the origins of species, now largely considered irrelevant and outdated, speculate on a gamut of possibilities. The most popular theory is that nonhumans were once in fact human, irrevocably changed by the chaos of the Reversion. Others argue that they were inhabitants of other worlds, transposed onto the Earth as it shifted out of the Abyss and through the ether. Even more controversial is the belief that all nonhumans are demons, citing the lack of tangible evidence for there being physical realms beyond the Earth and the Abyss. As it currently stands, the mystery continues to baffle the best minds of the age.

This chapter presents rules and information for all the races available for play in a DARK LEGACIES campaign. Where races similar to those in the *Player's Handbook* are presented, the rules presented herein supercede the core rules in their entirety.

Racial Ability Adjustments

Table 1-1: Racial Ability Adjustments lists the ability adjustments for each race and their favored class. Where more than one favored class is listed, choose only one; thereafter, that chosen class is the favored class for your character.

TABLE 1-1: RACIAL ABILITY ADJUSTMENTS

Race	Ability Adjustments	Favored Class
Human	None	Any
Assar	+2 Dexterity, +2 Charisma	Fighter
Brigg	+4 Strength, −2 Dexterity, −2 Intelligence, −2 Charisma	Barbarian
Dwerof	+2 Constitution, −2 Dexterity	Soldier
Eldrin	+2 Dexterity, +2 Intelligence, −2 Strength, −2 Constitution	Arcanist or Rogue
Hybrid	+2 Variable[1], −2 Wisdom	Barbarian or Rogue
Novag	+2 Constitution, −2 Strength	Fighter or Soldier

1 Hybrid characters receive a +2 racial bonus on an ability score of their choice, excluding Wisdom.

Race and Languages

Language selection for characters is limited as a result of the historical isolation of each of Earth's races from their neighbors, and in some case from their own culture. Human languages are the most prevalent within the Corelands, with Low Common – a bastardized derivative of many old human languages – being the standard trade language of all races wishing to get by in Earth's Corelands or bustling Eastern Ridge.

The native language for each race is given in Table 1-2: Languages. Human characters must select a regional language as their native language, specific to their region of birth or where they were raised. Regional human languages are given in Table 1-3: Human Regional Languages. Sarlat is unique in that it has two official languages: Sarlesse and Bralish. Sarlesse is the dominant language, native to the country since its founding, while Bralish was introduced during the Unification Wars, when droves of immigrants fled to Sarlat from the annexed nation of Braile on its northwestern border. When creating a character from Sarlat, choose only one available regional language as the character's native language.

Many races can speak a language but cannot read or write it; in these cases, the name of the partially known language is followed by a "spoken" descriptor. Complete fluency can be purchased with 1 skill point or acquired as a bonus language granted by a high Intelligence score. Other languages gained from Intelligence bonuses or purchased with skill points are fully researched and provide both spoken and written fluency. Languages not normally available to a character because of his race can be learned at character creation for double the normal skill point cost.

TABLE 1-2: LANGUAGES

Race	Native Language
Human	Varies by region
Assar	Assyric
Brigg	Briggan
Dwerof	Dwerkant
Eldrin	Eldraamik
Hybrid	Low Common
Novag	Novska

TABLE 1-3: HUMAN REGIONAL LANGUAGES

Region	Native Language
Ilfernac	Ilfernese
Precaea	Precaean
Sarlat	Sarlesse or Bralish
Eastern Ridge	Ilfernese or Low Common

Race and Age

The age categories for each race are given in Table 1-4: Aging Effects. Numbers given are in years. All effects of aging are as described in the *Player's Handbook*.

TABLE 1-4: AGING EFFECTS

Race	Adulthood	Middle Age[1]	Old[2]	Venerable[3]	Maximum Age
Human	15	35	53	70	100
Assar	60	165	250	320	500
Brigg	14	30	45	60	90
Dwerof	40	100	150	200	240
Eldrin	30	80	130	160	180
Hybrid	15	35	50	65	80
Novag	20	50	75	100	120

1 At middle age, −1 to Str, Dex, and Con; +1 to Int, Wis, and Cha.
2 At old age, −2 to Str, Dex, and Con; +1 to Int, Wis, and Cha.
3 At venerable age, −3 to Str, Dex, and Con; +1 to Int, Wis, and Cha.

Humans

"No one remembers when the demons came or why the sun fell from the sky. How could we, with nearly three thousand years past now since we took the Earth back? Did we bring it on ourselves? Most don't care and the rest pretend not to, but each time I kill another man, I feel those distant memories creep a little closer. Is history repeating? Will the sun fall again before the next millennium can rise?"

- Sergeant Gavidon Birrius, Red Sun Over Pelleton
(an infamous Precaean mercenary regiment)

Humans are the dominant and most populous species of Earth, having quickly risen from barbarism following the Reversion to reclaim their world. Despite endless conflict, from within and without, human nations endure where other civilizations have fallen. It was human armies that halted Azrae's hordes and it is human megacities that house the refugees of those fallen civilizations. Regardless of its achievements and a proclaimed superiority over nonhumans, however, humanity has failed as a unified race. Divergent from the outset, bound by force during the Unification Wars, then embattled again until the Kingdoms War exhausted them, humans chafe against one another over political and religious differences. Their conflicts are held at bay only by fragile ceasefires, half-hearted truces, and a common struggle against the rise of arcanism. This insidious threat, only recently beset upon the human domain, rises from the ashes of the burned eldrin homeland like a beast that cannot be killed, carried by chaotic winds into the heart of every human nation, and with each passing year casts its shadow farther.

Personality: Humans have the most diverse personalities of all the races of Earth. Whereas most of the other races can be defined by stereotypes that are more truth than prejudice, humans are unfailingly difficult to predict. What they do share is remarkable resilience, ingenuity, and adaptability, offset by a penchant for impulsive behavior and a tendency to forget the lessons of history.

Physical Description: The features of humans are as varied as their personalities. Countless skin tones, hair colors, and builds can be found among the urban and rural lands, especially within the melting pot of the Eastern Ridge. The solidification of nations within the Corelands, however, has resulted in visibly identifiable cultural backgrounds.

Ilfernese humans are often tall and fair-haired, with light skin and eyes, and strong cheek and jawbones. The humans of southern Ilfernac have a bronze skin tone and a stockier build than their northern neighbors. The features of Precaean humans vary from city to city, but most have a slight olive tone to their skin, thick dark hair, and strong noses. Sarlesse features are divided between people of native Sarlesse origin, those with Bralish backgrounds, and the descendants of mixed families. Pale skin, black hair, and slightly almond shaped eyes are trademark Sarlesse characteristics. Bralish humans are almost indistinguishable from Ilfernese humans.

Fashion also varies along geographic lines within the human domain. Nalterei, Sarlat – an affluent metropolis often considered the cultural capital of all the human nations – heavily influences fashion in the Corelands. In the Eastern Ridge, however, trends are as often drawn from savage cultures as they are from the west, and it is not uncommon to see its citizens sporting tattoos and piercings akin to their brigg neighbors in Ban Got.

Relations: Humans find fellowship with one another only so far as the reaches of their block, community, or country, depending on their individual disposition. A long history of cohabitation with novags has acclimated humans to the presence of other races, though the appearance of eldrin, hybrids, and assar following the Great War has fermented fresh anxiety in some quarters; an anxiety that is compounded by old prejudices. Among these xenophobic humans, other humans are viewed with greater favor while nonhumans are scorned.

Still, most humans look well upon novags, who have been steadfast neighbors and allies since the founding days of human civilization. Eldrin rarely receive respect even among tolerant humans, though they have yet to suffer the full brunt of human prejudice as hybrids have. Minimal interaction with dwerofs has produced little context between the two races, though Precaea presses for alliances with the dwerof nation to the west. Briggs are valued in the eastern lands as stalwart employees and companions, if not dedicated allies. And most look upon the mysterious assar with equal parts awe and suspicion, the latter fed by a nagging feeling that they played a more insidious role in ancient human history than is remembered.

Lands: The human domain is centered in the Corelands, a wide region that includes Ilfernac, Precaea, and Sarlat, which spans the majority of the continent's central geography, and the Eastern Ridge, which extends east into the Deadlands and south to abandoned dwerof, eldrin, and novag territories. Though large expanses of habitable wilderness exist throughout these regions, humans prefer the reassurance of dense urban living to small rural outposts. Since reclaiming the Earth, they have gathered together in large communities for mutual protection against the demons that roam the wilderness, no matter the impracticality of so many people living in such close quarters. Many of these communities are interdependent villages, towns, and cities, positioned in close proximity to one another. Others have grown into sprawling megacities that dot the land, where hundreds of thousands and sometimes more than a million humans – and now nonhumans – rub shoulders on overcrowded streets and residential complexes spilling over with filth, crime, and poverty.

Religion: Religion is a factor in most humans' lives and has been a major motivator of both progress and strife throughout history. Most nations have some measure of theocratic law, thus token piety – commonly measured by one's donations to the local church – is expected or required. But with the rise of arcanism and subsequent doubt regarding the existence of a divine authority beyond the facade of powerful religious institutions, humans in some quarters have come to scorn the priests that lord over them. In the Eastern Ridge in particular, where the influence of the Church of Deihass and its offshoots is marginal, humans are retreating from the religion that has guided and ruled them for the last three thousand years.

Language: The first years of human migration following the Reversion bore with them a mingling of cultures and languages, most of which were fragmented after an extended age of barbarism. The merger of these disparate peoples into nations, the influence of a domineering Church, and the rise of the Ilfernac Empire eventually eliminated all but a few of them, relegating the rest to obscurity and eventual death. What remained were the languages that exist to this day, each specific to a single country or in some cases carried by exiles of an annexed region into new territory. These regional languages continue to advance and propagate, largely due to the emergence of printing presses as a means to promote literacy and to spread propaganda.

Along with the entrenching of regional languages in the foundation years came the formation of Low Common, a conglomeration of these regional languages and also some that had long since passed into obscurity. Low Common has considerable roots in Ilfernese (which is sometimes called High Common), but many words are broken or misused. It also makes heavy use of slang, including numerous curses and colloquialisms borrowed from the briggs and novags. While most humans in the Corelands speak a proper regional language, Low Common has become a viable international trade language, favored by humans of the Eastern Ridge and nonhuman immigrants. It is rarely written, however, as it is less verbose than the languages from which it derives, and because the regions where it is exclusively spoken also tend to be heavily illiterate. Low Common is disdained by the upper class, by government, and by the clergy, all of which consider it to be a bastardized, diluted language, fit only for the lesser population.

Names: Humans have given names and family names, and sometimes also possess middle names or numerals denoting lineage. The origins of most human names have been lost to time, though many surnames are clearly derived from occupations, locations, or even events. Names taken from the Covenant – the core text of the Faith – and other religious texts are common, though they diverge in spelling and pronunciation from one country to another. The presence of nonhumans in some human quarters is also influential, and it is not uncommon to find humans with novag names or eldrin-inspired names where these alien cultures are given leave to thrive. Ilfernese names are common outside of Ilfernac, particularly in Precaea and Sarlat, which were both once provinces under the rule of the Ilfernac Empire prior to the Kingdoms War. Growing nationalism in the former provinces of the Empire has seen many of these names retained but altered along regional language lines. Where cultures blend in the Eastern Ridge, Ilfernese names are more common than any other, though again, subtle variations are commonplace.

Ilfernese Names

Ilfernese names tend to be short, with male first names and surnames ending in hard consonants while female names usually end with vowels, particularly "ine" and "a."

Male Names: Arn, Ferdrik, Korrad, Lucef, Torbir.

Female Names: Eline, Helle, Pia, Trine, Vola.
Family Names: Berngard, Grodner, Koft, Roner, Syben.

Precaean Names

Precaean names are short, to the point, and created to convey strength, whether male or female. They tend to have heavy pronunciations on the first syllable and a limited choice of suffix, usually "on," "or," and "us" for male names, and "a," "ine," and "ite" for female names. Most surnames end in "don" and "ius."

Male Names: Balthus, Egus, Nor, Pius, Volon.
Female Names: Coldine, Edrite, Lucia, Mera, Plourine.
Family Names: Divius, Glave, Illdon, Mirius, Serdon.

Sarlesse Names

Sarlesse names roll off the tongue as does the rest of the language. Most male names are short, ending in "an," "en," or "on", depending on whether the family's roots are old Ilfernese, Sarlesse, or Bralish, respectively. Female names are longer and prettier, often ending in "elle" or "ette." Sarlesse family names are many and varied, due to the integration of both Bralish and Sarlesse elements. They are often locative or descriptive, with "du" and "lu" meaning "of" and "the" respectively.

Male Names: Adren, Bastien, Egen, Oston, Rian.
Female Names: Adelle, Dielle, Miri, Plourette, Vinesse.
Family Names: Cede, Dutard, Gaveau, Lutrond, Regess.

Adventurers: Whether out of restlessness or courage, humans overwhelm other races with their willingness for adventure. Intrigue amongst human nations is rich, and the decimated regions beyond the Corelands, once feared and off limits, have become lucrative hunting grounds that inspire much bloodshed among competing parties. Governments and secret circles proposition adventurers to retrieve knowledge and artifacts from these realms in return for wealth and notoriety. Elsewhere, humans wage subtle wars for the blessing or coin of their church. And still others adventure for their own profit, journeying not only to the burned homelands of the eldrin and the novags, and the sealed cities of the dwerofs, but to the very edge of the Earth where the ancient taint of demonic passage still afflicts the land.

Favored Class: Any. Humans are the most adaptable race of all and have no racial predilection toward one class or another.

Human Racial Traits

+ **Medium:** As Medium creatures, humans have no special bonuses or penalties due to their size.
+ Human base land speed is 30 feet.
+ 1 extra feat at 1st level.
+ 4 extra skill points at 1st level and 1 extra skill point at each additional level.
+ Automatic Language: Varies by region. Bonus Languages: Any.

Assar

"These creatures are rats though they walk and talk… infesting my world, infesting my brain, infesting my sensibilities! I kill as many as I can before they can breed. And should one speak to me, I speak back pleasantly, as though I am also a rat, but truly I am a god. When I have taken what I want – for rats are imbeciles and will give it easily – and the talking rat turns to scurry away, I will strike it down as well, if only to punish it for speaking to me as though it was my equal."

- "Scourge of Man," notorious assar assassin

The assar are the fallen rulers of the world, displaced to its southern reaches when the Reversion destroyed their civilization and humanity reclaimed the Earth. They are the only non-human race that existed upon the Earth prior to that principal event, their origin unknown. Little as well is known of their greatest cities, which thrived during the dark times before the sun returned; their secrets are buried in the Deadlands under thousands of years of sand and silt and guarded by ancient demons. What remains of the race swelters in the heat of the Burning Wastes well south of the Corelands, patient during the wars and the growth of nations, only to return with the fall of Azrae. Assar emissaries walk human lands in increasing number, though no humans have been invited into assar lands. The number and motives of their race are a mystery, but each assar that walks the Corelands and the Eastern Ridge does so with the bearing of a ruler, spiteful of those who have usurped their place.

Personality: Assar are cool, arrogant, and possessed of a vicious wit suited to condescension. They view most everyone as inferiors, whom they manipulate to their advantage with a juggling act of patronizing civility and dismissive abruptness. Beneath this facade of calm control, however, lurks a homicidal rage that can erupt with frighteningly little provocation. Assar have a quick temper, and are as apt to react to adversity with a litany of articulate insults as they are with deadly violence. Despite these chaotic tendencies, most assar are capable of maintaining relationships, and can be satisfied indefinitely so long as a real or imagined position of authority is established to the satisfaction of their egos. In rare instances where they have eased their emotional blockade, some assar have been known to reveal uncharacteristic fatalism and a melancholy disregard for their own lives – qualities which, upon regaining composure, they uniformly reject as the reflected weakness of the ignorant observer's imagination.

Physical Description: Assar are the most exotic race on Earth. They stand 6 to 7 feet tall, with lithe figures possessed of all the grace of eldrin but none of the weakness. Their skin is impossibly smooth and free of any blemish, wrinkle, or defect that might serve as a physical hint of their age or experiences, and their faces are so sculpted as to appear to have been formed from a porcelain mold; cheekbones and jaws that are severe and chiseled, with a long stately nose, a dramatic brow ridge and small but perfectly curved lips. Almond shaped orbs appear more like inset gems than eyes and are devoid of pupils or irises; instead, they are solid, seemingly inorganic formations varying in tone from light yellow to dark red, which betray no hint of emotion. Assar prefer tight-fitting clothing that has been individually tailored to show off their physique, and they wear exotic perfumes crafted from rare flowers and spices unique to arid climes. Traditional assar jewelry consists of an intricate lattice of bone inset with precious metals and gems that is worn upon the head and through which they may thread their hair, and a severe diamond-shaped piercing which is fastened below the lips.

Relations: Assar display little of their trademark belittlement against their own kind. Instead, they greet one another with compliments, sweeping motions, and bows. This civil attitude is more about ritual than racial camaraderie however, as assar have no compunctions against killing one another when it benefits them. Despite their disdain for the "lesser races," they respect and recognize power. Thus, assar find humans – who they perceive as the current dominant species of the Corelands – to be the most palpable of these lesser races, though this measured respect rarely transcends into admiration and can easily regress into hateful jealousy. Most other races are dismissed as parasites that leech off of human civilization, particularly the dispossessed eldrin and novags. Briggs are disdained as wild animals and hybrids as little more than the offal of a breeding program gone wrong.

Lands: The Assar have survived in the deserts of the far south for three thousand years, based out of the city of Syrtris, which means "exile" in their language. Beyond the spires and highways of their home is an unwelcoming land of vast sprawl-

ing dunes, dry cracked soil, and rocky steppes, barely nourished by a pittance of underground tributaries and dying wells. Resources that once sustained them have been all but exhausted as the race rebuilt and reproduced following the Reversion, leaving few options other then a return to the Corelands, by force or diplomacy.

Religion: Assar are a fiercely devout people, though their devotion is centered upon themselves as potential gods rather than upon any one god or religion. Each assar is considered to have the potential to impose his will upon the world to such an extent that the memory of him – good or bad – will become history, thereby immortalizing him. Despite this, assar texts neither refute the presence of divine gods nor dismiss them as false powers. Both Deihass and Azrae are acknowledged, much to the curiosity of human priests, but they are known as betrayers rather than benefactors, with no solid distinction between the two. They are blamed equally for the Reversion, which is regarded by the assar as a curse rather than a boon as humanity views it, and for the fall of assar civilization. While no specific decree prohibits worship of these ambiguous powers, no assar in his right mind could conceive of worshiping anyone but himself.

Language: Assyric is the language of the assar – a whispery, impossibly articulate language that, when spoken, elicits shivers in any non-assar within earshot. The written language is just as complex, consisting of fluid characters and accents that combine in geometric patterns to form words and sentences. There are no languages like it in any other mortal culture. It does, however, bear a striking resemblance to demon cuneiform, so much so in fact that the two languages are thought by some to share the same Abyssal roots. The only other language spoken with frequency is Low Common; it is a savage language relative to Assyric, yet the assar manage to speak it with a grace that cannot be replicated by a human tongue. The trade language is valued as a means by which assar can get by in human lands without having to waste time learning multiple inferior human languages. Nonhuman languages are deemed worthless.

Names: Assar have a strict naming tradition, developed out of a belief that possessing another assar's true name grants power over that individual, and also that continuance of one's name assures a degree of immortality. They find the casual name-dropping of the lesser races more than a little discomfiting.

All assar are named at birth, but their name is kept a secret until their guardians consider them fit to possess and guard it. This single true name is unique, though it always contains portions of the true names of their guardians. Thus, when an assar names another, they create a vessel with which they pass on a portion of themselves. Thereafter, this name is shared reluctantly, usually only with mates and select confidants. Male names are distinguished by a prefix of "Xi" and female names with "Xa." All assar names end with "x." Assar maintain a descriptive title that they use to refer to themselves in place of their true name, and as a means to boast of their exploits with a simple introduction.

Assar are forbidden to name themselves; thus, an assar raised outside of his own culture or whose guardians are killed before they can reveal his true name lives a cursed life, never to propagate a portion of his own name, and thus damning his lineage to obscurity.

True Names: Xi Yen The Hela Dox, Xa Bel Azs Alne Fex.

Adventurers: Assar are driven by ego and ambition. They adventure to advance their skills and reputation, heedless of the bloodshed they leave in their wake. Assar rarely patronize causes or charities but when they do take on quests for the benefit of another, they do so with an eye to how it may also be of benefit to them. These adventures extend into all regions, however conflicted or foul, as the assar consider all of the Earth theirs by right and no territory off-limits.

Favored Class: Fighter. Assar are confident, cunning, and extremely lethal combatants who express their considerable egos with articulate, individualized fighting styles.

Other Classes: Assar generally prefer direct confrontation, but some delight in the cat and mouse game of the lurker. Assar that have exchanged their native homeland for the vast cities of the human nations often become rogues with a gift for assassination, applying their natural agility and cunning to the urban wilderness. Assar are too civilized to choose the life of a barbarian and too willful and independent to commit themselves to the life of a soldier. Assar approach arcanism with hesitance that betrays their normal self-confidence, but assar arcanists do exist. There are no priests among their race.

Assar Racial Traits

- +2 Dexterity, +2 Charisma: Assar are possessed of fluid bodies and personalities, both of which are capable of graceful feats of manipulation.
- Medium: As Medium creatures, assar have no special bonuses or penalties due to their size.
- Assar base land speed is 30 feet.
- Darksight: Assar can see perfectly in natural darkness, though they are still blinded by magical effects that cause unnatural darkness.
- Unreadable: The alien physiology of assar lends itself to concealing secrets or weakness that might otherwise be betrayed by subtle facial expressions or a glint in the eye. They receive a +2 racial bonus on Bluff checks and on level checks against Intimidation.
- Desert Survival: Assar receive a +2 racial bonus on Survival checks made in desert terrain due to their intimate familiarity with the unforgiving climes of the south.
- Adaptive Metabolism: Assar are largely unaffected by temperature variations. They do not suffer any ill effects from cold or heat exposure until the temperature becomes severe (below 0° F or above 110° F); at that point they need only make a Fortitude save every half hour rather than every 10 minutes. Extreme cold and heat affects them normally.
- True Name Vulnerability: When confronted in an aggressive manner by someone that has spoken their true name, assar suffer a −4 morale penalty to all attack rolls, saving throws, skill checks, and level checks against that aggressor.
- Automatic Language: Assyric. Bonus Language: Low Common.
- ECL +1: Assar are more powerful than the other races.

Briggs

"Briggs not dumb. Briggs know when evil is up and when to put an axe in it. Briggs just not bother with fancy talk and lying like little humans."

- Bregig Aft Treg ooft Frerek ooft Degek, warrior of Ban Got

Briggs are the brutes of the east; an insular race that subscribes to no church and scoffs at the arrogant pursuits of priests and arcanists. They have seen nations rise and fall and entire species displaced as a consequence of this arrogance, while their own people remained united. Despite this racial bond, a near constant struggle for survival throughout other races' wars has left its mark. Briggs suffer from a worsening deterioration of culture and quality of life in the hard mountains of the Crimson Reach and have long since fallen behind their human neighbors technologically and socially. Following in the footsteps of the very races they scorn, an increasing number of briggs leave their homeland each year to take residence in these human lands, assimilating themselves into human cultures while discarding their own heritage.

Personality: Life is hard for the briggs and always has been. They have suffered oppression and dislocation throughout their history on Earth and despite being deemed a simple people by most, are remarkably complex. Their behavior varies considerably depending on the present circumstances and company, switching rapidly from confrontational to passive. Status within tightly knit brigg communities traditionally revolves around ritual tests of physical strength, which leads to brutish and sometimes chaotic behavior, but this aggressive demeanor is often withheld in the company of outsiders. Rather, they are generally wary and standoffish, always judgmental, but they may quickly defer if they perceive someone as superior to them. Briggs are practical rather than impulsive, and will address the present needs even if it means demeaning themselves in the process. They are strong believers in gut feeling and rely on their inner wisdom to carry them through their lives. When an instinct calls for loyalty, it is given unselfishly – once an outsider has been accepted as a friend, they are accorded all the devotion and respect that would be given to a member of the brigg's own community.

Physical Description: Briggs are the largest of the common races, and tower over their neighbors in an intimidating mass of muscle, teeth, and tattoos. They typically stand 7 to 7 ½ feet tall and weigh as much as 600 pounds, with stout necks, barrel chests, and long muscular arms. There is no appreciable difference in size between males and females. Monstrously large mouths ringed with powerful teeth dominate brigg facial features; it gapes from their head in wicked contrast to small dark eyes and a flat nose. Briggs are a naturally hairy people but they typically shave their body hair down to the skin to better show off the traditional tattoos that they wear from adolescence; briggs without tattoos are considered outsiders – unfortunate youths that have been raised among the weaker races – and are shunned among their kind.

Relations: Briggs possess a strong and true racial loyalty that binds them together as one unified people, a relationship that diminishes only when a brigg leaves or has been cast out from brigg society. Outcasts are viewed with disdain, and traditionally receive less favor than even non-briggs do. Non-briggs are treated with equal suspicion regardless of race, with the exception of novags whom briggs actively dislike, and a soured alliance with the dwerofs many years ago has resulted in animosity between the two peoples. Briggs occasionally mingle with humans in the Eastern Ridge where they are welcomed as cheap swords and pack mules, but they find themselves limited by human prejudices and rarely ascend the ranks of human hierarchies.

Lands: The brigg race settled near the dwerofs for a time following the Reversion. But growing isolationism from their stoic neighbors and tension over inadequate resources pushed them out toward the southeastern seaboard, where they briefly made their homes. The novag migration followed not long after, forcing the briggs back to the southern tip of the Eastern Ridge, bloody and beaten, where they remain to this day in small numbers within scattered communities collectively known as Ban Got. Outside of their native territory, they are most often found in human cities on the east side of the Crimson Reach, and more rarely in the Corelands.

Religion: Briggs are a godless people whose beliefs extend no further than the physical world they stand upon. They are often critical of the human kingdoms, which they see as a single broken nation whose faith in too many churches has divided their race. This attitude and a general aversion to religion has left the brigg people bereft of welcome into any church. But it also makes them valuable mercenaries for those that desire completely impartial troops in religious conflicts.

Language: Briggan is the spoken language of the brigg people, and is a complicated, guttural affair of hard consonants and strongly pronounced vowels. Written Briggan uses the same alphabet and character set as the dwerofs' Dwerkant, though it makes use of only a third of the expansive dwerof vocabulary and the meanings of most of the characters have diverged over time. Despite the existence of a formalized written language, literacy levels are extremely low among the briggs. Most legends, moral lessons, and essential skills are passed down verbally through the generations. Though this has resulted in a rich tradition of storytelling that every brigg is privy to, apathy towards the written word, exacerbated by the daily struggle for survival, has resulted in cultural diffusion and the further deterioration of the brigg language.

Names: Brigg names consist of a short two-syllable given name followed by a descriptive name and a string of ancestral names that can span many generations of ancestors. Males and females share the same root names, which are differentiated only by their suffixes depending on sex; male names often end with "an," "ek," "ig," or "os," while female names often end with "at," "ef," "id," or "ot."

Male Names: Dagan, Fedrek, Gavig, Nanos.
Female Names: Dagat, Fedref, Gavid, Nanot.

Descriptive Names (translated): Aft Treg (Wise Son), Lags Iroot (Biting Wind), Oovot Giik (Mountain Hands).

Adventurers: Brigg adventurers are the most outgoing examples of their race. Rather than taking comfort among their own kind, they leave either by choice or after enduring some shame that has alienated them from the greater community. Many find work in the Eastern Ridge as physical laborers or hired muscle before moving on to the adventurer's guilds and beyond, into realms far beyond the scope of Ban Got.

Favored Class: Barbarian. Briggs are the least civilized of Earth's settled species, and favor brute strength and intimidation as the means to most ends.

Other Classes: Briggs that spend time among humans in the Eastern Ridge are often fighters, working as mercenaries or pack mules, while those with the wits and discipline to execute orders are recruited into local militias as soldiers. The more intelligent examples of the race are lurkers, specialized in the rocky terrain that surrounds Ban Got, where they are a bane to unwitting trespassers. Brigg rogues are rare due to impracticality of size and general ineptitude in matters of stealth, but some take a more blunt approach, operating as enforcers and thugs in crime circles. Briggs never take on the professions of priest or arcanist, due to their fundamental antipathy toward religion and magic.

Brigg Racial Traits

* +4 Strength, −2 Dexterity, −2 Intelligence, −2 Charisma: Briggs

are incredibly strong, but ponderous both physically and mentally, and slow to make friends.

* **Medium:** As Medium creatures, briggs have no special bonuses or penalties due to their size.
* Brigg base land speed is 30 feet.
* **Mighty Countenance:** Intimidate is a class skill for all briggs regardless of class, and they receive a +2 racial bonus on Intimidate checks and on level checks to resist intimidation.
* **Judge of Character:** Brigg's receive a +2 racial bonus on Sense Motive checks, due to their innate suspicion and an uncanny ability to see through lies.
* **Unshakable:** Briggs are especially resistant to the manipulation of priests, receiving a +4 racial bonus on saving throws against sermons.
* **Automatic Language:** Briggan (spoken).
  Bonus Languages: Low Common, Dwerkant, Novska.

Dwerofs

"They label us cowards, isolationists… they are blind to the terrors that lurk beyond the protective walls of Order and Community. We were forced into this place but no one can force us to associate with such idiots."

- Arseny-Arseny Volkoff,
Minister of External Affairs, Dwer Zotha

Dwerofs – often called "dwarfs" by their human neighbors – are a stubborn, steadfast people that have subsisted for countless generations on a policy of strict self-sufficiency, isolating themselves from all the other races of the Earth. While their neighbors suffered immensely in the Great War, the dwerof race escaped unscathed, uprooting their entire nation and retreating northwest as a horde of demons encroached on their borders. Though they survive in new lands, the dark shadow of the horde weighs heavily on the spirit of all dwerofs, and an imperceptible taint of chaos claws at the fabric of their society. As the dwerofs rebuild their nation, the Ministry of Preservation – their pseudo-religious governing body – struggles to maintain control over its citizens. Crimes committed against fellow dwerofs are on the rise and soldiers battle with arcanists in the streets.

Personality: Dwerofs are inundated with the tenets of dwerof community code and behavior from childhood. They are a reserved, dispassionate people, able to resist any manner of temptation that might distract them from the execution of their duties. Rewards are welcomed, but excessive ambition and unwarranted greed are discouraged. Though determined and intelligent, they are used to thinking within rigidly defined parameters and suffer considerable discomfort when forced to innovate outside of the norm. Conflicts are generally seen in black and white terms, and resolved according to the law, or by deeply ingrained morals in the absence of that law. Lawfulness, in general, is of paramount importance to dwerofs, and those that knowingly disrupt the accepted order of things are scorned. This set view and an upbringing rooted in steely nationalism leads dwerofs to a generally unfavorable view of outsiders and their selfish ambitions. Dwerofs that travel beyond the reach of their homeland take these values with them. While never fully transcending their dour nature, they prefer community to isolation and will seek out surrogates to their countrymen. Dwerofs are true to their word among these adopted companions, if not fully understanding, and do not hesitate when called to their defense.

Physical Description: Dwerofs are a broad and imposing race, with drab features that mirror the rock from which their first nation was carved. Despite an average height of only 4 to 4 ½ feet, their weight matches or exceeds that of humans, due to a wide girth, heavy bone structure, and dense muscles. They have an ashen, almost colorless skin tone, faded from centuries of seclusion underground, and pitch-black eyes that bulge in low-light conditions but shrink in bright light. Most dwerofs gray at an early age, their dark brown or black hair turning completely white by their middle years. Males traditionally maintain medium-length, square-trimmed beards and precisely cut hair, while females keep their hair short or pulled back. Dwerof fashion is reserved, centered on attire that is uniform and functional.

Relations: The institutionalized respect within dwerof culture, along with laws that promise severe punishment for harming a fellow dwerof, forges a majority population with strong racial solidarity, and a despised criminal minority that rebels against their own. Solidarity does not, however, extend beyond the walls of Dwer Zotha, as a history of isolation has left dwerofs with little basis on which to communicate with their neighbors. Eldrin are an old enemy, but so old that animosity is more of a formality among traditional elders than anything else. Relations with briggs are awkward due to an unceremonious parting between the two former allies in their middle history, when the dwerofs withdrew fully from the world and their neighbors. Dwerofs have a grudging respect for humans, particularly Prelacy-ruled Precaea, and acknowledge the engineering and military prowess of the novags, despite numerous small conflicts between the two peoples prior to the Great War. Their attitudes toward the other races are neutral, though the presence of hybrids has been known to make dwerofs exceedingly uncomfortable.

Lands: The nation of Dwer Zotha is the new home of the dwerof people, forged after their flight from the old halls of Dwer Betha. The old country is simultaneously revered and feared by dwerofs, and unspoken consent dictates that no dwerof shall ever return there. Dwer Zotha is a rigidly structured community where the greater good commands a higher priority over personal freedoms, and unquestioning loyalty to the state is required. Chief Ministers of the Ministry of Preservation serve as political leaders and direct the construction and expansion efforts of the young nation. All citizens are equals under the banner of the hammer. Dwerofs that leave the fortified gates of Dwer Zotha do so with the knowledge that they will not be welcomed back.

Religion: All dwerofs in Dwer Zotha pledge allegiance to the Ministry of Preservation, the sole spiritual authority of the dwerof people and an ancient bastion of order. Chiefs of the Ministry possess both spiritual and political authority as heads of state. Dwerofs who walk the adventurer's path sometimes pay homage to the churches of their human neighbors, particularly the Prelacy of the Divine Adjudicator, whose religious ideals so closely matches the tenets of their own Ministry, but cases of actual dwerof participation in human churches are extremely rare. To convert as such is to forsake all dwerof tradition and upbringing, and to invite the harsh punishments for defection that are instilled in every dwerof heart by their ministers.

Language: All dwerofs speak Dwerkant, an ancient language that has remained constant throughout their history. Spoken Dwerkant is a short, blunt language characterized by throaty exclamations. The written version is extremely complex and consists of an alphabet plus thousands of unique characters that are penned from right to left. Rarely, dwerofs learn the languages of their new neighbors and even then, usually only Low Common. The only other standard language archived in dwerof libraries is that of the eldrin: Eldraamik. Though conflict between the two races is now merely an artifact of his-

tory, fluency has been maintained by librarians for generations should the need for it ever arise again. Countless volumes of dwerof lore exist, detailing the work and stories behind the construction of their great cities, the events of their history on the Earth, and the heroics of those that tamed their former and current lands. Particularly sensitive works are closely guarded by the Ministry, whose vaults contain everything from scrolls that outline the formation of their institution to dark tomes of demon cuneiform that betray the dwerofs' arcane legacy.

Names: Dwerofs are given a "bestowed name" at birth, which they use along with their family name until they reach adulthood. As part of their Dokh Vod Oor – a coming of age ceremony that is endorsed and recorded by the government – they choose an "earned name". They may choose the same name as was given by their parents or a completely new one. Regardless, both names are retained as a double first name; their family name remains unaltered. Being unnamed – ejected from dwerof society before earning a second name – is synonymous with being a criminal, thus most renegade dwerofs change their names after being ejected. Doing so allows them to avoid shame and confrontation when encountering another dwerof on the outside, but it also brings with it a punishment of summary execution should the falsity of their name be revealed.

Male Names: Arseny, Brepa, Dalsh, Moskal, Veldmin.

Female Names: Aggad, Magyana, Nagada, Pusha, Yelene.

Family Names: Dobokof, Givny, Kourdef, Pitrin, Volkoff.

Adventurers: Dwerof adventurers typically come in two interconnected varieties: undesirables that have committed some crime, real or imagined, against the state; and those that pursue them when mere exile is insufficient punishment. As a result, the extremes of dwerof society are often found within human lands and devoted parties of soldiers are as likely to be encountered as manic, power hungry arcanists and their ilk. Dwerofs that leave voluntarily, with no intention of returning, inevitably make a name for themselves in the outside world, where they spend the rest of their days traveling to distant realms rather than resettling.

Favored Class: Soldier. Dwerof society is strict and militant, requiring all citizens to serve a term in the military upon reaching adulthood.

Other Classes: Many dwerof heroes are fighters that excel in individual combat and pave the way for expansion and the glory of the state. Lurkers are outsiders that feel restless within the confines of the urban realm, and are tasked with scouting and defense beyond the fringes of civilization. Dwerof barbarians are virtually unheard of, though tales do exist of exiles that turn to savagery after living alone for years outside the embrace of the greater community. Rogues are uncommon in dwerof society and individuals that repeatedly break the law are forced into exile, where they take up their old habits in human lands. A legacy of magical misuse has resulted in exceptionally few arcanists, and those that do practice either do so under heavy supervision from the Ministry, or take to the outside world in search of unfettered power. Though the Ministry has religious overtones, no actual dwerof priests exist within their own culture, and subsequently few feel compelled to join the alien churches of humanity.

Dwerof Racial Traits

- **+2 Constitution, −2 Dexterity:** Dwerofs are exceedingly tough and hardy but are short-limbed and encumbered by their own girth.
- **Medium:** As Medium creatures, dwerofs have no special bonuses or penalties due to their size.
- **Dwerof base land speed is 20 feet.** However, dwerofs can move at this speed even when wearing medium or heavy armor or when carrying a medium or heavy load.
- **Deepsight:** Dwerofs can see in the dark up to 60 feet. Deepsight is black and white only, but it is otherwise like normal sight, and dwerofs can function normally with no light at all.
- **Weapon Familiarity:** Dwerofs may treat the dwerof maul (see page 70) as a martial weapon rather than an exotic weapon.
- **Stability:** Dwerofs can hold their ground to a phenomenal degree in the face of opposition. When standing firmly on the ground, they receive a +4 bonus on ability checks made to resist being bull rushed and tripped.
- **Rigid Discipline:** Dwerofs are barraged from childhood with the virtues of discipline, the rewards of hard work, and the punishments for succumbing to temptation. They receive a +2 racial bonus on Concentration and Profession checks and a +2 racial bonus on Will saves.
- **Rigid Thinking:** Dwerofs are masters of deciphering arcane script but have difficulty directing the chaos of a spell's demonic energy. They receive a +2 racial bonus on Decipher Script checks and on Spellcraft checks to decipher and learn spells, but suffer a −2 racial penalty on Spellcraft checks to cast spells.
- **Isolationism:** Dwerofs struggle with the social intricacies and etiquette of cultures outside of their own, receiving a −2 racial penalty on all Charisma-based skill checks when dealing with non-dwerofs.
- **Automatic Languages:** Dwerkant. Bonus Languages: Briggan, Low Common, Eldraamik.

Eldrin

"The megacities suit us, whether we admit it or not, what with the anonymous throngs of people, the obscuring fog of the coal foundries, and entire neighborhoods abandoned to an overflow of shit and disease. What better place to hide from our people's own wretched, dying stench than in the everyday stench of humanity."

- Antaeri Lidius, eldrin thief-for-hire

The eldrin are a race on the verge of extinction. Where an entire civilization once prospered in the dark woods of Illgoth, a scant few now remain, scattered across human lands after the ruin of the Great War. Compounding their misery is a general lack of sympathy from the other races, for the knowledge that it was the eldrin who began that war by unleashing Azrae and her demon horde upon the world in an orgy of unchecked arcanism. This legacy gnaws at the heels of all eldrin, and even those without arcane proficiency are indiscriminately pursued by dark societies hungry for power. Most keep to the shadows, watching silently as their arrogant brethren guide human apprentices in the very science that destroyed their homeland and murdered its population.

Personality: Most eldrin are sullen, seething, and bitter, suffering from the shameful legacy of the Great War and subsequent exile from their own land. When motivated enough to surmount their racial slump, eldrin do so with a cold and mercenary attitude. Rather than acclimate socially to their new lot in human lands, most lead solitary lives or work with as few people as possible to facilitate self-serving goals rather than forming real relationships based on common cause. Even those that do manage marginal social bonds are reticent and protective of their weak egos.

Physical Description: Eldrin have features that are comely but frail, bordering at times on sickly. They are slim and slight of build, ranging in height from 5 to almost 6 feet and weighing between 80 and 150 pounds. Their delicate body shape lends an androgynous look to the race, though females have a slightly smaller and more curvaceous figure than their male counterparts. Straight, almost colorless blond hair crowns an angular head and pointed ears, but elsewhere their chalky white skin is completely hairless. Eldrin have almond-shaped eyes with deep red irises that vary in shade and intensity from one eldrin to another. They prefer bulky clothing that obscures their features from the casual glances of passersby, and rarely venture out in plain sight without the security of a hood or heavy jacket.

Relations: Eldrin are prone to vicious hypocrisy when dealing with their kin: eldrin that seek acceptance among humankind are viewed poorly by other eldrin, yet these same critics rarely care for the welfare of any eldrin other than themselves. Their only vestige of racial unity is based upon the transgressions of the eldrin peoples' former enemies, which they are loath to forget despite the greater tragedies forged by their own hand; it is in these small hatreds that their last threads of cultural identity are found. Previous wars with the dwerofs compounded by the dwerof retreat during the Great War burns in the hearts of eldrin and affairs between the two are rarely congenial. Likewise, skirmishes with the novags during Novdy Ottor's days of conquest taints relations, though the mutual loss of their homelands has tempered this animosity. Some eldrin maintain a traditionally low opinion of humans while others begrudge them some respect now that human lands are also eldrin lands. Hybrids are considered an outright abomination and an ugly reminder of the past. A lack of historical interaction with the assar and briggs leaves eldrin with no context on which to base their opinions of these two races, a fact that unnerves them when encounters are inevitable.

Lands: The native eldrin homeland of Illgoth is a burnt waste, haunted by demons and miserable creatures touched by the chaos of the Great War. Most of today's eldrin resign themselves to a life in human cities, particularly in the western nation of Ilfernac and the Eastern Ridge, while others cling to the periphery of Illgoth amongst the dead woods. Regardless of where they make their homes, most eldrin live secluded lives and the race as a whole is on the decline. Any hopes of restoring the eldrin homeland have long been lost, and it has for all intents and purposes been abandoned to its new dark lords.

Religion: The eldrin forsook religion long before the Great War, throwing out the divine in favor of personal transcendence achieved through study of magic. No eldrin church exists and any material evidence of such an institution has long been buried under the ruins of Illgoth along with the remains of its faithful. Exposure to human religion however, and a loss of touch with their own culture inspires some eldrin to take on priestly mantles, particularly within the Church of Deihass, which will take any convert it can, and within the self-serving ranks of Despinus Chapter. These deviant eldrin are viewed with abhorrence by the rest of their race, and in taking on this new lot, divorce themselves completely from the last remnants of their eldrin heritage.

Language: The old eldrin tongue of Eldraamik is a fluid affair characterized by double vowels and consonants, supported by a dying script. While all eldrin retain spoken fluency, the written word has fallen into obscurity due to the almost complete assimilation of their kind into human culture. Ironically, it is humans that have helped sustain the language, mostly in arcanist circles that spend considerable resources and lives recovering eldrin treatises on magic and demonic scrolls from Illgoth. Almost all other eldrin texts – literature, historical manuscripts, and official records – were lost or destroyed over the course of the Great War, as Illgoth was occupied and then sacked by demons; what has so far been found of these is horded by those same shadowy circles, no matter how mundane their content.

Names: True eldrin names have been on the decline ever since the remnants of the race settled out of Illgoth. Eldrin family names are extinct. A rare number, usually those raised by a traditional parent, possess an eldrin first name. Most others have eldrin names that have been diluted with human nuances or entirely human names suited to their region.

Male Names: Daeger, Jaanik, Pillax, Qorus, Xerso.
Female Names: Armalla, Illia, Melleion, Raasla, Yaeleth.

Adventurers: Eldrin adventurers are as often driven by base survival as they are by a need to find meaning in their lives, something they are unable to do as new members of a human

society to which they will never truly belong. Some keep to urban locales and take employment as mercenaries valued for their superior agility and loose conscience, while others are compelled to explore lands beyond the human realm, where no eldrin has tread before. Particularly ambitious eldrin use their races' magical legacy as a bargaining chip to acquire power in arcanist cabals and secret guilds.

Favored Class: Arcanist or Rogue (choose one). Eldrin have a natural affinity for magic, something that wiser eldrin recognize as a curse rather than a boon. Eldrin rogues are numerous, having long since become accustomed to living in the shadow of human civilization.

Other Classes: Lurkers are far more common than fighters among the eldrin, as few among them can manage the physical hardship of constant melee combat, and the shadows of the wilderness suits them. Eldrin are not trusted by any human nation to serve as soldiers in their armies, though some find their way into regimented mercenary companies. Barbarians are rare and typify those individuals that remain in the periphery of the ruined eldrin homeland, never having managed to acclimate to a new homeland. A small but growing number of eldrin become priests in human churches, choosing to devote themselves to an alien but available god rather than clinging to their own decimated culture.

Eldrin Racial Traits

- +2 Dexterity, +2 Intelligence, –2 Strength, –2 Constitution: Eldrin have sharp reflexes and minds, but a weak bloodline leaves them comparatively frail for their size.
- Medium: As Medium creatures, eldrin have no special bonuses or penalties due to their size.
- Eldrin base speed is 30 feet.
- Low-light Vision: Eldrin can see twice as far as a human in starlight, torchlight, and similar conditions of poor illumination. They retain the ability to distinguish color and detail under these conditions.
- Hypersensitivity: Eldrin receive a +2 racial bonus to Listen, Search, and Spot checks, due to extremely sensitive ears and eyes. But this same sensitivity makes them especially susceptible to external effects or spells that cause deafness or blindness, for which they suffer a –2 racial penalty to saving throws.
- Antisocial: Eldrin prefer to blend in with the crowd. They receive a +2 racial bonus on Disguise and Hide checks, but suffer a –2 racial penalty on Diplomacy and Gather Information checks.
- Abyssal Savior, Abyssal Damnation: The dark power that empowers eldrin also damns them. They receive a +2 bonus on Spellcraft checks, and the result rolled for each die of nonlethal casting strain is reduced by 1 (minimum 1 point of damage per d4). However, each time they cast a spell, eldrin accrue 2 points of taint instead of 1.
- Automatic Languages: Eldraamik (spoken), Low Common. Bonus Languages: Eldraamik (written), Novska.

Hybrids

"Come. Let me give you what you want: a little taste of the Abyss, without the guilt."

- Dierdrix, hybrid prostitute

"Hybrid" is just one name for this cursed race, which was born of the breeding of demons with eldrin prior to the onset of the Great War. They are also called "demonkin," "the never blessed," "misbegotten," or simply "scum." Few of the names they are called are flattering, and even fewer are welcoming; hybrids have no place to call home, and no lot in the world they have been thrust upon. Originally created as an indentured workforce and as soldiers of the horde, they served the will of Azrae until the close of the Great War, whereupon they fled from the blackened land of their birth and from the picket lines of the broken demon armies. Though the war is long over, their flight continues; a legacy of death pursues the unnatural hybrids, who are a material reminder of war, strife, and the proximity of demons to the mortal realm. Fanatical religious elements, antagonized by this window into the past, led an all out inquisition – the "Cleansing" – against them after the Kingdoms War. By its end, almost all hybrids that had escaped to the eastern Corelands had been hunted down and killed, along with their "coconspirators" and associates. Persecution against their kind has settled down in the years since, though they are ever wary. The few that survive today eek out a living in the underbelly of society, where they wallow in the wake of hatred and persecution.

Personality: Hybrids are constantly witnessed to the worst aspects of society and of themselves, becoming hardened and selfish in the bowels of the world. Survival and discretion are necessary factors in staying alive, leaving little opportunity or desire for extended social interaction. When they do interact, they are noncommittal – promiscuity, gambling, crime, and adventure provide brief reprieves from their life of misery. When a hybrid succumbs to passion, it is often excessive and always transitory, discarded with the next flight from persecution or late night in an underground brothel. A companion that has managed the company of a hybrid for an extended period is betrayed as easily as someone who has known them for only an hour, and a treasure trove is squandered on an evening of decadence without remorse. Hybrids recognize the fact that there is no place for them outside of the slums and back alleys, nor will there ever be, so see little need to carry forth such baggage into the next day.

Physical Description: Each hybrid is unique, subject to a random collection of physical attributes derived from his mixed heritage. The eldrin component of a hybrid's heritage is apparent in their body size and shape – which is usually eldrin or human-sized – and often within some aspect of their facial features, or hair and eye color. The demonic elements are exotic, whether they are subtle, such as metallic skin color or especially long fingers; or blatant, such as horns, a forked tongue or a tail; regardless, it is clear to most onlookers that hybrids are not natural creatures. What all hybrids have in common is a considerable presence – those that are attractive are especially so, possessed of an alluring, fiendish beauty that many find irresistible, and those that are grotesque elicit all the repulsion of their demonic forebears. The demonic bloodline of a hybrid is pervasive: all offspring of hybrids are also hybrids, regardless of the race of the other parent.

Relations: Hybrids are as unpredictable regarding racial unity as they are with most aspects of their disposition – a fact that is compounded by a lack of uniform origin or appearance within the hybrid race. Though they are likely to find greater acceptance among their own kind, more hybrids also means more competition when scavenging and more attention from zealous enemies of the misbegotten. Likewise, an inconsistent atmosphere of prejudice outside of their own kind leaves hybrids with few preferences for the company of one race over another, and necessitates careful consideration before exposing themselves in any region.

Lands: When the hybrids escaped their bondage from the demon horde, some returned to the fringes of Illgoth but most fled to the Corelands and the Eastern Ridge, taking refuge in the dark corners of human civilization. The Cleansing pushed them back out – east and south – following the Kingdoms War, and it is in the Eastern Ridge where most now take refuge. They can be found there in the underground, sewers, and back alleys of most cities. Those that remain in the Corelands keep to the megacitiy slums, where they can hide indefinitely amidst an unwanted mass of bodies.

Religion: Hybrids are frequently termed the "Never Blessed", a name they earn for the demonic taint that alienates them from Deihass and therefore the Faith. They find no comfort in hallowed halls and can never partake in the blessings of priesthood. While hybrids are almost exclusively nonreligious, some resort to worship of Azrae – the only patron available to them – for spiritual nourishment. These hybrids find a home in the many and varied demon cults that plague mankind, as clergy to chaos or as charismatic cult leaders.

Language: As refugees with no land or culture of their own, hybrids speak whatever language is appropriate to their immediate surroundings. Eldraamik and

Abyssal were once native but no longer. Their native tongue today is Low Common, which serves them well within the human domain where they linger. Other languages are frequently learned as a necessity of survival, particularly human regional languages.

Names: Hybrid names are as different from one another as are hybrid features. Most hybrids are named or choose their names based on specific circumstances, such as who raised them or where they grew up. Hybrids frequently change their names as they struggle to find their place in the world; some choose human or eldrin names, others claim the names of demons of legend, and many choose names that are based entirely on a physical feature or nickname, such as "Six Fingers" or "Scales." Few hybrids bother with any sort of family name that links them to their vulgar heritage.

Adventurers: Hybrids often adventure out of necessity, keeping one step ahead of those that would persecute them. They are rarely driven by greater ideals, preferring to satisfy base desires and needs, though some travel out of genuine wanderlust. These latter hybrids are fiercely independent and capable, strengthened by the considerable adversity of traveling within regions hostile to their race.

Favored Class: Barbarian or Rogue (choose one). The widespread persecution suffered by most hybrids either drives them to the outreaches of the world, where they persevere through ferocity, or to the urban underground, where they must survive by stealth or criminal means.

Other Classes: Hybrids often apply themselves as fighters if they can manage the mercenary lifestyle, or lurkers if they can find no sanctuary among stone, iron, or people. Even in those regions of the Eastern Ridge where hybrids can mingle with the populace without fear of extreme prejudice, their racial stigma bars them from entry into armies or militias as soldiers. Despite the common belief that hybrids are an inherently corrupt, magic-using race, they cannot command magic naturally as their demonic progenitors do and poor access to resourses and contacts leaves few willing or able to take up arcanism. That same demonic ancestry curses hybrids to a life devoid of the favor of any church, thus they can never become priests.

Hybrid Racial Traits

- +2 Strength, Dexterity, Constitution, Intelligence, or Charisma (choose one); –2 Wisdom: Hybrids vary wildly from one to the next, the only commonality being a penchant for rash and capricious behavior.
- Medium: As Medium creatures, hybrids have no special bonuses or penalties due to their size.
- Hybrid base land speed is 30 feet.
- Limited Darksight: Hybrids can see perfectly in natural darkness up to 60 feet, though they are still blinded by magical effects that cause unnatural darkness.
- Survivor: Hybrids are adept at surviving in the darkest, least-hospitable corners of the world. They receive a +2 racial bonus on Hide, Move Silently, and Survival checks, and can use the Survival skill in urban areas to scrounge for food and shelter.
- Scavenger: Hybrids are able to make the best use of other people's waste. They receive a +2 racial bonus on Craft (armorsmithing) checks to assemble piecemeal armor and suffer only a –2 penalty to attack rolls (rather than the standard –4) when using an improvised weapon that is similar to a proper weapon with which the hybrid is proficient.
- Face of Azrae: Hybrids are immune to demon fear and spells with demon-based fear effects such as *abyssal window* and *demonic visage*, as they see a reflection of themselves in the face of all demons.
- Mark of Azrae: Hybrids are viewed with suspicion or outright hostility in most lands. As such, the Difficulty Class for all Charisma-based skill checks, excluding Intimidation, is increased by 4. This modifier can be reduced at the GM's discretion in locales less hostile to hybrids, such as the slums of the Eastern Ridge.
- Poverty: Hybrids enter an unwelcoming world with little resources of their own. They multiply their starting gold dice by 2 instead of 10.
- Automatic Languages: Low Common. Bonus Languages: Any.

Novags

"The first thing a novag did when our race washed aground on this world was blow some poor bastard's brains out. Nothing personal mind you, it's just our way…"

- Doldek Gattlig, weapons dealer

Novags are a militant, technologically focused race that washed aground on Earth's southeastern seaboard during the Reversion, their massive battle fleet stranded upon a shore they would never leave. They are a race of warriors, masters of combat and military engineering, with little interest in magic or religion. Throughout their bloody history on Earth they have waged war against dwerofs, eldrin, and the briggs, displacing the latter from the rolling hills that would become their doomed homeland, before it in turn was destroyed by Azrae's hordes in a brutal, protracted battle. Only with humans have novags had a lasting peace, and it is amongst humans that they now live. It is largely due to the novag race that human civilization has come as far as it has. Their technical expertise can be seen in the construction of every human megacity, and the trail of bones that leads back to Novdy Ottor serves as a reminder of how many novags fell in battle against the demon armies before any human entered the Great War.

Personality: Novags have a gruff, somewhat bleak outlook on life, punctuated by rigid military tradition and little patience for cowardice or subterfuge. This impatience extends to most aspects of a novag's personality, thus they are rarely prone to procrastination – when a goal is set, it is worked at until completed to a high standard. Though fiercely independent, they recognize and respect the need for rules and will work within them when possible to meet their ends. A novag's word can be trusted, and when it is given, a novag will break it only under the most serious circumstances. Novag restlessness can lead them to bouts of depressive boredom when they go unchallenged physically or intellectually for too long, thus conflict is welcomed. They are most content when obstacles can be overcome by way of battle. Novags are quick to display their consummate bravery, throwing themselves into combat whenever the situation demands it, and often when it does not.

Physical Description: Novags stand 3 ½ to 4 feet tall and weigh 60 to 100 pounds. Though they can sometimes stand as tall as shorter dwerofs, their proportions and girth are similar to humans. Despite their deceivingly wiry frames, novags are naturally muscular and fit, and have strong, heavy bones. Most males have thick, ragged hair or shaved heads and finely trimmed and styled sideburns; females generally keep their hair short and functional. Their skin is a dusky pink and their eyes are dark and large. Novags enjoy the security of armor and almost always wear at least a rudimentary plate of steel or reinforced leather upon their bodies; among their own people, those that do not wear armor are mocked for "walking naked."

Relations: Prior to the Great War and the razing of their homeland, novags were unified as a people. That unity has suffered due to the lack of focus upon one novag nation. Swollen Novdytowns – novag communities that have existed within the cities of the Corelands since the early trade days – succumb to the inevitable discord of overpopulation and take up arms against one another on opposing ends of human conflicts. A mercenary trend has emerged that sees novags divesting themselves of old bonds of allegiance. Following that trend, novags tend to get along with whoever is paying them, regardless of race; no job is too dangerous and no employer too unsavory when a contract is at stake.

Novags have a modest admiration for humans based on many centuries of coexistence, though they prefer the company of soldiers to priests or dabblers in things demonic. Past experience with dwerofs and eldrin is largely limited to minor conflicts in the early days of novag expansionism. While they feel some pity for the eldrin for having lost their own homeland, they view the dwerofs with contempt for their hasty retreat in the Great War and their continued isolation. Despite their violent history with the briggs, novags hold no grudges and respect the ousted residents of Novdy Ottor for their tenacity and strength. Hybrids are viewed with extreme suspicion due to their ancestors' involvement with the enemy during the battle of Novdy Ottor, regardless of their claims of being unwilling participants. Assar are considered an unknown enemy.

Lands: All novags share a great love for Novdy Ottor, the decimated homeland of their past. Many years have passed since its fall during the Great War, and the novag race has survived admirably amongst humans, but the memory of Novdy Ottor has not been abandoned. Rather, it is preserved in countless Novdytowns, which now serve as the widely distributed homeland of the novag race. Most major human cities have Novdytowns, dense with bustling residential complexes, armament companies, construction guilds, and factories. This density increased many fold with the fall of Novdy Ottor, stretching the capacity of these communities to a breaking point as they became swollen with the refugees of the Great War. Most Novdytowns are subsequently overpopulated, and much like the human cities that surround them, are rife with poverty, homelessness, and crime. Surrounded by humans, novags find themselves becoming increasingly human in nature.

Religion: Traditionally, novags have little patience for religion, viewing deference to a divine power with much the same disdain as briggs do. Rather than submitting faith in a god or a church, they revere their great warriors and generals as cultural icons, maintaining the legacies of great battles in written texts to preserve novag culture. These texts are many and varied, scattered about the human nations in disparate Novdytowns. More often than not, completely different heroes and legends are acknowledged from city to city, resulting in varied belief sets across the novag population. These traditions are strong, and despite living amongst humans for far longer than the eldrin, there are still fewer novags than eldrin that have succumbed to the draw of human churches. Rather, they interact with religious institutions on an impersonal level as engineers and consultants. Many a novag can be found as an honored guest in the administrative halls of the Beyella Divinity's Red Spire, and in the war rooms of the Prelacy of the Divine Adjudicator.

Language: Despite their forced exile from Novdy Ottor, all novags retain spoken and written fluency in their native language of Novska. Novdytowns serve as bastions of novag culture, providing a foothold for their people in place of their ruined homeland. Rather than degrade or disappear entirely, Novska has in fact influenced the language of those cities and Low Common is peppered with words and expressions taken from the novag language. Further reinforcing this is a strong written tradition, anchored in military and technological texts that are treated with the same reverence that a priest might treat his holy books. Great volumes describe the conquests and violent history of the novags, the facts and legends surrounding their greatest generals, and technical schematics for powerful arms and armor. These tomes are embellished with prose and poetry, which novags ladle liberally upon their favorite subjects of combat and war. Human-bound Novdytowns carefully guard these tomes, but countless more remain in the burnt heart of Novdy Ottor where they lie abandoned after a rushed retreat from the demon horde.

Names: Novags are usually given the name of their father, mother, or a derivative of either, along with a numeral to designate their place in the family lineage. Thus, the son of an Irek Borta will likely be named Irek Borta II. New names are introduced into families usually as an honorific to a cultural icon or relative that fell in battle. Male names often end with hard consonants, "k" being very common, while female names usually end with soft vowels, particularly "a."

Male Names: Gregor, Irek, Lubo, Marek, Patyk, Stachek.
Female Names: Ansta, Katrin, Melka, Pina, Sylliva, Zania.
Family Names: Arnista, Banas, Borta, Grodny, Ranig, Wednig.

Adventurers: Novags typically take on adventure to mercenary ends, or as an opportunity to hone fighting skills that have become flaccid within the comfort of human borders. Many travel as a means to stave off the utter monotony of peace times, finding comfort in graven lands that others view with the deepest dread. The most patriotic novags are bound by a yearning to reclaim Novdy Ottor, and find their way to their blighted homeland sooner or later, armed to the teeth and ready to accept death before a second retreat.

Favored Class: Fighter or Soldier (choose one). All novags have a strong military ancestry and a penchant for taking up arms in the face of adversity. Novdy Ottor was brimming with soldiers in its heyday, but since its fall few novags have joined up with human armies except as consultants or mercenaries. Most of these mercenaries are fighters, skilled in heavy armor, ranged weapons, and any tactic that can help them survive on their own.

Other Classes: Novag lurkers are rare, but those that do exist are as fierce as their ground-pounding counterparts, using terrain and tactics to their advantage rather than weapons expertise. Novags have too much discipline and too little brute strength to make effective barbarians. In the overpopulated Novdytowns of the human domain, where neighbors battle one another over simple necessities, novag rogues prowl the streets, devoid of their race's characteristic racial loyalty. Novags have little use for religion but those that do find their calling often fall in with Despinus Chapter. And despite their natural intelligence in matters of warfare and engineering, few novags have the mind or inclination to take up arcanism.

Novag Racial Traits

- +2 Constitution, −2 Strength: Novags are hardy and resilient but smaller in stature and therefore weaker than larger humanoids.
- Small: As Small creatures, novags gain a +1 size bonus to Armor Class, a +1 size bonus on attack rolls, and a +4 size bonus on Hide checks, but they must use smaller weapons than humans use, and their lifting and carrying limits are three-quarters those of Medium characters.
- Novag base land speed is 20 feet.
- Low-light Vision. Novags can see twice as far as

humans in starlight, torchlight, and similar conditions of poor illumination. They retain the ability to distinguish color and detail under these conditions.

- Technological Savvy: Novags are second to none when tasked to build sophisticated structures or the tools of war. They receive a +2 racial bonus on Knowledge and Profession checks related to architecture, construction, and engineering, and a +2 racial bonus on Craft (mechanical weapons) checks.
- Warrior Bloodline: Novags are resistant to all but the most severe ailments, receiving a +2 racial bonus on saving throws against disease and poison.
- Fearless: Novags are possessed of legendary courage, receiving a +2 racial bonus on saving throws against fear effects and spells.
- Automatic Languages: Novska, Low Common. Bonus Languages: All regional human languages.

Chapter 2: Classes

"Everyone pays the Priest. You got no choice if you wanna stay in business around 'ere. But I reckon it's the muscle that keeps people in line. That man's got more swords and back-stabbers backin' 'im up than you can count. Some say e's even gotta spellcaster on the payroll. Oh well, that's life in the Ridge – no use pissin' 'bout it all day."

- Shopkeeper in Grozt

The following chapter details the new and variant classes available in a DARK LEGACIES campaign. Of the player character classes presented in the core rules, only the barbarian, fighter, and rogue are suitable for play; they have been included here with some modifications. Of the standard NPC classes, all except the adept are suitable for use in a DARK LEGACIES campaign. As with the wizard and sorcerer player character classes, the adept NPC class has been superseded by the arcanist.

Arcanists are the only magic-oriented class, though a character of any class can learn and cast spells to a lesser degree. Magic in DARK LEGACIES is rooted in the Abyss rather than the Earth, thus there is no natural magic or druidic tradition. Likewise, there is no magical bardic tradition; bard archetypes can be emulated by creating an expert or rogue with ranks in Perform and Spellcraft, or even a musically inclined priest. Priests are the only divine-oriented class, replacing clerics, with militant priests taking the place of paladins. Various forms of basic hand-to-hand combat are employed among the varied cultures of Earth but nothing as specialized or mystical as those practiced by the monk. The ranger has been reinterpreted as the lurker. The soldier is a new warrior class.

The seven player character classes, in the order in which they are presented in this chapter, are as follows:

Arcanist (Arc): A devious and resourceful practitioner of demonic magic.

Barbarian (Bbn): A savage warrior who uses brute violence and intimidation to defeat his enemies.

Fighter (Ftr): A warrior with unmatched weapons mastery potential and a diverse range of individualized fighting skills.

Lurker (Lrk): A highly skilled tracker, marauder, and survivalist who leverages natural environments for both offense and defense.

Priest (Prs): A religious devotee and master manipulator, possessed of extraordinary and supernatural abilities that allow him to impose his will on enemies and allies alike.

Rogue (Rog): A highly mobile and lethal scout, spy, and assassin who achieves his goals through stealth and subterfuge.

Soldier (Sol): A disciplined and hardy warrior with exceptional endurance and the capacity to quickly overwhelm his enemies when fighting alongside other soldiers.

Arcanist

"The feeling is like nothing else. An exhilarating tingle as you speak the spell's ancient words. The rush of energy flowing wildly through your veins, desperate for you to take control. And then, as you bend the very Abyss to your will, a gush of explosive euphoria... Your priests say Heaven is beyond the reach of mortals. I can tell you they are wrong."

- Sergi-Ishmane Gurkin, dwerof arcanist

Magic is the stuff of demons, the glue that binds their chaotic spirits to physical forms and the power they wield to bring misery down upon all the races of Earth. Since the Reversion, that power has fallen into mortal hands in the form of arcanism: a dark science that combines demonic incantation with mortal alchemy to transmute demonic energy into spells. Loath to be buried amidst the rubble of fallen races, this science has endured war and decay with great tenacity, biding its time between civilizations. As new races emerge, arcanism takes hold of the hearts of those among them that exhibit a single-minded yearning for unfettered personal power, eventually leading them to corruption and chaos.

Only recently has this ubiquitous power come to humankind, born on the back of the eldrin exodus as Illgoth burned. Renegades and power-seekers, some newly exposed and others well acquainted with the ruin that can come of arcanism, practice their dark science from within the protective shadow of the world's last great civilization. Secret arcanist societies and demonic cults fester within the heart of this human domain, formed during the upheaval of the Great War and given unwitting leave to prosper amidst the chaos of the ensuing Kingdoms War. Only in the last century have justifiably paranoid governments and religious authorities been able to exert their will and resources against the arcanist threat.

As the noose tightens around their throats, fewer and fewer arcanists are able to excel beyond basic experimentation for fear of persecution and lack of access to essential materials. Many abandon the practice altogether, while a lesser number converge within secret organizations that are devoted to arcanism, so as to share resources and knowledge. Fewer still persevere on their personal path to power, surviving threats from home and from the demon-infested wastes where fragments of lost spells and priceless spell components call to them. Regardless of their approach, all arcanists are equally susceptible to the dangers of immersing themselves in magic; they walk a dark road in order to gain power, whether with a purposeful step or the haphazard stumbling of one blinded by denial and ignorance. Demonic roots emerge as the scientific facade of arcanism is peeled away, drawing those that would venture too far down the road ever closer to Azrae and the Abyss.

Adventurers: The proliferation of arcanism throughout human realms is the source of much consternation amongst the religious institutions of humankind, who perceive it as the greatest threat to their foundation of order and control since the chaos of the Great War and the loosing of Azrae's legions. The seeds of paranoia have been planted within lawmakers and the general populace alike, spawning military actions with ghastly collateral damage and inciting ordinary folk to burn their own neighbors out of their homes, and often within them. An arcanist that practices openly in such regions quickly becomes a dead arcanist, and even those that adventure there with reasonable discretion do so at great risk to themselves and their companions.

Some realms, however, exhibit a lesser degree of danger to arcanists. This is due as much to an absence of religious influence as it is to a heavier emphasis on survival than status quo. It is in those places, many of which lie in the chaotic Eastern Ridge, that arcanists find safe haven, though even there they are rarely forthright about their occupation, and carefully consider when and how to use their talents for fear of attracting unwanted notice and retribution from afar. More often than not, they travel to stay one step ahead of those that fear or covet their power, burdened by rare alchemical concoctions and priceless demonic scripts that they bear on their person. These travels often extend beyond the fringes of civilization, where they seek out old and forbidden knowledge in the darkest pits of the world.

Characteristics: Arcanists are consumed by their desire for power, and the source of their power is in their spells. While anyone able to read the language of demons and to acquire the requisite materials can cast spells regardless of their class, the single-minded focus of arcanists gives them the greatest potential to cast spells repeatedly and successfully. Though they do not automatically gain spells as they increase in level, arcanists are the only class that can cast spells from memory, without the need to reference the actual spell formula. As they gain experience, they can memorize a greater number of spells and delve into more complex and powerful spells with greater confidence. Their proficiency with many languages and knowledge of all things arcane and unnatural is also a great asset when traveling down the dark road. The risk of being identified as an arcanist and the lack of guaranteed success when casting spells requires that arcanists also be able to survive by mundane methods; they are poor combatants, but what they lack in combat ability they make up for in resourcefulness and deceptive talent. All arcanists are necessarily smooth of tongue and wise to the street.

Religion: Arcanism represents unfettered personal power, free from the mantle of worship and outside the hierarchy of any church. Thus, at its very roots it exists in opposition to religion. Still, most arcanists, regardless of any private antipathy, display some token piety to placate local religious authorities and to avoid undue notice. Truly religious arcanists juggle their faith with their practice; inevitably, they must abandon one or the other as they become increasingly exposed to demonic cabals and to cults that ascribe their magical accomplishments to excessive ritual in Azrae's name.

Background: Arcanists emerge from all walks of life, with little commonality among them other than a desire for power, which in turn usually conceals a deeper yearning. A noble of medium bearing might study as a means to gain entrance into a society that he would otherwise be too lowborn to access, while a hybrid cultist of Azrae is as likely to pursue arcanism as his only road to salvation. This lonely drive for power and the fear of exposing oneself to church agents isolates arcanists from one another; encounters between them are cool at best, with few displays of camaraderie. Nonhuman arcanists, particularly eldrin, are an exception to this rule and often find themselves harassed by their human counterparts due to the widespread belief that they possess great magical power as a birthright.

Other Classes: Whichever tool fits the job is the view of most arcanists. Should they need a force of arms to protect themselves in threatening lands, they will rely upon fighters. When traversing a dangerous stretch of wilderness or requiring the skills of an herbalist for their spell components, they will leverage the talents of a lurker. Should they require possession of a demonic text being held in a church vault, they will requisition the services of a rogue. Arcanists are loath to associate with soldiers, even under a deceptive guise, as their agendas often conflict with those of nations and governments. Barbarians are typically deemed too careless of where they step and what they destroy. Only in rare and secret circumstances would an arcanist and a priest ever find themselves on the same side.

Role: Arcanists use their magic sparingly, but when a seemingly impossible situation requires an unconventional solution, they can be counted on more than any other class to successfully cast spells on demand. Where spellcasting is impractical or unsafe, arcanists contribute with skill and cunning: they are often fluent in many languages and possess a great deal of knowledge that can serve a party well in unfamiliar lands, and their uncanny talent for deception and twisting words can be a boon. However, this same predilection for deceptive behavior, exacerbated by the corruption that comes with excessive spellcasting, often creates an atmosphere of distrust in parties that contain arcanists, and they are rarely afforded the same camaraderie as other classes.

GAME RULE INFORMATION

Arcanists have the following game statistics.

Abilities: Intelligence determines how powerful a spell an arcanist can learn and cast (see Chapter 6: Magic), and how many spells he can memorize. It is also important for many of an arcanist's essential skills. High Constitution allows the arcanist to cast more spells before becoming fatigued or unconscious and helps him manage spellcasting distractions and the harsh physical consequences of spellcasting failure. A high Charisma is useful for arcanists as it allows them to talk their way out of precarious situations. High Dexterity is helpful for arcanists, who wear little or no armor, because it provides them with an Armor Class bonus.

Hit Die: d6.

Class Skills

The arcanist's class skills (and the key ability for each skill) are Appraise (Int), Bluff (Cha), Concentration (Con), Craft (Int), Decipher Script (Int), Diplomacy (Cha), Gather Information (Cha), Heal (Wis), Knowledge (all skills, taken individually) (Int), Profession (Wis), Sleight of Hand (Dex), Speak Language (n/a), and Spellcraft (Int).

Skill Points at 1st Level: (6 + Int modifier) × 4.
Skill Points at Each Additional Level: 6 + Int modifier.

Class Features

All of the following are class features of the arcanist.

Weapon and Armor Proficiency: Arcanists are proficient with all simple weapons and with light armor. However, armor interferes with an arcanist's handling of material spell components, which can cause his spells to fail (page 75).

Bonus Languages: An arcanist's bonus language options include Abyssal, the language of magic. This choice is in addition to the bonus languages available to the arcanist because of his race. Fluency in Abyssal is required to learn and cast spells.

Dark Road: An arcanist devotes himself to arcanism above all else and thus gains several advantages over lay practitioners as described below.

Spellcraft Bonus: An arcanist gains a bonus on Spellcraft checks equal to his arcanist level. This bonus applies to all uses of the Spellcraft skill, including deciphering, learning, and casting spells.

Spell Memorization: An arcanist, and only an arcanist, can memorize spells, thus eliminating the need for a spell reference when casting them. He can memorize one spell level worth of known spells per arcanist level per day, modified by his Intelligence modifier. Thus, a 4th level arcanist with an Intelligence score of 15 can memorize six levels worth of spells (four for his arcanist level plus two for his Intelligence bonus). He could choose to memorize six 1st-level spells; four 1st-level spells and one 2nd-level spell; one 6th-level spell; or any other combination not exceeding his allowed maximum. These spells remain in memory after being cast and can be cast repeatedly, but all memorized spells fade from memory after a day. An arcanist must spend two hours studying in the morning in order to memorize spells for that day, though he is not obligated to do so if he instead wishes to cast spells from their references.

Casting Resistance: Long hours of experimentation and discipline train the arcanist to better contain and disperse the demonic energy channeled through him when he casts spells. Each time he gains casting resistance, the total damage incurred when casting spells is reduced. For every point of resistance bonus gained, treat spells as one level lower for purposes of calculating nonlethal damage only. Thus, a 7th-level arcanist (with casting resistance +2) casting a 3rd-level spell treats it as a 1st-level spell for casting damage purposes. A spell's effective level can never be reduced below 1st level, thus the caster always suffers at least 1d4 nonlethal damage when casting a spell.

See Chapter 6: Magic for complete rules on learning and casting spells.

Spells: If arcanist is the character's starting character class, he possesses a spellbook, a set of scrolls, or some other written medium that contains either two uncommon spells of up to 3rd-level or one rare spell of up to 2nd-level. He has the necessary components to cast each spell 1d4 times. This represents the meager resources that he has managed to scrounge as an independent practitioner. If a character multi-classes into arcanist, he does not automatically gain this class benefit. Arcanists do not automatically gain spells as they increase in level.

Arcanist Ability: In the course of his trade, an arcanist acquires talents that assist him in getting what he needs while staying clear of those that would harm him. He can also develop specific skills unavailable to those who do not devote themselves entirely to arcanism. At first level, he may choose a special ability from the list below. He gains a new ability at 2nd level and every three levels thereafter (5th, 8th, 11th, 14th, 17th, and 20th level). Where noted, an arcanist can choose the same ability more than once to increasing effect.

Black-Market Trading: The arcanist is forced to become quick of tongue and wise to the street by his need for rare goods. He gains a +2 bonus on Appraise, Diplomacy, and Gather Information checks made to buy or sell illicit or illegal goods. This ability can be taken more than once; the bonuses stack.

Demonspeak: The arcanist can use the Abyssal tongue and dark words of power to cow his enemies. When using this ability, he applies half his arcanist level as a bonus on Intimidate checks, but in doing so, exposes himself as a practitioner of arcanism.

Expert Channeling: The arcanist is able to modify the violent energies that are unleashed as a result of a spell failure, refactoring them at the last moment. Once per day, he may reroll a spell failure side effect (page 100), but he must apply the result of the new roll, even if it is worse than the original. This ability can be taken more than once; each time it is taken, the arcanist can use it once more per day.

Extended Spell Retention: By experimenting with advanced memorization techniques, an arcanist can retain memorized spells for an additional number of days equal to half his arcanist level. He must spend four hours rather than two to memorize his spells, and must repeat the process any time he wants to change his repertoire of memorized spells.

Linguistic Expertise: An arcanist with linguistic expertise is better able to decipher dead languages and ancient text due to his extensive experience with multiple languages. He gains a bonus to Decipher Script skill checks equal to the number of languages that he knows. Thus, an arcanist that knows three languages receives a +3 bonus. This bonus increases as more languages are learned.

Obscure Eye: An eye for exotic goods helps the arcanist distinguish genuine spell components from fakes. He gains a +2 bonus on all skill checks to identify spell components. This ability can be taken more than once; the bonuses stack.

Skill Diversity: The arcanist may choose any three skills that are not normally class skills. They are now arcanist class skills for him. This ability can be taken more than once.

Smooth Talker: An arcanist is apt at evading incarceration and manipulating the law. He gains a +2 bonus on all Bluff, Diplomacy, and Knowledge (local) checks when parleying with authorities or courts. This ability can be taken more than once; the bonuses stack.

Smuggler: Arcanists are constantly paranoid of being found with contraband on their person. By taking the smuggler ability, an arcanist gains a +3 bonus on Sleight of Hand checks to conceal items. This ability can be taken more than once; the bonuses stack.

Unbreakable: An Arcanist with this ability gains a +3 bonus on Will saves against disclosing secrets that would compromise or harm him if revealed. The bonus applies in all circumstances, whether mundane, magical, or supernatural. This ability can be taken more than once; the bonuses stack.

Bonus Feat: An arcanist may choose a feat drawn from the following list in place of an arcanist ability: Combat Casting, Craft Incendiary, Create Demonic Item, Deceitful, Diligent, Negotiator, Persuasive, Seductive, Self-Sufficient, Skill Focus, Stealthy, Street Smart, Toughness.

Table 2-1: The Arcanist

Level	Base Attack Bonus	Fort Save	Ref Save	Will Save	Special
1st	+0	+2	+0	+2	Arcanist ability, dark road, spells
2nd	+1	+3	+0	+3	Arcanist ability
3rd	+1	+3	+1	+3	Casting resistance +1
4th	+2	+4	+1	+4	
5th	+2	+4	+1	+4	Arcanist ability
6th	+3	+5	+2	+5	
7th	+3	+5	+2	+5	Casting resistance +2
8th	+4	+6	+2	+6	Arcanist ability
9th	+4	+6	+3	+6	
10th	+5	+7	+3	+7	
11th	+5	+7	+3	+7	Arcanist ability, casting resistance +3
12th	+6/+1	+8	+4	+8	
13th	+6/+1	+8	+4	+8	
14th	+7/+2	+9	+4	+9	Arcanist ability
15th	+7/+2	+9	+5	+9	Casting resistance +4
16th	+8/+3	+10	+5	+10	
17th	+8/+3	+10	+5	+10	Arcanist ability
18th	+9/+4	+11	+6	+11	
19th	+9/+4	+11	+6	+11	Casting resistance +5
20th	+10/+5	+12	+6	+12	Arcanist ability

Barbarian

"Forget the women. Get the metal!"

- Tank, hybrid warlord, during a raid on Vagred

While the majority of the world's population has converged within cities and towns to form civilized nations, there are those who have little envy of such a life, and others that have been thrust from it in the wake of war and ruin. These barbarians, who are also referred to as "savages," "wildmen," or even "demon men," exist on the periphery, in isolated communities or as solitary victims of circumstance. They make a basic life for themselves in regions that no one else could endure, taming unforgiving lands with necessary brutality, and enduring the unspeakable chaos of regions affected by the Great War with unmatched resiliency.

Most folk in the Corelands and other islands of civilization perceive the behavior of barbarians as reckless, savage and wanton. Humankind, in particular, has long since forgotten its own history of barbarism prior to the Reversion. Despite this obvious prejudice, mistrust of barbarians is due as much to where they live as it is to how they live. Laws and normality are distressingly absent in the periphery, where demons and other unnatural creatures inflict terror upon any that venture there; memories of destruction wrought by Azrae's hordes and subsequent flight from these lands remain fresh and are handed down with each new generation. The fact that barbarians continue to survive and even prosper in such regions, combined with their rough impropriety, elicits anxiety and suspicion in most civilized folk that they encounter, leading to baseless accusations against them when crimes or tragedy occur in or near their presence.

Adventurers: Few can boast of having the same physical mettle and courage as a barbarian, which makes them well suited to adventure. They are strangers to neither hardship nor danger. Some migrate from one unaccommodating locale to the next, pursued by or pursuing enemies or simply to escape a region of exhausted or polluted resources. Others flee the smothering monotony of their communities, driven by curiosity and a desire to see the world and take from it, though more commonly in the form of experience than material wealth. The typically unaligned nature of barbarians makes them a precious commodity within mercenary companies and militias, where they are appreciated as capable (and cheap) grunts and laborers.

Characteristics: Barbarians are brutish warriors of the wilderness, unconcerned with tactics or fancy swordplay. They are able to move with terrifying speed and to absorb minor injuries without flinching. But they are most deadly when employing their powerful rage, during which they become stronger and tougher, and better able to both intimidate their foes and resist manipulative forces. Though their potential to enter these rages is limited each day, the carnage that results from each episode is usually sufficient to last them until their next encounter.

Religion: More by choice than by circumstance, barbarians care little for organized religions and the institutions that promote them. Most keep to lands that are either beyond the reach of these institutions or that have long since been abandoned to godlessness. Some maintain a simpler set of beliefs, more cultural than religious in nature, and often steeped in superstition. However, barbarians that spend prolonged periods of time in lands ruled by religious laws and practices may eventually embrace them, though more often out of necessity than true faith. Far in the east, where the Abyss on the horizon can seem closer than the civilization to the west, some barbarians revere demons as living gods upon the Earth, though the relationship is usually based on fear and manipulation rather than authentic devotion.

Background: With the exception of the briggs, who have reached a plateau in terms of their social and technological development, most barbarians emerge as the result of war and political and religious upheaval; the conflicts of the recent past have driven many outlying communities to the brink. Whether he is a survivor of recent turmoil or the offspring of such a person, a barbarian may cling to the fringes of his wasted homeland, unwilling or unable to acclimate to a civilized existence. Most of those that do undertake the journey into civilized lands find their way as pack mules, mercenaries, or conscripts in foreign conflicts before making a life for themselves as an independent adventurer. Outside of tribal territories such as Ban Got and the feudal gangs that plague the wastelands, there is no bond among barbarians; they share little in common other than a knack for survival and an origin rooted in misery and hardship.

Other Classes: As blunt warriors accustomed to the most basic methods of survival, barbarians tend to exhibit a bias against those classes that they consider to be unnecessarily complicated. Thus, they prefer the company of fighters with whom they share an affinity for violence, and lurkers whose wilderness sense they can understand and respect. Excessive tactics and deceit are generally frowned upon, tainting barbarians' relationships with soldiers and rogues. Arcanists and priests are viewed as one and the same – underhanded practitioners of strange and manipulative power – and are avoided. This last prejudice is the hardest for a barbarian to overcome, even if he has evolved to accept an otherwise well-rounded group of companions.

Role: Barbarians are best suited for duty on the front-line as combatants and deterrents. From there they can inflict and absorb tremendous amounts of damage, prevent altercations by intimidating their enemies, or use their considerable speed to pursue and intercept those that flee before them.

GAME RULE INFORMATION
Barbarians have the following game statistics.

Abilities: Strength and Constitution are important for barbarians because of their roles in combat. Dexterity is important for barbarians who wear little or no armor.

Hit Die: d12.

Class Skills
The barbarian's class skills (and the key ability for each skill) are Climb (Str), Craft (Int), Handle Animal (Cha), Intimidate (Cha), Jump (Str), Listen (Wis), Ride (Dex), Survival (Wis), and Swim (Str).

Skill Points at 1st Level: (4 + Int modifier) × 4.
Skill Points at Each Additional Level: 4 + Int modifier.

Class Features
All of the following are class features of the barbarian.

Weapon and Armor Proficiency: A barbarian is proficient with all simple weapons, all martial melee weapons, all bows (short, composite short, long, composite long), and with light armor, medium armor, and shields (except tower shields).

Brute Force: A barbarian is accustomed to intimidating others with simple brute strength. He may use his Strength score rather than his Charisma score to determine his modifier for the Intimidate skill.

Fast Movement (Ex): A barbarian's land speed is faster than the norm for his race by +10 feet. This benefit applies only when he is wearing no armor, light armor, or medium armor and not carrying a heavy load. Apply this bonus before modifying the barbarian's speed because of any load carried or armor worn.

Illiteracy: Barbarians are the only characters who do not automatically know how to read and write. A barbarian may spend 2 skill points to gain the ability to read and write all languages he is able to speak. A barbarian who gains a level in any other class automatically gains literacy. Any other character who gains a barbarian level does not lose the literacy he or she already had.

Rage (Ex): A barbarian can fly into a frenzied rage of terror a certain number of times per day. In a rage, a barbarian temporarily gains a +4 bonus to Strength, a +4 bonus to Constitution, and a +2 morale bonus on Will saves, but he takes a −2 penalty to Armor Class. The increase in Constitution increases the barbarian's hit points by 2 points per level, but these hit points go away at the end of the rage when his Constitution score drops back to normal. (These extra hit points are not lost first the way temporary hit points are.)

While raging, a barbarian cannot use any Charisma-, Dexterity-, or Intelligence-based skills (except for Balance, Escape Artist, Intimidate, and Ride), the Concentration skill, or any abilities that require patience or concentration, nor can he cast spells, use the Voice, or activate items of power that require a command word to function. He can use any feat he has except Combat Expertise.

A fit of rage lasts for a number of rounds equal to 3 + the character's (newly improved) Constitution modifier. A barbarian may prematurely end his rage. At the end of the rage, the barbarian loses the rage modifiers and restrictions and becomes fatigued (−2 penalty to Strength, −2 penalty to Dexterity, can't charge or run) for the duration of the current encounter (unless he is a 17th-level barbarian, at which point this limitation no longer applies; see below).

A barbarian can fly into a rage only once per encounter. At 1st level he can use his rage ability once per day. At 4th level and every four levels thereafter, he can use it one additional time per day (to a maximum of six times per day at 20th level). Entering a rage takes no time itself, but a barbarian can do it only during his action, not in response to someone else's action.

Uncanny Dodge (Ex): At 2nd level, a barbarian retains his Dexterity bonus to AC (if any) even if he is caught flat-footed or struck by an invisible attacker. However, he still loses his Dexterity bonus to AC if immobilized. If a barbarian already has uncanny dodge from a different class, he automatically gains improved uncanny dodge (see below) instead.

Damage Reduction (Ex): At 3rd level, a barbarian gains Damage Reduction. Subtract 1 from the damage the barbarian takes each time he is dealt damage from a weapon or a natural attack. At 6th level and every three barbarian levels thereafter (9th, 12th, 15th. and 18th level), this damage reduction rises by 1 point. Damage reduction can reduce damage to 0 but not below 0.

Improved Uncanny Dodge (Ex): At 5th level and higher, a barbarian can no longer be flanked. This defense denies a rogue the ability to sneak attack the barbarian by flanking him, unless the attacker has at least four more rogue levels than the target has barbarian levels. If a character already has uncanny dodge (see above) from a second class, he automatically gains improved uncanny dodge instead, and the levels from the classes that grant uncanny dodge stack to determine the minimum level a rogue must be to flank the character.

Fearsome Aspect (Ex): While in a rage, a barbarian of 7th level and higher can attempt to demoralize an opponent with an Intimidate check as a move action rather than a standard action.

Greater Rage (Ex): At 11th level, a barbarian's bonuses to Strength and Constitution during his rage each increase to +6, and his morale bonus on Will saves increases to +3. The penalty to AC remains at −2.

Indomitable Will (Ex): While in a rage, a barbarian of 14th level or higher gains a +4 bonus on Will saves to resist all charm and compulsion spells and effects. This bonus stacks with all other modifiers, including the morale bonus on Will saves he also receives during his rage.

Tireless Rage (Ex): At 17th level and higher, a barbarian no longer becomes fatigued at the end of his rage.

Mighty Rage (Ex): At 20th level, a barbarian's bonuses to Strength and Constitution during his rage each increase to +8, and his morale bonus on Will saves increases to +4. The penalty to AC remains at −2.

TABLE 2-2: THE BARBARIAN

Level	Base Attack Bonus	Fort Save	Ref Save	Will Save	Special
1st	+1	+2	+0	+0	Brute force, fast movement, illiteracy, rage 1/day
2nd	+2	+3	+0	+0	Uncanny dodge
3rd	+3	+3	+1	+1	Damage reduction 1/−
4th	+4	+4	+1	+1	Rage 2/day
5th	+5	+4	+1	+1	Improved uncanny dodge
6th	+6/+1	+5	+2	+2	Damage reduction 2/−
7th	+7/+2	+5	+2	+2	Fearsome aspect
8th	+8/+3	+6	+2	+2	Rage 3/day
9th	+9/+4	+6	+3	+3	Damage reduction 3/−
10th	+10/+5	+7	+3	+3	
11th	+11/+6/+1	+7	+3	+3	Greater rage
12th	+12/+7/+2	+8	+4	+4	Damage reduction 4/−, rage 4/day
13th	+13/+8/+3	+8	+4	+4	
14th	+14/+9/+4	+9	+4	+4	Indomitable will
15th	+15/+10/+5	+9	+5	+5	Damage reduction 5/−
16th	+16/+11/+6/+1	+10	+5	+5	Rage 5/day
17th	+17/+12/+7/+2	+10	+5	+5	Tireless rage
18th	+18/+13/+8/+3	+11	+6	+6	Damage reduction 6/−
19th	+19/+14/+9/+4	+11	+6	+6	
20th	+20/+15/+10/+5	+12	+6	+6	Mighty rage, rage 6/day

Fighter

"In the wastelands, the sword is final adjudicator."

- Ferad Gurthal, former fighter

Adventure and exploration have been constant since the Great War, which made the Earth seem smaller and more accessible to adventurers, and since the conclusion of the Kingdoms War, whereupon nations began supplementing their shrunken armies in earnest, with mercenaries hired out of fighter guilds. These adventures sometimes arise out of need but more often out of want; regardless of the cause, where there is need or want in civilized lands and out upon the afflicted territories of the Earth, there is usually a will to commit violence to get it. Eager employers desire skilled warriors that can be bought at a moment's notice, and it is amongst these official and secretive organizations that fighters find their niche.

Fighters are consummate warriors, concerned more with developing themselves and their reputation than they are with subscribing to political or religious partisanship. They fight and kill whomever and wherever they can to earn a living, working as bound mercenaries as often as of their own accord. Their numbers are many, thus they compete for the favor of prospective employers, often through mercenary companies and adventurer guilds. Should they survive the fool's errands and suicide missions in which all fighters of low reputation partake, the resulting coin provides sustenance for another day at worst or a life of decadence at best. Those that survive these trying initiations, in the guise of a hero or a tyrant, become extremely valuable commodities, and quickly find themselves in the company of those with power, wealth, and a great number of enemies.

Characteristics: Fighters are dedicated and uncontested masters of combat, able to hold their own against enemies in melee combat more than any other individual class. They are familiar with all but strictly military armaments, and can master their weapons quickly as a result of a dedicated focus to the art of combat. They are free to specialize in whatever form of combat they desire, be it brutal power moves, evasive combat, ranged expertise, or any combination of techniques.

Religion: The mercenary nature of most fighters requires a malleable soul, which can patronize whatever religious authority is paying their fee. Rarely does a fighter become so attached to one institution or another that he loses the wider perspective on prospective clients. Some fighters, however, do find themselves choosing a side in the violent struggle between religious law and arcanism. These aligned fighters restrict themselves to serving one group or the other, and can become fiercely pious or impious in the process.

Background: Fighters have many and varied backgrounds. Some studied combat in private armies, militias or federal armies but chose the life of

a mercenary rather than committing themselves as soldiers. Others are self-taught and forged in blood, having taken advantage of the current age of exploration to escape their mundane lives. An abundance of mercenary companies, adventurer houses, and armed gangs exist where a weak commoner can make the transition to a respected combatant. The competitive nature of these institutions and general distrust leaves little room for camaraderie however. There is no global brotherhood of fighters, and friendship often extends only so far as a fighter's immediate allegiances.

Other Classes: Fighters, more so than any other class, are capable of handling themselves in life-threatening combat situations. However, their travels usually draw them into situations where they require specialized support. Though they may find themselves uncomfortable in the presence of arcanists or sluggish alongside a lurker in the woods, they quickly learn to appreciate being part of a diverse team and rarely turn down such resources.

Role: A fighter is suited to combat, especially against individual enemies of considerable power, though his specific role is governed by the fighting style with which he chooses to specialize. Most fighters are counted on as melee combatants who can be supported from afar. Fighters that opt for a quick and agile form of melee combat or ranged weapon mastery are a terror on the battlefield, but they can find themselves quickly outflanked if not given additional melee support.

GAME RULE INFORMATION

Fighters have the following game statistics.

Abilities: Strength is the most important asset for fighters because of its direct impact on their ability to inflict damage. Constitution is important as it provides the fighter with the ability to outlast his opponents in combat. Dexterity can be important for fighters that choose to wear light armor and practice agile fighting styles, though most opt for a second skin of heavy iron instead.

Hit Die: d10.

Class Skills

The fighter's class skills (and the key ability for each skill) are Climb (Str), Craft (Int), Handle Animal (Cha), Intimidate (Cha), Jump (Str), Ride (Dex), and Swim (Str).

Skill Points at 1st Level: (2 + Int modifier) × 4.
Skill Points at Each Additional Level: 2 + Int modifier.

Class Features

All of the following are class features of the fighter.

Weapon and Armor Proficiency: The fighter is proficient with all simple and martial weapons, with all types of armor (light, medium, and heavy), and with shields (except tower shields).

Bonus Feats: At 1st level, a fighter gets a bonus combat-oriented feat in addition to the feat that any 1st-level character gets and the bonus feat granted to human characters. The fighter gains an additional bonus feat at 2nd level and every two fighter levels thereafter (4th, 6th, 8th, 10th, 12th, 14th, 16th, 18th, and 20th). These bonus feats must be drawn from the following list: Blind-Fight, Combat Expertise (Improved Disarm, Improved Feint, Improved Trip, Whirlwind Attack), Combat Reflexes, Dodge (*Improved Dodge*, Mobility, Spring Attack), Exotic Weapon Proficiency*, Improved Critical*, Improved Initiative, Improved Unarmed Strike (Improved Grapple, Deflect Arrows, Snatch Arrows, Stunning Fist), Mounted Combat (Mounted Archery, Ride-By Attack, Spirited Charge, Trample), Point Blank Shot (Far Shot, Precise Shot, Rapid Shot, Manyshot, Shot on the Run, Improved Precise Shot), Power Attack (Cleave, Great Cleave, Improved Bull Rush, Improved Overrun, Improved Sunder), Quick Draw, Rapid Reload, Improved Shield Bash, *Signature Weapon**, Two-Weapon Fighting (Two-Weapon Defense, Improved Two-Weapon Fighting, Greater Two-Weapon Fighting), Weapon Finesse*, Weapon Focus* (Weapon Specialization*, Greater Weapon Focus*, Greater Weapon Specialization*).

Some of the bonus feats available to a fighter cannot be acquired until the fighter has gained one or more prerequisite feats; these feats are listed parenthetically after the prerequisite feat. A fighter can select feats marked with an asterisk (*) more than once, but it must be for a different weapon each time. A fighter must still meet all prerequisites for a feat, including ability score and base attack bonus minimums. Feats shown in italics can be found in Chapter 3: Skills & Feats.

TABLE 2-3: THE FIGHTER

Level	Base Attack Bonus	Fort Save	Ref Save	Will Save	Special
1st	+1	+2	+0	+0	Bonus feat
2nd	+2	+3	+0	+0	Bonus feat
3rd	+3	+3	+1	+1	
4th	+4	+4	+1	+1	Bonus feat
5th	+5	+4	+1	+1	
6th	+6/+1	+5	+2	+2	Bonus feat
7th	+7/+2	+5	+2	+2	
8th	+8/+3	+6	+2	+2	Bonus feat
9th	+9/+4	+6	+3	+3	
10th	+10/+5	+7	+3	+3	Bonus feat
11th	+11/+6/+1	+7	+3	+3	
12th	+12/+7/+2	+8	+4	+4	Bonus feat
13th	+13/+8/+3	+8	+4	+4	
14th	+14/+9/+4	+9	+4	+4	Bonus feat
15th	+15/+10/+5	+9	+5	+5	
16th	+16/+11/+6/+1	+10	+5	+5	Bonus feat
17th	+17/+12/+7/+2	+10	+5	+5	
18th	+18/+13/+8/+3	+11	+6	+6	Bonus feat
19th	+19/+14/+9/+4	+11	+6	+6	
20th	+20/+15/+10/+5	+12	+6	+6	Bonus feat

Lurker

"I keep to the periphery where no laws exist. Here I am god and demon alike, partaking in divine retribution upon those that trespass. I have acted as a plague upon human, brigg, and novag, as each violated my territory. I have laid a swath of destruction so bloody through the wild lands of southern Ilfernac that the children of Hildrie weep to their mothers when night falls, begging for sanctuary against the demon that lives in the woods. This domain is mine. Enter at your own risk."

    - Aelig of Illgoth, eldrin lurker

Though the world has become civilized, peppered with sprawling megacities that house millions of souls, the combined might of all civilization is still dwarfed by the raw wilderness that dominates the Earth. These wild regions, many of which have been scoured and abandoned repeatedly over the course of centuries, are home to natural and ungodly hazards that threaten all who stray from the beaten path. While civilizations have risen and fallen, these dangers have only increased, fed by the fallout of constant war and the chaos that spreads unabated out of sight of provincial interests.

Lurkers claim these lands as their homes, their rightful and wholly owned territory. Stalkers, bounty hunters, woodsmen and guerilla warriors, they thrive in the chaos of the wilds and in once civilized areas that have been reclaimed by the Earth. Where other adventurers falter, terrorized by unfamiliar shadows and the legacy of those who came and bloodied the way before them, lurkers excel. They blend effortlessly into these surroundings and stalk their prey with demonic cunning. When they strike, they do so quickly and indirectly before sinking back into the shadows. Many haunted landscapes, described by legends as being plagued by demons, are in actual fact the home of a lurker that struck to lethal and lasting effect.

Adventurers: Lurkers benefit themselves or an employer by leveraging their rare and specialized knowledge of wild and ruined places. Whether their ultimate goals are rooted in personal ambition or are purely mercenary, there is no shortage of work to carry them along the way; individuals and organizations from every level of society, official and otherwise, have a vested interest in the natural and unnatural treasures that lie beyond the fringes of civilization. Lurkers prefer to keep to a particular region of wilderness where they have become intimately familiar with the lay of the land, its hiding places and the traps which they have carefully placed there, but they do not hesitate to move on when the region's potential has been exhausted or their advantage compromised.

Characteristics: A lurker's extensive skills, special abilities and keen senses allow him to survive and excel in the wilderness and beyond. He is a master tracker, able to pursue his enemies at great speed through rough terrain or hide his own tracks. A lurker has a sharp eye for environmental irregularities and can detect traps in any environment. His survival training also allows him to build traps entirely from available natural resources and geographic features. While not a dedicated warrior, a lurker possesses respectable weapon skills and is often the first to act due to an extraordinary awareness of his surroundings. Discretion is usually preferred over melee combat however; the lurker is a master of camouflage, ambushes, and attacking from concealment. Lastly, lurkers familiarize themselves with the local ecology and learn to produce salves that both heal and poison, that can be used immediately or preserved for resale to the highest bidder.

Religion: Lurkers have no categorical predilection for or against religion. Each lurker is defined by the circumstances of his unique background and is as likely to isolate himself from every aspect of the civilized world, religion included, as he is to have a vested interest in the goals of a particular church or cult. Regardless of his core beliefs, exposure to demonic forces in the wilderness and prolonged isolation can color a lurker's perspective on the world a shade darker, leading him to adopt controversial views on what is natural and right.

Background: There is no common origin among lurkers, except that most are loners who despise the urban throng rather than nature-lovers. Some choose the life while others are forced into it by circumstance; the murder of entire civilizations during the Great War ejected many refugees into the wild, where they eventually learned to survive and stave off barbarism after a generation or two of culling. All lurkers make their coin off the "in-between" territories where many fear to tread, hiring themselves out as mercenaries, dealers of rare ecology, or comprising a special unit attached to a military or church. There is little camaraderie among those that are not also members of the same organization. More often than not, the opposite is true: they constantly wage war against one another in the wild places as opposing sides of territorial disputes, military missions, and bounty hunts.

Other Classes: Though lurkers tend to prefer operating alone, they have no particular bias against any particular class as long as their own goals are not compromised in the process. Only when they find themselves encumbered by a particularly clumsy "civy" – their term for city-bound adventurers unaccustomed to life in the wilds – do they protest, as wont to leave them to die in a festering swamp or parched dune as they are to suffer their incompetence.

Role: The lurker is a consummate guide, scout, and assassin, able to negotiate wild lands and confusing tracks that would leave others lost or walking into certain death. He is most effective against his enemies when employing stealth, relying on ranged attacks and traps, or utilizing poison to disable or kill them, though he can also serve as a formidable secondary combatant when needed.

GAME RULE INFORMATION

Lurkers have the following game statistics.

Abilities: Dexterity and Strength are important for a lurker because they tend to wear little in the way of protective armor and they invariably find themselves in combat situations. Wisdom is important as it determines a lurker's potential to avoid danger, the complexity of poisons he is able to fabricate, and is also the basis for many of his skills. Constitution is important, as a lurker must often make due on meager supplies and in harsh climes.

Hit Die: d8.

Class Skills

The lurker's class skills (and the key ability for each skill) are Climb (Str), Craft (Int), Disable Device (Int), Handle Animal (Cha), Heal (Wis), Hide (Dex), Jump (Str), Knowledge (dungeoneering) (Int), Knowledge (geography) (Int), Knowledge (monsters) (Int), Knowledge (nature) (Int), Listen (Wis), Move Silently (Dex), Profession (Wis), Ride (Dex), Search (Int), Spot (Wis), Survival (Wis), Swim (Str), and Use Rope (Dex).

Skill Points at 1st Level: (6 + Int modifier) × 4.
Skill Points at Each Additional Level: 6 + Int modifier.

Class Features

All of the following are class features of the lurker.

Weapon and Armor Proficiency: A lurker is proficient in the use of all simple weapons, all light and one-handed martial melee weapons, all martial ranged weapons, all bows (short, composite short, long, composite long), plus the blowgun and net. Lurkers are proficient with light armor, but not with shields.

Improved Sniping (Ex): Lurkers are master snipers (see the Hide skill), able to leverage camouflage and the concealment benefit of their surroundings to maximum effect. If hiding in any sort of natural terrain, a lurker's penalty to his Hide check made following a ranged attack is reduced by 1 per lurker level. Thus, a 1st level lurker suffers only a –19 penalty to hide while sniping instead of the normal –20, while a 20th level lurker suffers no penalty at all. This ability can be combined with the camouflage ability but not with hide in plain sight. The benefits of improved sniping apply only when the lurker wears light or no armor. All other normal rules for sniping apply.

Track: A lurker gains Track as a bonus feat.

Wilderness Edge (Ex): A lurker performs best when operating in natural environments. He gains a +2 bonus on Knowledge (geography), Knowledge (nature), and Survival checks. He also applies this bonus on Climb, Craft (when applied to natural objects such as rafts, shelters, or traps), Hide, Listen, and Spot checks when in a natural environment.

Combat Acuity (Ex): A lurker has extreme perceptive abilities gleaned from his experience surviving in the wild. At 2nd level, he may add his Wisdom modifier (if positive) to his Initiative score in addition to his Dexterity modifier. This bonus stacks with Improved Initiative and other abilities that grant bonuses to initiative checks.

Fabricate Healing Salve (Ex): At 2nd level, a lurker with 5 ranks in Survival can create a healing salve from natural resources found in the wilderness. The lurker must spend one hour obtaining materials and preparing his salve, after which he makes a Survival check (DC 15). He can rush the process but the Difficulty Class for his Survival check increases by 5 for every 10 minutes of reduction, to a minimum of 10 minutes (against DC 40). A healing salve converts hit point damage equal to 1d4 plus 1 point per lurker level to nonlethal damage; the damage is converted at a rate of 1 point per minute. Each salve is enough for only one application and a creature can only benefit from one salve per day. If not used immediately, the salve retains its potency for a number of hours equal to twice the lurker's level. This ability cannot be used in afflicted environments, such as Novdy Ottor or the Deadlands.

Covert Attack (Ex): Starting at 3rd level, a lurker can attack with deadly accuracy and effect from a concealed position. If the lurker has successfully hidden and is able to study a victim for at least 2 rounds without being spotted, on the next round he gains a +1 bonus on ranged attack rolls against that target and his weapon's critical range increases by 1. The attack bonus increases to +2 at 7th level, +3 at 11th level, +4 at 15th level, and +5 at 19th level. If the lurker is sniping, he may only make one attack with the listed bonus, following which he must make a Hide check. If he is not sniping, he can make as many attacks as he has that round with the listed bonus on each attack.

Trap Sense (Ex): Starting at 3rd level, a lurker's eye for anomalies and deceptions alerts him to danger from both natural and mechanical traps, giving him a +1 bonus on Reflex saves made to avoid traps and a +1 dodge bonus to AC against attacks made by traps. These bonuses increase by +1 every three lurker levels thereafter (6th, 9th, 12th, 15th, and 18th level). Trap sense bonuses gained from multiple classes stack.

Trapping: At 3rd level, a lurker can build traps with a CR up to 1/3 his lurker level (maximum CR 4) entirely out of materials that are present in his surrounding natural terrain, assuming the necessary resources are available. He can also use the Search skill to locate traps built in this fashion (but not manufactured mechanical traps) when the task has a Difficulty Class higher than 20. Additionally, a lurker who beats such a trap's Disable Device DC by 10 or more can study it, figure out how it works, and bypass it (with his party) without disarming it.

To create a trap, a lurker follows the standard rules as described in the *DMG* for manufacturing traps using the Craft (trapmaking) skill, except that there is no actual cost involved. The effective price, which is used to determine craft time only, is equal to 1% of the trap's market price. Natural traps cannot be repaired. Because natural traps are constructed from imprecise materials and suffer from environmental exposure, there is a 25% chance minus 1% per lurker level that such a trap will not activate every time it would normally be triggered. Natural traps last 1d4 days (rolled by the GM) per lurker level before being consumed by nature. Some commonly built lurker traps are listed below.

Camouflaged Pit Trap: A simple pit that has been dug out and covered over with foliage and other natural coverings. CR 1; location trigger; manual reset; DC 20 Reflex save avoids; 10 ft. deep (1d6, fall); Search DC 20; Disable Device DC 16. Effective Price: 6 gp.

Falling Rocks: A man-made rockslide, loosed from above when a bracing object is shifted or broken. CR 2; location or touch trigger (choose one); no reset; Atk +10 melee (2d6, rocks) multiple targets (all targets in two adjacent 5-ft. squares); Search DC 20; Disable Device DC 20. Effective Price: 10 gp.

Large Net Snare: A net, usually fashioned from rope, which lifts from a camouflaged spot on the ground to ensnare one or more victims when stepped on. CR 2; location trigger; manual reset; Atk +5 melee (see note); Search DC 20; Disable Device DC 25. Note: Characters in a 10-ft. square are grappled by net (Str 18) if they fail a DC 14 Reflex save. Effective Price: 30 gp.

Spear Trap: A spear held taught with rope or vines, then released when the trap is triggered. CR 1; location trigger; manual reset; Atk +10 ranged (1d8/×3, spear); Search DC 20; Disable Device DC 20. Note: 200-ft. max range, target determined randomly from those in its path. Effective Price: 10 gp.

Spiked Pit Trap: An exposed pit, lined with sharp rocks or sticks. CR 1; location trigger; manual reset; DC 20 Reflex save avoids; 10 ft. deep (1d6, fall); pit spikes (Atk +10 melee, 1d4 spikes per target for 1d4 +1 each); Search DC 18; Disable Device DC 15. Effective Craft Price: 3 gp.

Swinging Log Trap: A large log, fastened so that it swings out vertically or horizontally to strike a target with considerable force. CR 1; location or touch trigger (choose one); manual reset; Atk +6 melee (2d6, Large wood log); Search DC 20; Disable Device DC 20. Effective Price: 6 gp. If hit, the affected creature must make an opposed Strength check with the trap (Str 20, size category Large). If it loses, it is pushed back 5 feet plus an additional 5 feet for every 5 points that the trap's Strength check exceeds the creature's, and is also knocked prone.

Poison Use: At 4th level, a lurker has acquainted himself with the use of poison and never risks accidentally poisoning himself when applying poison to a weapon or ammunition. Additionally, he gains a +2 bonus on Heal checks used to treat poison.

Fabricate Poison: Just as each natural environment has the power to heal, each has the potential to poison and destroy. At 4th level, a lurker learns to fabricate one poison entirely from natural materials found in the wilderness. Available poisons, along with their Fabrication DC and effects are given on Table 2-4: Lurker Poisons. Contact and inhaled poisons are harder to fabricate, modifying this DC by +5 and +10 respectively. A lurker cannot fabricate a poison with a Fabrication DC greater than twice his lurker level plus his Wisdom modifier.

Fabricating a poison requires that the lurker spend 1d3 full days (rolled by the GM) sourcing and combining materials, after which he makes a Survival check against the poison's Fabrication DC. If the check is successful, one dose of the poison has been created. If the check fails, the lurker cannot make another attempt to fabricate that poison from materials in the immediate vicinity until either 7d4 days (rolled by the GM) have passed or he gains a rank in Survival. A lurker can test a poison's efficacy by taking minute doses to which he is resistant, thus he always knows whether it was fabricated correctly or not. A lurker's poison retains its potency for a number of days equal to his lurker level. Multiple doses of the same poison inflicted upon a target within the same day have no additional effect.

The Fortitude save DC of a lurker's poison is equal to 10 + half the lurker's level at the time of learning how to fabricate the poison. A lurker can fabricate a new poison at 8th level and every four lurker levels thereafter (12th, 16th, and 20th level). Thus, a 16th-level lurker knows how to fabricate four poisons, which have save DCs of 12, 14, 16, and 18. He can choose to relearn a poison he has learned previously in order to increase the save DC or to fabricate an alternative delivery type; regardless, the poisons are treated as unique.

Woodland Stride (Ex): Starting at 5th level, a lurker may move through any sort of undergrowth (such as natural thorns, briars, overgrown areas, and similar terrain) at his normal speed and without taking damage or suffering any other impairment. However, thorns, briars, and overgrown areas that are enchanted or magically manipulated to impede motion still affect him.

Swift Tracker (Ex): At 6th level, a lurker can move at his normal speed while following tracks without taking the normal −5 penalty. He takes only a −10 penalty (instead of the normal −20) when moving at up to twice normal speed while tracking.

Table 2-4: Lurker Poisons

Poison	Fabrication DC	Initial Damage	Secondary Damage
Psychoactive	8	1 Cha, Int, or Wis[1]	2d4 Cha, Int, or Wis[1]
Paralytic	10	Paralysis[2]	0
Knock-out	15	Unconsciousness[3]	Unconsciousness for 2d4 hours
Debilitating	15	1 Str	2d4 Str
Destabilizing	15	1 Dex	2d4 Dex
Wounding	20	2d12 hp	1d6 Con
Lethal	25	1d4 Con	2d4 Con

1 The affected attribute is chosen when the lurker learns to fabricate this poison.
2 Paralysis lasts for 2d6 minutes.
3 Unconsciousness lasts for 1d3 hours.

Hide Tracks (Ex): Beginning at 8th level, a lurker is able to conceal his own tracks and the tracks of those that travel with him if he moves at half his normal speed. Anyone attempting to track the lurker, and a number of additional people equal to half the lurker's level, adds +10 to their Track DC. This increases to +20 at 14th level and +30 at 20th level. A lurker can move at full speed while hiding his tracks but he only gains half the listed bonus.

Camouflage (Ex): A lurker of 11th level or higher can use the Hide skill in any sort of natural terrain, even if the terrain does not grant cover or concealment.

Hide in Plain Sight (Ex): While in any sort of natural terrain, a lurker of 17th level or higher can use the Hide skill even while being observed.

Table 2-5: The Lurker

Level	Base Attack Bonus	Fort Save	Ref Save	Will Save	Special
1st	+0	+2	+2	+0	Improved sniping, Track, wilderness edge
2nd	+1	+3	+3	+0	Combat acuity, fabricate healing salve
3rd	+2	+3	+3	+1	Covert attack +1, trap sense +1, trapping
4th	+3	+4	+4	+1	Fabricate poison, poison use
5th	+3	+4	+4	+1	Woodland stride
6th	+4	+5	+5	+2	Swift tracker, trap sense +2
7th	+5	+5	+5	+2	Covert attack +2
8th	+6/+1	+6	+6	+2	Fabricate new poison, hide tracks +10
9th	+6/+1	+6	+6	+3	Trap sense +3
10th	+7/+2	+7	+7	+3	
11th	+8/+3	+7	+7	+3	Camouflage, covert attack +3
12th	+9/+4	+8	+8	+4	Fabricate new poison, trap sense +4
13th	+9/+4	+8	+8	+4	
14th	+10/+5	+9	+9	+4	Hide tracks +20
15th	+11/+6/+1	+9	+9	+5	Covert attack +4, trap sense +5
16th	+12/+7/+2	+10	+10	+5	Fabricate new poison
17th	+12/+7/+2	+10	+10	+5	Hide in plain sight
18th	+13/+8/+3	+11	+11	+6	Trap sense +6
19th	+14/+9/+4	+11	+11	+6	Covert attack +5
20th	+15/+10/+5	+12	+12	+6	Fabricate new poison, hide tracks +30

Priest

"Faith is my shield. Believe in it, and I shall protect you. Faith is my sword. Defile it, and I will show you no mercy."

- Prelacy of the Divine Adjudicator prayer.

Religious authorities cite the introduction of the Faith to humanity as the preeminent event to shape the world as it exists today. As the sun rose with the Reversion, the First Priest endowed humanity with the ability to reclaim the Earth from demonkind by imbuing a human ministry with knowledge and power. The influence of religious institutions permeates every civilized nation, fully dominating some through entrenched theocratic law. The Faith has also taken the hearts of a great number of nonhumans, who would rather submit to an alien but whole culture rather than cling to the fragments of their own.

Priests are the agents of the Faith, and are both revered and feared throughout society. They act as confessors to kings, judge and jury of the profane, and crusaders against not only demonkind and arcanism, but against those who would challenge their will or the will of the church. Priests exert this will upon the world through righteous conviction and the truly supernatural power of the Voice. This unique ability, originally taught to the priesthood by the First Priest at the dawn of the Reversion, permits them to compel the masses, heal the sick, and destroy the heretical elements that would taint the Earth once more.

Adventurers: Priests of established Corelands denominations – the Church of Deihass, the Prelacy of the Divine Adjudicator, and the Beyella Divinity – usually adventure at the behest of ecclesiastical superiors. They go forth as crusaders, diplomats, information gatherers, and missionaries, either in an official capacity for a particular mission or under their own discretion. Priests that stray too long from an organizational hierarchy invariably find themselves caught up in personal or secret quests, but they must be ever conscious of the higher goals of their church and the long reach of their superiors. Priests of the outlaw Despinus Chapter aspire to less grandiose aspirations than their Corelands counterparts, driven more by personal motivation than by church decree; these pariahs typically adventure to satisfy mercenary and self-serving goals, while remaining fully devoted to their cursed denomination.

Characteristics: Priests manipulate the world around them with the tools of their faith, but the specific manner in which they do so varies greatly from one priest to another. All priests can recite sermons to inspire their allies, terrorize their enemies, and sway the emotions of the masses in their path. Likewise, all priests, and only priests, can use the Voice – a supernatural speech augmentation achieved through prayer, meditation, and self-discipline – to produce miraculous effects. As a priest increases in level, the power and range of his Voice increases accordingly. The specific abilities of each priest, however, and the manner in which he can use the Voice are determined by his selection of holy dominions. Each of these schools of ecclesiastic training grants the priest with specific applications of the Voice as well as other conventional abilities or knowledge.

Each holy dominion focuses on a single guiding principle of the Faith, as taught by the First Priest three thousand years ago: Piety, which guides a priest so that he never wavers in his worship; Consecration, to bless holy items of power; War, to wield those items against the enemies of Deihass; Forbiddance, to cast out demons from the Earth; Knowledge, to amass and leverage the secrets of the world; Dominance, to control and guide the weak; Sanctity, to disrupt demonic magic that rots the foundations of law and order; and Purity, to purge civilization of disease so that it might spread the glory of Deihass, unabated, to the corners of the world.

Religion: Priests, by definition, are both advocates and functionaries of one of the four denominations of the Faith, each descended from the original Church of Deihass. The specific rituals and icons of worship differ among these denominations and they are so segregated at times as to appear as distinct religions, but all priests of the Faith share the belief that Deihass is a supreme being, the god of humanity, and the bringer of the sun. Likewise, Azrae, her demons, and their cults are unanimously viewed as the bane of civilization.

Background: All of the Faith's denominations are based out of longstanding institutions that are organized into complex hierarchies and divided further into factions along regional, political, dominion, and ideological lines. Even outlawed Despinus Chapter, confined to the nether regions of society, is a structured institution, composed of officially ordained members that swear their souls to the ideals and goals of their church. Each denomination has its own method of recruitment and prerequisites for entry into the clergy. Most priests enter service at an early age through direct application, often submitted by a parent or guardian who cannot afford to raise the child or who wishes to garner favor from the offering. A church may also request the heir of an influential or highborn family enter the priesthood at a designated age; this contract, signed at birth, is broken only at great risk to the family name and its members.

Once enrolled into the service of a church, priests are bound to their fellow clergymen. Schisms have beset servants of the Faith upon one another throughout history, leading to four divergent and frequently embattled denominations. Citing the dangers of such chaos, high priests and their ruling councils enact constant reformations, edicts, and punishments to suppress internal conflict that could lead to the deterioration or dissolution of their denomination. Still, denominational division is common, especially in contested jurisdictions outside the control of a church authority and between factions with conflicting agendas; direct conflict is rare, however, and when it erupts it usually does so in the form of political maneuvers and secret wars.

No bond exists between priests of different denominations. Each sees the other as heretical to varying degrees – fallen from the true path or otherwise incorrect in their methods of delivering the Faith. Within regions where multiple denominations coexist but one has a strong majority over the other, this animosity manifests as restrained contempt, vicious politics, or, at its most extreme, crusades with an aim to eliminate the weaker faith. Within neutral territory, priests of opposing denominations are reluctant neighbors bound by law or circumstances. Not since the Kingdoms War have entire denominations battled against one another in outright warfare.

Other Classes: Priests serve as a valuable commodity to adventuring parties. Their force of will, broad connections, and command of the Voice often places them at the heads of these groups, where they dictate commands at their leisure. The disposition of a priest's denomination or faction affects his attitude toward other classes, though more often than not, immediate needs override any official edict against associating with specific characters. However, this willingness to work with others rarely extends to priests of other religions or to arcanists. Some terse relationships exist among the Faith's antagonistic denominations, but a priest will rarely associate directly with a priest of another denomination unless specifically ordered to do so or given no other choice. Priests do not mix with arcanists – at least not officially – as these wielders of demonic magic have been uniformly branded as insidious enemies that practice their vile science in opposition to the will of Deihass and all his institutions of faith.

Role: A priest's role is largely defined by his holy dominions; a priest with the War dominion may act as a capable secondary combatant while priests with the Forbiddance dominion are often their party's only hope against demonkind. So long as he travels within friendly or neutral lands, a priest serves well as party leader, using his charisma, knowledge, authority, or – barring conventional measures – the Voice to sway anyone that the party may encounter to their favor. Though the Voice is considerably less diverse in its applications than the varied spells of an arcanist, a priest is usually better received than an arcanist even in lands hostile to his religion. Where diplomacy fails, a priest can provide considerable support through his sermons.

GAME RULE INFORMATION
Priests have the following game statistics.

Abilities: Charisma determines how effective a priest's sermons are, how often a priest can use the Voice to command supernatural effects, and how hard his Voice is to resist. Strength and Constitution are important for priests that take up arms in the service of their church, while high Intelligence is important for those that wield knowledge as a weapon. Charisma and Intelligence are important for many of the priest's class skills.

Hit Die: d6.

Class Skills
The priest's class skills (and the key ability for each skill) are Bluff (Cha), Concentration (Con), Craft (Int), Diplomacy (Cha), Gather Information (Cha), Intimidate (Cha), Knowledge (history) (Int), Knowledge (local) (Int), Knowledge (religion) (Int), Preach (Cha), and Sense Motive (Wis).

Dominions and Class Skills: A priest who chooses the Forbiddance dominion adds Knowledge (demonism) (Int) to the priest class skills listed above. A priest who chooses the Knowledge dominion adds Decipher Script (Int), all Knowledge (Int) skills, and Speak language (n/a) to the list. A priest who chooses the Purity dominion adds Heal (Wis) to the list. A priest who chooses the Sanctity dominion adds Knowledge (magic) (Int) and Spellcraft (Int) to the list. A priest who chooses the War dominion adds Jump (Str), Ride

(Dex), and Swim (Str) to the list. See Holy Dominions, below, for more information.

Skill Points at 1st Level: (4 + Int modifier) × 4.
Skill Points at Each Additional Level: 4 + Int modifier.

Dominions and Skill Points: A priest who chooses the Knowledge dominion gains an additional 16 skill points at 1st level and 4 additional skill points each level thereafter. These bonus skill points must be spent on Intelligence-based skills or on languages.

Class Features

All of the following are class features of the priest.

Weapon and Armor Proficiency: Priests are proficient with all simple weapons and with light armor. A priest who chooses the War dominion is also proficient with all martial weapons, with medium and heavy armor, and with shields (except tower shields).

Holy Dominions: Holy dominions are schools of ecclesiastic training that grant a priest with additional class skills and features. While all priests share the same fundamental abilities, each is differentiated by the dominions he embraces as being definitive of his religion: Consecration, Dominance, Forbiddance, Knowledge, Piety, Purity, Sanctity, and War. All priests automatically gain the Piety dominion, which provides their ability to sermonize and their confidence of faith (see below). In addition to this default dominion, a priest must choose three additional holy dominions that represent the specific focus of his faith. Refer to the Holy Dominion Features section below for details.

Sermonize (Ex): Once per day per priest level, a priest can inspire his allies and terrorize his enemies by invoking powerful passages from scripture and preaching with religious fervor. Each sermon requires both a minimum priest level and a minimum number of ranks in the Preach skill to qualify.

Starting a sermon is a standard action. Sermonizing requires concentration, which means that the priest must take a standard action each round to sustain the sermon. Sermonizing only provokes attacks of opportunity if the sermon is being referenced (see below). A priest can sustain a sermon for up to 3 rounds plus 1 round per priest level. A priest cannot communicate with his voice in any other way (giving orders, calling for help, casting a spell, etc) while sermonizing. A deaf priest has a 50% chance to fail when attempting to sermonize. If he fails, the attempt still counts against his daily limit.

A priest might take cues from written material over the course of a sermon, but he preaches largely from memory and with much improvisation. At his option, a priest can instead preach a sermon with the full assistance of his holy books, to which he then refers in order to bolster and extend his dicta-tion. Such referenced sermons require a full-round action to start and full-round actions each round to sustain, and provoke attacks of opportunity. While preaching in this manner, a priest can sustain his sermon for an additional 3 rounds and gains a +2 competence bonus to all Preach checks made during the sermon. A priest cannot alternate between standard and referenced preaching during a sermon.

Sermonizing is a mind-affecting, language-dependent ability. Some sermons are also compulsion or fear abilities. All sermons have a range of 30 feet. Language barriers (including a creature's ability to hear) can be circumvented and range increased by augmenting a sermon with the Voice (see The Voice, below). Unless otherwise noted, the Difficulty Class for a saving throw against a priest's sermon is 10 + ½ the priest's level + the priest's Charisma modifier. A creature can attempt to save against a sermon even if the effects are beneficial. If a creature makes a successful save against a priest's sermon, it is immune to any further sermons (harmful or beneficial) from that priest for a period of 24 hours.

Binding Rapture: A priest with 3 or more ranks in Preach can fascinate an audience of one or more humanoid creatures with potent passages from scripture. To be affected, each creature must hear the priest sermonize for a full round, and must be able to see him and pay attention to him. The distraction of nearby combat or other dangers prevents the sermon from working. Binding Rapture has no effect upon a creature that is sermonizing or casting a spell. The priest can fascinate one creature at 1st level, and an additional creature every three levels thereafter (two at 4th level, three at 7th level, etc).

To use the sermon, the priest makes a Preach check. His check result is the DC for each affected creature's Will save against the effect. Any creature that fails its Will save becomes fascinated for the duration of the sermon, and can take no actions. While fascinated, a creature takes a −4 penalty on skill checks made as reactions, such as Listen and Spot checks. Any potential threat, such as an ally of the priest approaching the fascinated creature, requires that the priest make another Preach check and allows the creature a new saving throw against a DC equal to the new Preach check result. Any obvious threat, such as someone drawing a weapon, casting a spell, or aiming a ranged weapon at the target, automatically breaks the effect. Binding Rapture is a compulsion ability.

Courage of the Blessed: A priest with 3 or more ranks in Preach can inspire courage in his allies (including himself), bolstering them against fear and improving their combat abilities. To be affected, each ally must hear the priest sermonize for a full round. Affected allies receive a +1 morale bonus on saving throws against charm, compulsion, and fear effects and a +1 morale bonus on attack and weapon damage rolls. At 7th level, and every six priest levels thereafter, this bonus increases by 1 (+2 at 7th, +3 at 13th, +4 at 19th). The effect lasts as long as the priest sustains the sermon and for an additional number of rounds after he stops (or after the ally can no longer hear him) equal to his Charisma modifier (if positive).

Violent Reclamation: A priest with 3 or more ranks in Preach can attempt to free a compelled or frightened ally by unleashing a violent litany upon him. If successful, this sermon negates any single compulsion or fear spell or effect, including that of the following sermons: Binding Rapture, Heretic's Distress, Fear of God, and Tide of the Masses. To be affected, the ally must hear the priest sermonize for a full round. Each round thereafter, the priest makes a Preach check. The ally gains another saving throw each round that it hears the sermon, using the priest's Preach check result for its save. If the saving throw is successful, he is freed of the harmful effect but is dazed for the duration of the round in which that effect ends. Violent Reclamation is powerless against effects that don't allow saves.

Heretic's Distress: A priest of 3rd level or higher with 6 or more ranks in Preach can induce anxiety in all hostile creatures within range, diminishing their morale and combat effectiveness. To be affected, each creature must hear the priest sermonize for a full round. Any creature that fails its Will save suffers a −1 morale penalty on all saving throws and a −1 morale penalty on attack and weapon damage rolls. These penalties increase at higher priest levels, to −2 at 9th level and −3 at 15th level. The effect lasts only so long as the priest sustains the sermon. Heretic's Distress is a compulsion ability.

Purity of Thought: A priest of 6th level or higher with 9 or more ranks in Preach can expound upon the heretical nature of a single creature's behavior, disrupting any one of that creature's actions that are subject to a Concentration check (including sermonizing and spellcasting). To be affected, the creature must hear the priest sermonize for a full round, following which it makes an opposed Concentration check against the priest's Preach check. If the creature wins, the sermon is ineffectual; otherwise, the creature immediately loses concentration.

Divine Might of the Righteous: A priest of 9th level or higher with 12 or more ranks in Preach can reference and embellish the righteous exploits of a single ally, greatly boosting his confidence and combat effectiveness. To be affected, the ally must hear the priest sermonize for a full round. The affected ally gains temporary hit points equal to 1d8 + the priest's level, a +2 competence bonus on attack rolls, and a +2 competence bonus on all saving throws. The effect lasts as long as the priest sustains the sermon and for an additional number of rounds after he stops (or after the ally can no longer hear him) equal to his Charisma modifier (if positive).

Fear of God: A priest of 12th level or higher with 15 or more ranks in Preach can call forth extreme and intimidating scripture to cow a single creature. To be affected, the creature must hear the priest sermonize for a full round. If it fails its Will save, the creature cowers, frozen in fear and unable to take actions for the duration of the sermon or until the priest ap-proaches within 10 feet of it, thus negating the effect. It suffers a −2 penalty to Armor Class and loses its Dexterity bonus (if any) during this time. Fear of God is a fear ability.

Tide of the Masses: A priest of 15th level or higher with 18 or more ranks in Preach can incite a mob of the faithful, setting them to action under his instruction. He can attempt to rouse a number of Hit Dice of humanoids equal to his priest level to follow him. To be affected, each humanoid must hear the priest sermonize for 1 minute (10 rounds). Those affected by this sermon may make a Will save to negate its affects. Members of the crowd that are normally antagonistic toward the priest's denomination receive a +2 bonus to their saving throw. The sermon has no effect on priests of a different denomination than the sermonizing priest. Affected creatures treat the priest as a trusted friend and ally and are considered to have a friendly attitude toward him. The priest may incite the mob to perform a number of different actions, from creating a diversion to punishing suspected heretics, so long as their actions are not blatantly self-destructive. Instructing them to take actions that are obviously harmful immediately terminates the effect. The mob remains under the influence of the priest for the duration of the sermon plus an additional number of rounds after he stops (or after a member of the mob can no longer hear him) equal to his Charisma modifier (if positive). At the GM's discretion, a rowdy mob may continue along their given course of action even after the priest's influence has expired. Tide of the Masses is a compulsion ability.

True Faith: A priest of 18th level or higher with 21 or more ranks in Preach can invoke passages that harshly decry another priest's beliefs and practices, shaking that priest's faith to the point where he temporarily loses many of his class abilities. To be affected, the target must hear the priest sermonize for 1 minute (10 rounds). If the enemy priest fails his Will save he loses his ability to sermonize, his confidence of faith, and his ability to use the Voice. This sermon cannot be used against a priest of the same denomination as the sermonizing priest. The effect lasts 1d6 minutes per priest level; if the priest has twice as many priest levels as the target or more, the effect lasts 1d6 hours per priest level.

Confidence of Faith (Ex): A priest's will is bolstered by his conviction, thus he is not easily swayed by the sermons of other priests. He receives a +2 bonus on saves against sermons. This bonus increases to +4 if the priest's assailant is of the same denomination as he is.

The Voice (Su): At 2nd level, a priest can use the Voice, also known as the Voice of God or the Voice of Authority, to amplify his speech beyond its natural limits, and to invoke supernatural effects specific to his holy dominions. This unique power, which comes as a result of extended meditation, prayer, and self-discipline, is what truly distinguishes priests from the masses. A priest can initially use the Voice once per day plus his Charisma moderfier (whether positive or negative), gaining an additional use per day every second level thereafter (2/day at 4th level, 3/day at 6th level, etc).

The Voice in all its applications has an initial range of 30 feet, but within that range it can be heard over any obstructive noise. Range extends to 60 feet at 5th level, 90 feet at 11th level, and 120 feet at 17th level, though a priest can speak with the Voice out to a lower available range if desired. Some applications of the Voice are also language-dependent or require a line of effect or touch.

Regardless of the manner in which the Voice is delivered, it is an augmentation of normal speech and therefore audible to those within earshot; its use cannot be concealed. When he uses this ability, a priest's voice becomes supernaturally resonant and penetrating, as though accompanied by a baritone choir. The actual words spoken with the Voice depend on the desired effect. If using it to augment speech (see below) the priest is doing just that – augmenting his usual words with supernatural force. If using the Voice to produce an effect specific to a given holy dominion, the priest may utter a brusque command, invoke the name of a key religious figure or his own name, or issue a slow, acidic warning. The actual words spoken are irrelevant unless the priest is required to give an explicit command, such as with the Dominance dominion's Compelling Voice ability.

When using the Voice in a hostile manner against a creature, the creature must make a Will save (DC = 10 + ½ priest's level + priest's Cha modifier) or be affected as described for that application of the Voice.

When using the Voice to influence an item or effect, the priest must make a special Voice check against a specified Difficulty Class. A Voice check is a d20 roll with a bonus equal to ½ the priest's level + his Charisma modifier. Voice checks can be bolstered by an empowering litany (page 61).

When using the Voice in a beneficial or mundane manner, the effect is generally automatic and has an effect that is commensurate with the priest's level.

Augment Speech: All priests can use the Voice to augment their normal speech as a free action, regardless of their chosen holy dominions. This augmentation can be used in combination with another free action, such as calling out a warning over the cacophony of battle, or with any Charisma-based skill check that incorporates speech, including Preach checks used for the sermonize ability. If used to augment a skill check, a priest gains a bonus to his check result equal to half his priest level. This bonus stacks with all other bonuses to that skill check. The Voice has no beneficial effect if used in conjunction with spellcasting, and doing so is considered high heresy.

Common Voice (Su): At 8th level, a priest's Voice is no longer constrained by language-dependencies; it is spoken in the native language of the listener, regardless of whether the priest can normally speak that language or not. Thus, a priest need not speak the language of his audience if using the Voice to augment speech or when using the Dominance dominion's Compelling Voice ability (see below). The Common Voice does not, however, grant the priest with the ability to understand those languages if they are spoken back to him.

Table 2-6: The Priest

Level	Base Attack Bonus	Fort Save	Ref Save	Will Save	Special	War Attack Bonus	War Fort Save
1st	+0	+0	+0	+2	Confidence of faith, holy dominions, sermonize (binding rapture, courage of the blessed +1, violent reclamation)	+0	+2
2nd	+1	+0	+0	+3	Voice 1/day (30 ft.)	+1	+3
3rd	+1	+1	+1	+3	Sermonize (heretic's distress –1)	+2	+3
4th	+2	+1	+1	+4	Voice 2/day	+3	+4
5th	+2	+1	+1	+4	Voice 60 ft.	+3	+4
6th	+3	+2	+2	+5	Sermonize (purity of thought), Voice 3/day	+4	+5
7th	+3	+2	+2	+5	Sermonize (courage of the blessed +2)	+5	+5
8th	+4	+2	+2	+6	Common Voice, Voice 4/day	+6/+1	+6
9th	+4	+3	+3	+6	Sermonize (divine might of the righteous, heretic's distress –2)	+6/+1	+6
10th	+5	+3	+3	+7	Voice 5/day	+7/+2	+7
11th	+5	+3	+3	+7	Voice 90 ft.	+8/+3	+7
12th	+6/+1	+4	+4	+8	Sermonize (fear of god), Voice 6/day	+9/+4	+8
13th	+6/+1	+4	+4	+8	Sermonize (courage of the blessed +3)	+9/+4	+8
14th	+7/+2	+4	+4	+9	Pervasive Voice, Voice 7/day	+10/+5	+9
15th	+7/+2	+5	+5	+9	Sermonize (heretic's distress –3, tide of the masses)	+11/+6/+1	+9
16th	+8/+3	+5	+5	+10	Voice 8/day	+12/+7/+2	+10
17th	+8/+3	+5	+5	+10	Voice 120 ft.	+12/+7/+2	+10
18th	+9/+4	+6	+6	+11	Sermonize (true faith), Voice 9/day	+13/+8/+3	+11
19th	+9/+4	+6	+6	+11	Sermonize (courage of the blessed +4)	+14/+9/+4	+11
20th	+10/+5	+6	+6	+12	True Voice, Voice 10/day	+15/+10/+5	+12

Pervasive Voice (Su): At 14th level, the priest's Voice penetrates directly into the minds of the intended recipients, circumventing deafness or any attempt they make to inhibit their hearing.

True Voice (Su): At 20th level, a priest speaks with the True Voice, as spoken by the First Priest, and cannot be prevented from using it by any means. Thus, a priest who is gagged, magically silenced, or even has his tongue cut out can communicate normally if he augments his speech with the Voice (see Augmenting Speech, above). Likewise, he can use all of his dominion-specific powers that incorporate the Voice under those same circumstances.

Holy Dominion Features

Upon becoming an agent of the Faith, a priest must choose three holy dominions from the list below. He gains all of the associated class skills and features for those dominions.

Consecration: Consecration is the most mystical and focused of the dominions. It confers a single exceptional ability upon the priest: the ability to consecrate holy items of power. Consecration requires a Voice check, which is usually reinforced by an empowering litany and grand ritual. The number and type of powers that a priest can confer upon an item are commensurate with his priest level and other holy dominions. A priest can confer one holy quality upon an item for every five priest levels he has, thus a 4th- or lower-level priest can only assist in consecration rituals. The creation and function of items of power are fully detailed in the *Dark Legacies Campaign Guide*.

Dominance: Control is key to the power of Earth's churches. Priests must have the means to dominate their fellows so that the will of Deihass can be enforced. A priest with the Dominance dominion is a master manipulator, able to use the Voice to control the actions of others, and to resist the advances of those that would do the same to him. Just the threat of using the Voice to force a creature's hand is often enough to cow them into obedience.

Obstinate Will: A priest with the Dominance dominion is especially resistant against those who would try to dominate him in return. He gains a +1 bonus on saving throws against compulsion spells and effects and on level checks to resist intimidation. At 5th level and every five priest levels thereafter (10th, 15th, and 20th) this bonus increases by +1.

Compelling Voice: As a standard action, a priest with the Dominance dominion can use the Voice to compel a humanoid creature to obey a single command. Possible commands include, but are not limited to: revealing a single truth, approaching the priest, fleeing, halting, falling to the ground, dropping an item, attacking another creature, and even harming itself. A creature cannot, however, be compelled to cast a spell or use a spell-like ability or supernatural ability. Only creatures with Hit Dice equal to or less than the priest's level plus his Charisma modifier are affected.

If the creature fails its Will saving throw (DC 10 + ½ the priest's level + the priest's Charisma modifier), it must follow the command to the best of its ability at its earliest opportunity; it can take no actions of its own free will on that turn, even if the command does not consume all its available actions. If the command would force the creature to do something against its nature, such as attacking an ally or giving up a treasured item, it gains a +2 bonus to its saving throw. If the command would force the creature to harm itself, such as placing its hand into a fire, it gains a +5 bonus. If the command would clearly result in the creature's death, such as slitting its own throat, it receives a +10 bonus to its saving throw. The creature is free to act as it wishes on its next turn, unless it is again compelled with the Voice.

If the creature's Will save is successful, it is paralyzed by indecision (effectively dazed) for 1 round rather than compelled. While in such a state, the creature can take no actions but suffers no penalty to Armor Class.

If a compelled creature has not yet acted on the command given to it by a priest, another priest can attempt to compel it to his own will instead. The creature must make another Will saving throw, though it can forego it if desired. If the save succeeds, the intervening priest's Voice has no effect. If the saving throw fails, the compelling priests must make an opposed level check (1d20 + priest level + Charisma modifier), and the creature only follows the command of the winner. Any number of priests can attempt to compel the same creature with the Voice in this manner.

The Compelling Voice is a compulsion, language-dependent, mind-affecting ability.

Forbiddance: A priest with the Forbiddance dominion is empowered against demons, no matter the form they take. He is resistant to their unholy aura of fear and can root them out from hiding or banish them altogether from the Earth, but by being in such close proximity to them, he also puts his body and soul at great risk. Corruption is common, as the modern age finds immoral priests using their gifts to parlay with and enslave demons for their own ends, rather than destroying them outright.

Class Skill: Knowledge (demonism) (Int).

Bonus Language: A priest with the Forbiddance dominion can select Abyssal as a bonus language, in addition to the bonus languages available to him because of his race.

Many Faces of the Abyss: The terrors of the Abyss have been challenged and overcome. The priest gains a +1 bonus on saving throws against demon fear and fear spells based on demonic stimuli, such as *abyssal window*. At 5th level and every five priest levels thereafter (10th, 15th, and 20th) this bonus increases by +1.

Censure Demon: As a standard action, a priest with the Forbiddance dominion can use the Voice to exorcize a demon from a creature he believes to be possessed, force a creature he suspects of being a demon disguised by *shapeshift* to revert to its true form, or rebuke or destroy multiple demons that are in their natural form. Up to 2 Hit Dice of demons per priest level can be targeted, but no demon with HD greater than the priest's level plus his Charisma modifier can be affected. Censuring a demon also requires a line of effect. Any demon that fails its Will saving throw (DC 10 + ½ the priest's level + the priest's Charisma modifier) is subject to the censuring effect.

If the censure succeeds against a possessing demon, the demon is immediately and violently expelled from the host creature, but may attempt to possess another creature in the near vicinity, including the exorcizing priest. If the possessing demon's Will saving throw succeeds, it is instead only suppressed for a number of minutes equal to the priest's level minus the demon's HD (minimum 1 minute). While the demon is suppressed, the host creature regains total control over its own actions, though it may suffer serious dementia as a result of having been possessed. See Chapter 7: Grit & Consequences for complete details on possession.

If the censure succeeds against a demon disguised by *shapeshift*, the demon immediately reverts to its true form and cannot use its *shapeshift* ability for 24 hours. This reversion process still requires the standard amount of time (1 round per size category). If the disguised demon's Will saving throw succeeds, it instead only spawns temporary features that betray its demonic form. These abnormalities shift and waver in and out of existence for a number of minutes equal to the priest's level minus the demon's HD (minimum 1 minute) before expiring.

If the censure succeeds against one or more demons in their natural form, they cower in awe for 1d10 rounds. A cowering demon seethes with anger but is frozen, unable to take actions, takes a –2 penalty to Armor Class, and loses its Dexterity bonus (if any). If the priest approaches within 10 feet of a cowering demon, or attacks it with a melee weapon, the effect is broken; it remains intact if the priest attacks with ranged weapons at or beyond 10 feet, or anyone else attacks the demon in any fashion. If the censuring priest has twice as many levels (or more) as an affected demon has HD, that demon is destroyed outright, obliterated in an explosive flash of demonic energy and gore. If a targeted demon's Will save is successful, it is instead only dazed for 1 round. While dazed, a demon can take no actions but suffers no penalty to Armor Class.

If a demon would be destroyed by a censuring effect, a priest can instead choose to inflict the lesser effect of the censure (or no effect at all) and gain control of that demon. Only one demon can be controlled at a time regardless of its HD. The demon becomes subject to the priest's will for 1d10 hours (rolled by the GM) plus 1 hour per priest level. During this time, the demon cannot harm the priest directly. By using the Voice again (a standard action), a priest can compel the subjugated demon to commit to a single course of action; giving orders without using the Voice has no effect. A demon gains a new Will saving throw each time it is issued orders. If the saving throw succeeds, it is not compelled to carry out the order (though it may pretend to be thusly compelled) but it remains under control. Unlike a humanoid controlled by the Compelling Voice, a subjugated demon may not interpret its orders exactly as the priest would expect, and it will never bring any harm upon itself in performing them.

Commanding a demon in such a manner is formally rejected by all denominations of the Faith as a heretical application of the Voice.

Knowledge: Few institutions can boast of as extensive a repository of knowledge as that which can be found within the churches of humanity. A priest with the Knowledge dominion immerses himself in it, cataloging rare facts and dark secrets in his mind and within private volumes. Such librarian priests are known to wield great power within their churches, their fellow priests ever mindful of the blackmail that can be wielded against them.

Class Skills: Decipher Script (Int), Knowledge (all skills taken individually) (Int), Speak Language (Int).

Skill Points Increase: The priest gains an additional 16 skill points at 1st level and 4 additional skill points each priest level thereafter. These bonus skill points must be spent on Intelligence-based skills or on languages.

Bonus Languages: A priest with the Knowledge dominion can select any language as a bonus language.

Ecclesiastic Knowledge: A priest with the Knowledge dominion has access to facts and knowledge that are both relevant and obscure. He may make a special ecclesiastic knowledge check with a bonus equal to his priest level + his Intelligence modifier to see whether he knows some relevant information about local notable people, organizations, or places. If the priest has 5 or more ranks in Knowledge (history), he gains a +2 bonus on this check. Failed checks cannot be retried. The GM determines the Difficulty Class of the check by referring to the table below. Ecclesiastic knowledge can also be used to identify a quality of a demon or item of power, just as though the priest was using the relevant Knowledge skill. He may not take 10 or 20 on any of these checks.

DC	Type of Knowledge	Examples
10	Common, known by at least a substantial minority of the local population.	A local priest's reputation for lewd behavior; common legends about a nearby region infested with demons.
20	Uncommon but available, known by a few people in the area.	A local priest's dabbling in the criminal underworld; the fact that a nearby church is in possession of a demonic item.
25	Obscure, known by few, hard to come by.	A local priest's subversion by an arcanist guild; a government official's role in a notorious demon cult; legends about an item of power lost in the region during the Great War.
30	Extremely obscure, known by very few, possibly forgotten by most who once knew it, possibly known only by those who don't understand the significance of the knowledge.	An assar's true name; the name of a city or region long since dead.

Purity: Preserving the health of principal members of the church and of society is the focus of the Purity dominion.

With it, a priest can use the Voice to heal wounds and purge disease. Normally, a priest must be specifically sanctioned to use the Voice in this manner, upon select members designated by his church. Only Despinus Chapter, which advocates the sale of all uses of the Voice to the highest bidder, permits indiscriminate healing.

Class Skill: Heal (Wis).

Whole Body: Exposure to toxins and plague hardens the priest's immunity, granting him a +1 bonus on saving throws against disease. At 5th level and every five priest levels thereafter (10th, 15th, and 20th) this bonus increases by +1.

Healing Voice: With this application of the Voice, a priest can convert regular damage to nonlethal damage in a single recipient of his choosing. There are two different methods by which he can do so, but both require that he establish physical contact with the subject. Regardless of the manner in which a character is healed, severed or brutally mangled limbs cannot be restored. Using the Healing Voice to convert damage automatically stabilizes a dying character. The subject of a priest's Healing Voice can resist if desired, making a Will saving throw (DC 10 + ½ the priest's level + the priest's Charisma modifier) to negate the effects.

With the first method, the priest can convert 1d4 points of damage per priest level, but only 1d4 points are converted on the first round in which contact is made, and an additional 1d4 points are converted on each subsequent round for which it is maintained, up to the maximum. A priest must use a standard action (an application of the aid another action) each round to continue healing a creature. If a priest is healing himself in this manner, he need take no additional actions beyond first using the Voice, but he still converts only 1d4 points of damage per round.

The second method confers a lesser benefit but requires only a single full-round action to complete, and can therefore be more practical in combat. By touching the recipient, the priest immediately converts 1d4 points of damage for every two full priest levels. However, the sudden and violent manner in which this effect is conveyed can overwhelm the recipient, thus he must make a Fortitude save (DC = half amount of damage converted) or be dazed for 1 round. A dazed character can take no actions but has no penalty to Armor Class.

Cleansing Voice: A priest with the Purity dominion can use the Cleansing Voice to rid a person of disease. As with the Healing Voice, the subject can resist if desired, making a Will saving throw (DC 10 + ½ the priest's level + the priest's Charisma modifier) to negate the effects.

To cure disease, the priest must maintain physical contact with the subject for 1d12 hours (rolled by the GM) + 1 hour per year (or portion of a year) that the subject has suffered from the disease – 1 hour per priest level, with a minimum of 1 hour required. A priest generally invokes prayers for the recipient during this time. This purification process, which begins after 1d6 minutes of uninterrupted contact have passed, is torturous, causing the subject to be wracked with painful spasms, unable to defend itself. It takes 1 point of temporary Constitution damage for each hour (or portion of an hour) of the process. If the subject survives the cleansing, it is exhausted afterward; the priest is fatigued. Being cured of a disease does not prevent reinfection after a new exposure to the same disease at a later date, and if the disease is transmitted by touch, the priest may become infected himself. Purifying a subject does not remove scars or deformations that were caused by the disease.

The purifying process is terminated automatically if contact is broken. Regardless of the reason, the likelihood that the disease is removed in this case is based on the amount of time passed compared to the time required, rounded down to the closest hour. Thus, if a priest requires 6 hours to cure a subject of disease, but the process is interrupted after 4 hours and 45 minutes, there is only a 67% chance (4/6 × 100) that the subject is rid of disease. If a priest is purifying himself of disease, he cannot end the process prematurely.

Sanctity: In assuming the Sanctity dominion, a priest acquires knowledge of magic and the power to resist and disrupt it. As with the Forbiddance dominion, this knowledge can lead to corruption should a priest attempt to use the very thing he opposes to his own gain.

Class Skills: Knowledge (magic) (Int), Spellcraft (Int).

Bonus Language: A priest with the Sanctity dominion can select Abyssal as a bonus language, in addition to the bonus languages available to him because of his race.

Holy Warding: Iron will and dedication empowers the priest against magic. He gains a +1 bonus on saving throws against spells and spell-like abilities. At 5th level and every five priest levels thereafter (10th, 15th, and 20th) this bonus increases by +1.

Disrupt Magic: A priest with the Sanctity dominion can use his Voice to disrupt the demonic energies that give form to magical effects. This power allows him to terminate the ongoing effects of a spell upon an object or creature and to seal (suppress) or unseal (restore) the magical qualities of demonic items of power. Using the Voice to disrupt magic requires a Voice check. If this check fails, the priest cannot attempt to affect the same spell instance or demonic item until he gains another priest level.

Using the Voice to dispel a magical effect is a standard action that requires a Voice check against DC 10 + twice the spell's level. If the check succeeds, the spell ends as if its duration had expired, or as though it was dismissed if it was a permanent effect. A summoned creature cannot be targeted in this manner.

The process for affecting items of power is more complex, as the magic that binds a demonic item is far greater than that which is present in spells. Sealing or unsealing a demonic item of power is a standard action that requires a Voice check against DC 15 + 5 per demonic quality present; the priest must also be touching the item in order to produce the effect. A priest does not automatically know how many qualities an item has; he must make the appropriate Knowledge check (page 60), ecclesiastic knowledge check (see above), or find out by some other means. If he is unable to determine the item's power, he may still make his Voice check against a blind DC, known by the GM. Because of the difficulty involved, the handling of such items is normally accompanied by an empowering litany (page 61).

Sealing a demonic item suppresses its powers, effectively making it a mundane item, but it does not eliminate any side effects that the item possesses. Sealing lasts a number of years equal to the difference of the Voice check result and the DC, or until such a time as the demonic item is unsealed or destroyed. Unsealing a demonic item restores it to full power and is usually performed in secrecy or against the will of the priest's church, without the assistance of an empowering litany.

War: Priests with the War dominion forego some ecclesiastic training in order to pursue the martial arts. Such militant priests are as much soldiers as they are clergymen, enforcing the will of their church with steel and blood.

Class Skills: Jump (Str), Ride (Dex), Swim (Str).

Combat Training: A priest with the War dominion has a higher base attack bonus and Fortitude save than his non-militant counterparts, as shown on Table 2-6: The Priest.

Weapon and Armor Proficiency: The priest gains proficiency with all martial weapons, with medium and heavy armor, and with shields (except tower shields).

Fallen Priests

Though a priest is officially bound by the code of conduct and worship appropriate to his denomination, he cannot lose his priestly abilities regardless of personal indiscretions or general corruption. If a priest betrays his institution, however, or commits crimes that result in expulsion from his church, he cannot gain further levels as a priest until he makes amends or converts. If a priest veers down the dark road, to worship of Azrae or any other demon, he loses his ability to sermonize and his confidence of faith, as a consequence of devotion to his new path. At the GM's discretion, he may retain these abilities if he remains convinced of his piety, whether as a result of madness or a severely deluded sense of reality; however, a fallen priest can never consecrate holy items of power. Though practicing magic is heretical, it alone does not constitute demon worship.

Rogue

"War is foolish. Why waste so many resources when you can accomplish the same thing with a dodge, a roll, and a knife in the throat. Now that's efficiency."

- "Quick Knife," assar rogue

The Earth is in turmoil, though a somewhat stable political climate and rare reprieve from war might suggest otherwise. Human civilization continues to expand; megacities swell beyond sane limits, bloated further by the convergence therein of nonhuman refugees; and a new dwerof nation struggles to reestablish order. Though the world's battlefields have become quiet, fresh battles erupt from the chaos of these regions each day. Rogues have taken the place of soldiers, mingling anonymously among the population where they propagate their own brand of conflict – gang wars over megacity districts, increased crime as the fabric of ecclesiastic rule frays, and bloody competition over the pillaging of lucrative territories abandoned during the wars.

This trend toward lawlessness exists in all races and sexes, from the Corelands courts, where upper class human assassins blend poison with politics, to the gutters of the Eastern Ridge, where hybrid street thieves scurry from one mark to the next. In the former case, deception and subterfuge are promoted as viable alternatives to direct conflict; in the latter, they are simply a means to survive. The motives that drive the rogue are numerous, and the manner in which each views his occupation is just as varied. What they share as a class is precise skill, resourcefulness, versatility, and a life based around unlawful activity. They exploit what is exposed, steal what is hidden, and murder whoever has their back turned in order to sate their indulgences.

Adventurers: Rogues adventure mostly out of need or want, though the distinction between the two blurs as they gain in ambition and experience. Most prefer urban jungles where a lucrative living can be made off of the dense population, with the help of the right connections, careful exploitation, and knives in a few backs. Some take on adventure as independents or thieves-for-hire, concerning themselves only with their own immediate needs, while rogues attached to larger institutions adventure to further the agendas of their liege, gang, or church. Regardless of their allegiances, rogues with especially potent ambition often journey beyond the safety of cities into ruined lands, where treasures far beyond the norm await.

Characteristics: Rogues are the most skilled of the classes and can apply themselves to numerous and varied disciplines. This quality not only facilitates their occupational mastery with stealth and subterfuge, but makes them second only to the arcanist as the most likely class to experiment with magic. In combat, rogues are less capable than the warrior classes when meeting an enemy face-to-face, but they can deliver devastating sneak attacks when they catch an opponent off guard. Likewise, a rogue's exceptional agility and his ability to avoid traps make

him an incredibly hard target. As a rogue's experience increases, he can choose from an array of extraordinary abilities; whether these are oriented toward assassination, extreme defensive talent, or even greater skill mastery is up to him.

Religion: Unless they are part of a church-sanctioned organization, such as the Daughters of Beyella, rogues are typically nonreligious. Some rogues do maintain a token level of religious adherence despite themselves, their faith ministered to in underground chapels by outlaw priests of Despinus Chapter. Rogues that operate only in the service of a church may be as religious as any other holy servant of that institution. Parallel to the pious rogues are those that have been wooed by demon cults, particularly in the Eastern Ridge where the word of Deihass exerts little influence. It is not uncommon for these groups to come in conflict with one another, especially where control of territory is at issue.

Background: There is no shortage of chaos in the world and most rogues are born of that chaos, whether as an extension of it or out of an effort to control it. Sprawling neighborhoods rank with poverty and violence can be found in most cities, though some governments hide it better than others. Many rogues emerge from these urban sprawls, plying their trade as their only means of survival or out of a desire to ascend to a more affluent life. Inevitably, gangs emerge and battle against one another for control of criminal industries, leaving independent rogues with little choice but to join a gang or die. On the opposite end of the class divide, spies and infiltrators are raised and groomed by official institutions, where they are trained in grace and manners as well as stealth. Betrayal and intrigue are a fact of life in any rogue's career regardless of the nature of his environment, and a rogue that blindly trusts another rogue outside of his own gang or organization – and sometimes even then – risks a violent and lonely death in a dark alley.

Other Classes: Rogues tend to get along with anyone they need to get along with, and exhibit equal distrust of their peers regardless of their profession. They find clunky armored warriors to be especially obtuse, though rogues are the first to fall back behind a living iron shield when the need arises. The superior skill that lurkers possess in the wilderness can be disruptive to a rogue's sense of superiority, resulting in a dangerous atmosphere of one-upmanship where mutual respect is absent. Unless they are operating as agents of a particular nation or church, rogues rarely ever associate with soldiers and priests, the exception being valued priests of Despinus Chapter, who live and work alongside rogues in the underbelly of human civilization.

Role: Rogues are perhaps the most diverse class in terms of what they can offer to a group. They are largely defined by their skill set and chosen specialties rather than their ability in combat, though a rogue's stealth and sneak attack can be a great boon where discretion is required. Regardless of their area of focus, rogues are generally counted on to provide access to places, people, and objects that would be otherwise unattainable.

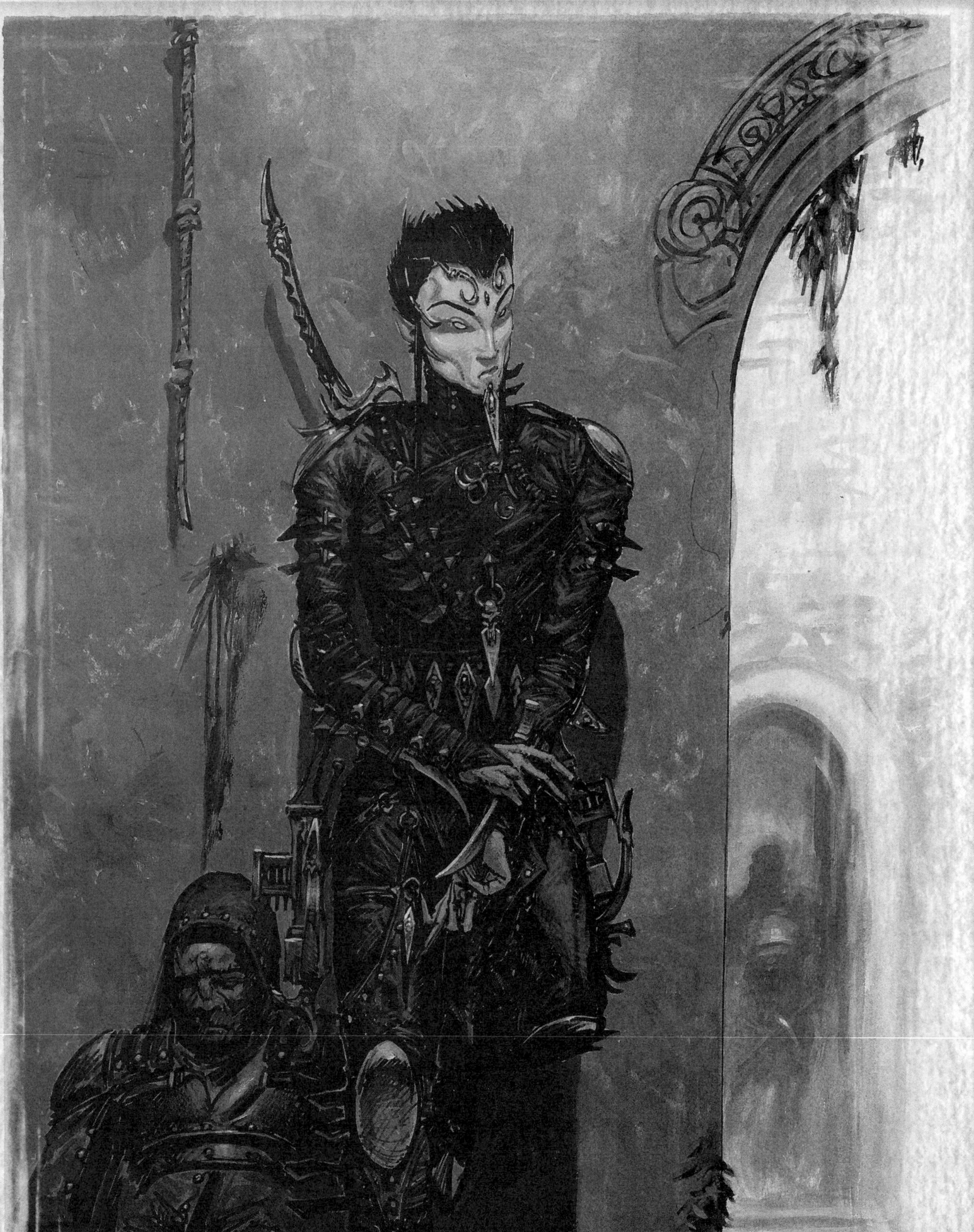

GAME RULE INFORMATION

Rogues have the following game statistics.

Abilities: Dexterity allows the lightly armored rogue to avoid attacks and bypass obstacles. Dexterity, Intelligence, and Wisdom are important for many of the rogue's class skills. A high Charisma scores also helps him outwit and manipulate his mark.

Hit Die: d6.

Class Skills

The rogue's class skills (and the key ability for each skill) are Appraise (Int), Balance (Dex), Bluff (Cha), Climb (Str), Craft (Int), Decipher Script (Int), Diplomacy (Cha), Disable Device (Int), Disguise (Cha), Escape Artist (Dex), Forgery (Int), Gather Information (Cha), Hide (Dex), Intimidate (Cha), Jump (Str), Knowledge (local) (Int), Listen (Wis), Move Silently (Dex), Open Lock (Dex), Perform (Cha), Profession (Wis), Search (Int), Sense Motive (Wis), Sleight of Hand (Dex), Spot (Wis), Swim (Str), Tumble (Dex), and Use Rope (Dex).

Skill Points at 1st Level: (8 + Int modifier) × 4.
Skill Points at Each Additional Level: 8 + Int modifier.

Class Features

All of the following are class features of the rogue.

Weapon and Armor Proficiency: A rogue's combat training focuses on agility and concealability. He is proficient with all simple weapons, plus the sap, short sword, hand repeater, retractable punching dagger, and wrist crossbow. Rogues are proficient with light armor but not with shields.

Sneak Attack: If a rogue can catch an opponent that is unable to defend himself effectively from his attack, he can strike a vital spot for extra damage. The rogue's attack deals extra damage any time his target would be denied a Dexterity bonus to AC (whether the target actually has a Dexterity bonus or not), or when the rogue flanks his target. This extra damage is 1d6 at 1st level, and it increases by 1d6 every two rogue levels thereafter. Should the rogue score a critical hit with a sneak attack, this extra damage is not multiplied.

Ranged attacks can count as sneak attacks only if the target is within 30 feet. With a sap (blackjack) or an unarmed strike, a rogue can make a sneak attack that deals nonlethal damage instead of lethal damage. He cannot use a weapon that deals lethal damage to deal nonlethal damage in a sneak attack, not even with the usual –4 penalty.

A rogue can sneak attack only living creatures with discernible anatomies – undead, constructs, oozes, plants, and incorporeal creatures lack vital areas to attack. Any creature that is immune to critical hits is not vulnerable to sneak attacks. The rogue must be able to see the target well enough to pick out a vital spot and must be able to reach such a spot. A rogue cannot sneak attack while striking a creature with concealment or striking the limbs of a creature whose vitals are beyond reach.

Trapfinding: Rogues can use the Search skill to locate manufactured or natural (lurker) traps when the task has a Difficulty Class higher than 20. Additionally, a rogue who beats a trap's Disable Device DC by 10 or more can study a trap, figure out how it works, and bypass it (with his party) without disarming it.

Table 2-7: The Rogue

Level	Base Attack Bonus	Fort Save	Ref Save	Will Save	Special
1st	+0	+0	+2	+0	Sneak attack +1d6, trapfinding
2nd	+1	+0	+3	+0	Evasion, trap sense +1
3rd	+2	+1	+3	+1	Sneak attack +2d6
4th	+3	+1	+4	+1	Uncanny dodge
5th	+3	+1	+4	+1	Sneak attack +3d6, trap sense +2
6th	+4	+2	+5	+2	
7th	+5	+2	+5	+2	Sneak attack +4d6
8th	+6/+1	+2	+6	+2	Improved uncanny dodge, trap sense +3
9th	+6/+1	+3	+6	+3	Sneak attack +5d6
10th	+7/+2	+3	+7	+3	Special ability
11th	+8/+3	+3	+7	+3	Sneak attack +6d6, trap sense +4
12th	+9/+4	+4	+8	+4	
13th	+9/+4	+4	+8	+4	Sneak attack +7d6, special ability
14th	+10/+5	+4	+9	+4	Trap sense +5
15th	+11/+6/+1	+5	+9	+5	Sneak attack +8d6
16th	+12/+7/+2	+5	+10	+5	Special ability
17th	+12/+7/+2	+5	+10	+5	Sneak attack +9d6, trap sense +6
18th	+13/+8/+3	+6	+11	+6	
19th	+14/+9/+4	+6	+11	+6	Sneak attack +10d6, special ability
20th	+15/+10/+5	+6	+12	+6	Trap sense +7

Evasion (Ex): At 2nd level and higher, a rogue can avoid even magical and unusual attacks with great agility. If he makes a successful Reflex saving throw against an attack that normally deals half damage on a successful save, he instead takes no damage. Evasion can be used only if the rogue is wearing light armor or no armor. A helpless rogue does not gain the benefit of evasion.

Trap Sense (Ex): At 2nd level, a rogue gains an intuitive sense that alerts him to danger from traps, giving him a +1 bonus on Reflex saves made to avoid traps and a +1 dodge bonus to AC against attacks made by traps. These bonuses rise to +2 when the rogue reaches 5th level, to +3 when he reaches 8th level, to +4 when he reaches 11th level, to +5 when he reaches 14th, to +6 at 17th level, and to +7 at 20th level. Trap sense bonuses gained from multiple classes stack.

Uncanny Dodge (Ex): Starting at 4th level, a rogue can react to danger before his senses would normally allow him to do so. He retains his Dexterity bonus to AC (if any) even if he is caught flat-footed or struck by an invisible attacker. However, he still loses his Dexterity bonus to AC if immobilized. If a rogue already has uncanny dodge from a different class he automatically gains improved uncanny dodge (see below) instead.

Improved Uncanny Dodge (Ex): A rogue of 8th level or higher can no longer be flanked. This defense denies another rogue the ability to sneak attack the character by flanking him, unless the attacker has at least four more rogue levels than the target does. If a character already has uncanny dodge (see above) from a second class, he automatically gains improved uncanny dodge instead, and the levels from the classes that grant uncanny dodge stack to determine the minimum rogue level required to flank the character.

Special Abilities: On attaining 10th level, and at every three levels thereafter (13th, 16th, and 19th), a rogue gains a special ability of his choice from among the following options.

Assassination (Ex): If the rogue studies his victim for 3 rounds and then makes a sneak attack with a melee weapon that successfully deals damage, the sneak attack has the additional effect of possibly either paralyzing or killing the target (rogue's choice). While studying the victim, the rogue can undertake other actions so long as his attention stays focused on the target and the target does not detect him or recognize him as an enemy. If the victim of such an attack fails his Fortitude saving throw (DC 10 + ½ the rogue's class level + the rogue's Intelligence modifier) against the kill effect, he dies. If the saving throw fails against the paralysis effect, the victim's mind and body become enervated, rendering him completely helpless and unable to act for 1d6 rounds plus 1 round for every two levels of the rogue. If the victim's saving throw succeeds, the attack is just a normal sneak attack. Once the rogue has completed the 3 rounds of study, he must make the assassination attempt within the next 3 rounds. If it is at-

tempted and fails (the victim makes his save) or if the rogue does not make the attempt within 3 rounds of completing the study, 3 new rounds of study are required before he can make another assassination attempt.

Crippling Strike (Ex): A rogue with this ability can sneak attack opponents with such precision that his blows weaken and hamper them. An opponent damaged by one of his sneak attacks also takes 2 points of Strength damage. Ability points lost to damage return on their own at the rate of 1 point per day for each damaged ability.

Defensive Roll (Ex): The rogue can roll with a potentially lethal blow to take less damage from it than he otherwise would. Once per day, when he would be reduced to 0 or fewer hit points by damage in combat (from a weapon or other blow, not a spell or special ability), the rogue can attempt to roll with the damage. To use this ability, the rogue must attempt a Reflex saving throw (DC = damage dealt). If the save succeeds, he takes only half damage from the blow; if it fails, he takes full damage. He must be aware of the attack and able to react to it in order to execute his defensive roll – if he is denied his Dexterity bonus to AC, he can't use this ability. Since this effect would not normally allow a character to make a Reflex save for half damage, the rogue's evasion ability does not apply to the defensive roll.

Improved Evasion (Ex): This ability works like evasion, except that while the rogue still takes no damage on a successful Reflex saving throw against attacks he henceforth takes only half damage on a failed save. A helpless rogue does not gain the benefit of improved evasion.

Opportunist (Ex): Once per round, the rogue can make an attack of opportunity against an opponent who has just been struck for damage in melee by another character. This attack counts as the rogue's attack of opportunity for that round. Even a rogue with the Combat Reflexes feat can't use the opportunist ability more than once per round.

Poison Use: The rogue has mastered the use of poison, and no longer risks accidentally poisoning himself when applying it to a blade. Additionally, he has grown resistant to toxic effects, gaining a +2 bonus on Fortitude saving throws against poison.

Skill Mastery: The rogue becomes so adept in the use of certain skills that he can use them reliably even under adverse conditions. Upon gaining this ability, he selects a number of skills equal to 3 + his Intelligence modifier. When making a skill check with one of these skills, he may take 10 even if stress and distractions would normally prevent him from doing so. A rogue may gain this special ability multiple times, selecting additional skills for it to apply to each time. The Spellcraft skill cannot be chosen with the skill mastery ability.

Feat: A rogue may gain a bonus feat in place of a special ability

Soldier

"My repeater is my life. I must take care of it so that it takes care of me. When my brothers have fallen, it is my last defense. When it is out of ammo, I must strike with its blade until my enemy is dead. My repeater is my life. I must take care of it so that it takes care of me."

— Soldier's mantra

Though the threat of the demon horde has passed and the battlefields of the Kingdoms War have grown still with cease-fire, war looms upon the Earth, given leave in the absence of a meaningful truce to inevitably resume where it left off. Dwerof soldiers stand guard in strictly regimented ranks over their new and fragile nation as alliances are drawn out with the human nations. The armies of the Corelands, diminished during the attrition of the Kingdoms War, grow once more in a renewed arms race. And the surly militias of the Eastern Ridge gain confidence, having been spared much of the destruction suffered by their counterparts during the wars.

Soldiers form these armies – men and women trained to defeat their enemies as individual cogs in a greater war machine. Alone, they appear as conventional warriors, but when duly accompanied by others of their kind, they become a scourge, fighting and dying in great iron formations. Soldiers carry themselves with confidence in this company, finding courage in their fellows and extending their endurance beyond natural limits. So long as homelands and enemies exist, to love and to hate, soldiers trudge onward where other warriors yield. Their legacies are enduring, as evidenced by the uncounted remains of the fallen that litter Earth's battlefields, and by the cities that survive or rot on the perimeter of those same fields.

Adventurers: No force of change on Earth has been so constant as war, providing ample employment for soldiers in service to their countries. When not occupied with strictly wartime actions, they often adventure in some official capacity for the benefit of a patron – usually a church, noble, or government official. Rarely, they are given leave to pursue their own ambitions. Regardless of where their journeys take them, soldiers are content to charge into battle for honor and glory, and to find meaning as part of something greater than themselves.

Characteristics: Though not as diverse in their individual fighting styles as fighters are, soldiers are a devastating force when working together and when called to do battle in unfavorable conditions. Soldiers are familiar with the tools of war and heavy weaponry, and develop an affinity with heavy armor superior to that of conventional fighters. As soldiers gain experience, they become even more deadly when fighting in formation with their comrades. They also become hardier, able to persist through physical and mental hardship long after others succumb, and better able to hold the line or charge down their enemies.

Religion: Soldiers are surrounded by death and destruction every day, and often find religion to be their only solace on the battlefield. Most governments encourage piety in their soldiers and provide the services of priests whenever possible to strengthen their faith and maintain their resolve in the face of adversity. Precaea's soldiers in particular, many of who share duty as servants of the Faith, are known for tearing into their enemies with a vicious determination fueled by righteous zeal.

Background: Soldiers find their way into their profession from all walks of life. Many come from poor families in rural districts, unsatisfied with life as a farmhand, escaping to military service after a drought or famine, or as a result of forced conscription. Others seek glory on the battlefield for personal reasons or to preserve a family tradition. Regardless of their origins, soldiers share an enduring bond with one another and commit themselves to protect and advance the goals of king and country. This bond extends even to their enemies, whose fallen are generally treated with dignity and respect.

Other Classes: While soldiers are most comfortable in the company of other soldiers, they are usually willing to work with anyone that has expertise beneficial to their mission. Lurkers are often recruited or developed within armed units, where they serve as scouts and tactical specialists in wild terrains. Priests are welcomed as traveling companions for the spiritual nourishment that they provide and the healing and morale-boosting powers of the Voice. Though soldiers respect the fighting prowess of fighters and barbarians, they have a hard time acclimating to their individual fighting styles and lack of discipline. Rogues and arcanists are viewed with varying levels of suspicion, depending on the disposition of the soldier and his nation or employer.

Role: Soldiers are combatants first and foremost, though they are most effective when accompanied by other soldiers. Regardless of their company, superior determination and training enables them to hold the line or rush into the chaos of battle with formidable aptitude. Their endurance and ability to shrug off fatigue and the effects of wearing armor for long periods of time also makes them reliable sentinels.

GAME RULE INFORMATION

Soldiers have the following game statistics:

Abilities: Strength and Constitution are equally important to soldiers, as they are the primary abilities that soldiers rely upon in combat. Strength allows then to not only hit better and harder, but it allows them to effectively don heavy plate armor. A high Constitution score helps them to absorb damage and outlast their foes on the battlefield.

Hit Die: d8.

Class Skills

The soldier's class skills (and key abilities for each skill) are Climb (Str), Craft (Int), Handle Animal (Cha), Heal (Wis), Intimidate (Cha), Jump (Str), Knowledge (geography), Knowledge (military tactics) (Int), Knowledge (nobility and royalty) (Int), Ride (Dex), Spot (Wis), Survival (Wis), and Swim (Str).

Skill Points at 1st Level: (4 + Int modifier) × 4.
Skill Points at each other Level: 4 + Int modifier.

Class Features

All of the following are class features of the soldier:

Weapons and Armor Proficiency: The soldier's armament training is unmatched by any other class. He is proficient with all simple and martial weapons, all bows (short, composite short, long, composite long), assault weapons (assault crossbow and assault repeater), with all types of armor (light, medium, and heavy), and with shields (including tower shields).

Formation Defense (Ex): When a soldier fights in formation with other soldiers, he gains a +1 bonus to Armor Class and a +1 bonus on saving throws against fear effects. A formation is established any time two or more soldiers are fighting next to one another. On a 5 ft. grid map, they must be in adjacent squares. Soldiers need not have the same facing to be in formation.

At 6th level, both the Armor Class bonus and save bonus increase to +2. At 11th level, a soldier is better able to manage the flanks of those soldiers that are nearest to him. No adjacent soldiers can be flanked, except by a rogue or soldier of four levels higher than the actual soldier being targeted. At 16th level, no adjacent soldiers can be flanked under any circumstances.

Military Provisions: At 1st level, the soldier receives two melee weapons and one ranged weapon of his choice, the total value of which cannot exceed 150 gp, as well as a set of composite armor. His government, liege, or company officially owns these items, thus they do not count against his starting gold.

Salary: As long as he is in active service, a soldier receives a monthly salary of 5 gp per soldier level.

Brothers in Arms (Ex): Starting at 2nd level, a soldier's attacks are more effective when fighting alongside his comrades. If he is in formation with one or more allied soldiers (see formation defense, above), he receives a +1 circumstance bonus on all attack rolls and a +1 circumstance bonus on damage rolls with melee weapons. This bonus increases by +1 at 5th level and every five levels thereafter (10th, 15th, and 20th level).

Endurance: A soldier gains Endurance as a bonus feat at 2nd level.

Pack March (Ex): At 3rd level, the soldier is conditioned to carry more than his strength would normally allow. When determining carrying capacity and encumbrance, he is considered to have a +2 Strength score.

Iron Skin (Ex): At 4th level, a soldier is so accustomed to wearing heavy armor that he can sleep in it without suffering from fatigue. He can also don and remove any type of armor hastily without penalty.

Quick Readying (Ex): At 5th level, a soldier can ready a weapon against a charge as a move action.

Many As One (Ex): At 8th level, a soldier's mind and body are tuned to the other soldiers in his formation, so that they can fight together as a single cohesive unit. All allied soldiers of at least 8th level that are also in formation can act on the highest initiative score rolled amongst them. The highest-level soldiers act first, followed by those with the highest Dexterity score. If the soldier with the highest initiative score is incapacitated or killed, the next highest score is used.

Mighty Charge (Ex): At 11th level, a soldier can run down his enemies with great ferocity. When attacking on a charge, he gets an additional +2 bonus on attack rolls.

Hold The Line (Ex): At 14th level, a soldier is treated as one size larger when resisting a bull rush or blocking an overrun.

Maximize Cover (Ex): By 17th level, a soldier has learned how to maximize the cover available to him, even in the least defensible of positions. His bonuses to AC and Reflex saves are doubled for the turn, to +8 and +4, respectively, but he cannot attack. Maximizing cover takes no time itself, but a soldier can do it only during his action, not in response to someone else's action. Some limited degree of cover must be available in order for a soldier to maximize it.

TABLE 2-8: THE SOLDIER

Level	Base Attack Bonus	Fort Save	Ref Save	Will Save	Special
1st	+1	+2	+0	+2	Formation defense, military provisions, salary
2nd	+2	+3	+0	+3	Brothers in arms +1, Endurance
3rd	+3	+3	+1	+3	Pack march
4th	+4	+4	+1	+4	Iron skin
5th	+5	+4	+1	+4	Brothers in arms +2, quick readying
6th	+6/+1	+5	+2	+5	Formation defense (improved defense)
7th	+7/+2	+5	+2	+5	
8th	+8/+3	+6	+2	+6	Many as one
9th	+9/+4	+6	+3	+6	
10th	+10/+5	+7	+3	+7	Brothers in arms +3
11th	+11/+6/+1	+7	+3	+7	Formation defense (guarded flanks), mighty charge
12th	+12/+7/+2	+8	+4	+8	
13th	+13/+8/+3	+8	+4	+8	
14th	+14/+9/+4	+9	+4	+9	Hold the line
15th	+15/+10/+5	+9	+5	+9	Brothers in arms +4
16th	+16/+11/+6/+1	+10	+5	+10	Formation defense (impenetrable flanks)
17th	+17/+12/+7/+2	+10	+5	+10	Maximize cover
18th	+18/+13/+8/+3	+11	+6	+11	
19th	+19/+14/+9/+4	+11	+6	+11	
20th	+20/+15/+10/+5	+12	+6	+12	Brothers in arms +5

Chapter 3: Skills & Feats

"Father Glorifus was quite a preacher, God bless 'im. He could convert men right in the thick'a battle – dodgin' and weavin', barely squintin' an eye when a blow actually landed on 'im. But when one'a those blows turned out ta be from a weapon of demonic qualities – wielded by some cesspool-dwellin' hybrid no less – all that grace poured out in a gush like it was nuthin'."

- Fraebek Jonnes, mercenary attached to the Church of Deihass

This chapter presents new and modified skills and feats for use in a DARK LEGACIES campaign.

Skills

Table 3-1: Skill Points Per Level shows the number of skill points that all available player character classes get.

TABLE 3-1: SKILL POINTS PER LEVEL

Class	1st-level Skill Points[1]	Higher-level Skill Points[2]
Arcanist	(6 + Int modifier) × 4	6 + Int modifier
Barbarian	(4 + Int modifier) × 4	4 + Int modifier
Fighter	(2 + Int modifier) × 4	2 + Int modifier
Lurker	(6 + Int modifier) × 4	6 + Int modifier
Priest	(4 + Int modifier) × 4	4 + Int modifier
Rogue	(8 + Int modifier) × 4	8 + Int modifier
Soldier	(4 + Int modifier) × 4	4 + Int modifier

1 Humans add +4 to this total at 1st level.
2 Humans add +1 each level.

Skill Changes

The Use Magic Device skill is not used in DARK LEGACIES, as magic is not limited to specific classes, and magic items have been superseded by demonic and holy items of power. All characters, regardless of their class, use the Spellcraft skill to decipher, learn, identify, and cast spells. Identification and understanding of items of power is achieved through Knowledge checks. Such items cannot be manipulated into operating differently regardless of the user's finessing.

Skill Descriptions

The following section describes new skills as well as additions or changes to existing skills.

Concentration (Con)

The Concentration skill has been extended in DARK LEGACIES to facilitate sermonizing, and also to properly characterize the greater difficulty of casting spells under duress. Consequently, maintaining concentration while casting a spell is more difficult and the ramifications of failing a Concentration check while casting are farther reaching.

Check: You must make a Concentration check whenever you might potentially be distracted (by taking damage, by being the target of a sermon or spell, etc) while engaged in some action that requires your full attention. Such actions include casting a spell, concentrating on an active spell (such as *cardiac assassin*), directing a spell (such as *vermin eyes*), using a spell-like ability (such as a demon's *shapeshift* ability), sermonizing, or using a skill that would provoke an attack of opportunity (such as Disable Device, Open Lock, and Use Rope, among others). In general, if an action wouldn't normally provoke an attack of opportunity, you need not make a Concentration check to avoid being distracted.

Concentration DC[1]	Distraction
10 + damage dealt	Damaged during the action.[2]
10 + half of continuous damage last dealt	Taking continuous damage during the action.[3]
Distracting spell's save DC	Distracted by nondamaging spell.[4]
Distracting sermon's save DC	Sermon.[5]
10	Vigorous motion (on a moving mount, in a small boat in rough water).
15	Violent motion (on a galloping horse, in a small boat in rapids).
20	Extraordinarily violent motion (earthquake).
15	Entangled.
20	Grappling or pinned (You can cast only spells for which you have the required material components in hand, and which require no specific placement of those components that would be impossible under the circumstances).
5	Weather is a high wind carrying blinding rain or sleet.
10	Weather is wind-driven hail, dust, or debris.
15	Spell component is briefly disrupted during casting.[6]

1 If you are trying to cast, concentrate on, or direct a spell when the distraction occurs, add the level of the spell to the indicated DC.
2 Such as during the casting of a spell with a casting time of 1 round or more, the preaching of a sermon, or the execution of an activity that takes more than a single full-round action (such as Disable Device). Also, damage stemming from an attack of opportunity or readied attack made in response to the spell being cast or the action being taken.
3 Such as from *bone spasm*.
4 If the spell allows no save, use the save DC it would have if it did allow a save.
5 Beneficial sermons are only distracting if you are casting a spell.
6 If the Concentration check succeeds but the disruption is so severe that it leaves no conceivable means of completing the spell (such as a vital component being smashed), you must terminate the spell on your next turn.

If the Concentration check succeeds, you may continue with the action as normal. If the check fails, the action automatically fails and is wasted. If you were in the process of casting a spell when you lost concentration, the spell fails and there may be additional consequences; you must immediately make a Spellcraft check as though the casting process completed, adding the difference of the Concentration check DC and the Concentration check result to the Spellcraft DC. If this Spellcraft check succeeds, there are no further consequences; if the check fails, you suffer a spell failure side effect (see Chapter 6: Magic for complete rules on casting spells and spell failure). If you were concentrating on an active spell when your concentration failed, the spell ends without consequence. If you were directing a spell, the direction fails but the spell remains active. If you were using a spell-like ability, that use of the ability is lost. If you were sermonizing, the sermon ends immediately. A skill use also fails, and in some cases a failed skill check may have additional ramifications.

The table above summarizes the various types of distractions that necessitate a Concentration check. If the distraction occurs while you are trying to cast a spell, you must add the level of the spell that you are trying to cast to the appropriate Concentration DC. If multiple distractions are present, make a check for each one; any failed Concentration check indicates that the task is not completed. The latter is especially important since most spells in DARK LEGACIES have a casting time longer

Table 3-2: Skills is a listing of available skills and their relevant information, including for which classes they are class skills (C) and for which classes they are cross-class (cc) skills.

TABLE 3-2: SKILLS

Skill	Arc	Bbn	Ftr	Lrk	Prs	Rog	Sol	Untrained	Key Ability
Appraise	C	cc	cc	cc	cc	C	cc	Yes	Int
Balance	cc	cc	cc	cc	cc	C	cc	Yes	Dex¹
Bluff	C	cc	cc	cc	C	C	cc	Yes	Cha
Climb	cc	C	C	C	cc	C	C	Yes	Str¹
Concentration	C	cc	cc	cc	C	cc	cc	Yes	Con
Craft	C	C	C	C	C	C	C	Yes	Int
Decipher Script	C	cc	cc	cc	cc	C	cc	No	Int
Diplomacy	C	cc	cc	cc	C	C	cc	Yes	Cha
Disable Device	cc	cc	cc	C	cc	C	cc	No	Int
Disguise	cc	cc	cc	cc	cc	C	cc	Yes	Cha
Escape Artist	cc	cc	cc	cc	cc	C	cc	Yes	Dex¹
Forgery	cc	cc	cc	cc	cc	C	cc	Yes	Int
Gather Information	C	cc	cc	cc	C	C	cc	Yes	Cha
Handle Animal	cc	C	C	C	cc	cc	C	No	Cha
Heal	C	cc	cc	C	cc	cc	C	Yes	Wis
Hide	cc	cc	cc	C	cc	C	cc	Yes	Dex¹
Intimidate	cc	C	C	cc	C	C	C	Yes	Cha
Jump	cc	C	C	C	cc	C	C	Yes	Str¹
Knowledge (architecture and engineering)	C	cc	cc	cc	cc	cc	cc	No	Int
Knowledge (demonism)	C	cc	cc	cc	cc	cc	cc	No	Int
Knowledge (dungeoneering)	C	cc	cc	C	cc	cc	cc	No	Int
Knowledge (geography)	C	cc	cc	C	cc	cc	C	No	Int
Knowledge (history)	C	cc	cc	cc	C	cc	cc	No	Int
Knowledge (industry)	C	cc	cc	cc	cc	cc	cc	No	Int
Knowledge (local)	C	cc	cc	cc	C	C	cc	No	Int
Knowledge (magic)	C	cc	cc	cc	cc	cc	cc	No	Int
Knowledge (military tactics)	C	cc	cc	cc	cc	cc	C	No	Int
Knowledge (monsters)	C	cc	cc	C	cc	cc	cc	No	Int
Knowledge (nature)	C	cc	cc	C	cc	cc	cc	No	Int
Knowledge (nobility and royalty)	C	cc	cc	cc	cc	cc	C	No	Int
Knowledge (religion)	C	cc	cc	cc	C	cc	cc	No	Int
Listen	cc	C	cc	C	cc	C	cc	Yes	Wis
Move Silently	cc	cc	cc	C	cc	C	cc	Yes	Dex¹
Open Lock	cc	cc	cc	cc	cc	C	cc	No	Dex
Perform	cc	cc	cc	cc	cc	C	cc	Yes	Cha
Preach	cc	cc	cc	cc	C	cc	cc	No	Cha
Profession	C	cc	cc	C	C	C	cc	No	Wis
Ride	cc	C	C	C	cc	cc	C	Yes	Dex
Search	cc	cc	cc	C	cc	C	cc	Yes	Int
Sense Motive	cc	cc	cc	cc	C	C	cc	Yes	Wis
Sleight of Hand	C	cc	cc	cc	cc	C	cc	No	Dex¹
Speak Language	C	cc	cc	cc	cc	cc	cc	No	None
Spellcraft	C	cc	cc	cc	cc	cc	cc	No	Int²
Spot	cc	cc	cc	C	cc	C	C	Yes	Wis
Survival	cc	C	cc	C	cc	cc	C	Yes	Wis
Swim	cc	C	C	C	cc	C	C	Yes	Str³
Tumble	cc	cc	cc	cc	cc	C	cc	No	Dex¹
Use Rope	cc	cc	cc	C	cc	C	cc	Yes	Dex

1 Your armor check penalty, if any, also applies.

2 Your armor check penalty, if any, applies to Spellcraft checks only when casting a spell.

3 Double the normal armor check penalty applies to checks.

than 1 round, thus exposing you to multiple potential distractions over the course of casting such spells.

Action: None. Making a Concentration check doesn't take an action; it is either a free action (when attempted reactively) or part of another action (when attempted actively).

Try Again: Yes, though a success doesn't cancel the effect of a previous failure, such as the loss of a spell you were casting or the disruption of a spell you were concentrating on.

Special: You can use Concentration to cast a spell, use a spell-like ability, sermonize, or use a skill defensively, so as to avoid attacks of opportunity altogether. This does not apply to other actions that might provoke attacks of opportunity (such as movement or reloading a repeater). The DC of the check is 15 (plus the spell's level, if casting a spell or using a spell-like ability defensively). If the Concentration check succeeds, you may attempt the action normally without provoking attacks of opportunity. If the Concentration check fails, the related action also fails (with any appropriate consequences), just as though it had been disrupted by a distraction.

A character with the Combat Casting feat gets a +4 bonus on Concentration checks made to cast a spell or use a spell-like ability while on the defensive or while grappling or pinned. A character with the Battle Preaching feat gets a +4 bonus on Concentration checks made to sermonize under the same circumstances.

Craft (Int)

The Craft skill has additional uses in DARK LEGACIES. It can be used to create masterpiece armaments, to build piecemeal armor from scrap, and to clear a jam in a repeating weapon.

Creating Masterpiece Armaments: You can make a masterpiece armament: a weapon, piece of ammunition, or suit of armor that conveys a bonus on its use through one or more superior qualities. Creating masterpiece armaments requires at least 10 ranks in the relevant Craft skill: Craft (weaponsmithing) for most conventional weapons, Craft (bowmaking) for bows, Craft (mechanical weapons) for repeaters, and Craft (armorsmithing) for armor. To create a masterpiece armament, you create each quality as though it were a separate item in addition to the base item. Each quality has its own price and a Craft DC of 20. Once both the base item and all of the desired qualities are completed, the masterpiece armament is finished. Note: the cost you pay for the masterpiece components is one-third of the given amount, just as it is for the cost in raw materials. See page 77 for details on each masterpiece quality.

Assembling Piecemeal Armor: Piecemeal armor (page 76) can be assembled using Craft (armorsmithing) with minimal tools, from actual armor sources or other materials which may be suitable as armor, such as a metal plate salvaged from an industrial ruin. It can also be continually upgraded to a higher Armor Bonus as more parts are found. Upgraded piecemeal armor assumes all of the characteristics of piecemeal armor with the new Armor Bonus.

When evaluating source material, assume that any suit of standard armor can be broken down into piecemeal armor with an Armor Bonus that is ¼ of its original value. If the armor being salvaged is one size smaller than you are, halve this number. If it is one size larger, double it. Armor Bonus equivalencies of unconventional sources (such as scrap metal) are calculated at the GM's discretion.

When determining assembly time, treat piecemeal armor as costing 1gp per point of Armor Bonus added (there is no actual cost associated with building piecemeal armor from scavenged materials). The Craft DC is 7 + the final Armor Bonus of the armor. Thus, building Piecemeal Armor AB3 from scratch and upgrading Piecemeal Armor AB2 to Piecemeal Armor AB3 would both be DC 10, though the existing set would take less time to upgrade than the new set would take to build from scratch (1gp for 1 point of Armor Bonus vs. 3gp for 3 points of Armor Bonus).

Clearing a Repeater Jam: When a repeater jams (page 71), it cannot be fired again until the jam is cleared. Clearing a jam requires a Craft (mechanical weapons) check (DC8 for clip-fed repeaters or DC12 for chain-fed repeaters). This is a full-round action that provokes attacks of opportunity. If the check is successful, the jam is cleared (the offending bolt is ejected) and you can attack again normally on your next turn. If the Craft check fails by less than 5, the jam is cleared but the clip or ammunition belt is destroyed and the repeater must be reloaded (the actual bolts can be recovered later). If you fail your Craft check by 5 or more, the clip or ammunition belt is destroyed and the repeater is damaged so badly that it cannot be fired again until repaired. Regardless of the check result, the ammunition that would have normally been used when the jam occurred is always destroyed.

When using the Craft skill to make one of the unique items described in Chapter 4: Equipment, refer to the following table for the required Craft skill and DC.

Item	Craft Skill	Craft DC
Flashpowder, matches	Alchemy[1]	15
Fire bomb, flash bomb, smoke bomb	Alchemy[1]	20
Expanding smoke bomb, rocket flare	Alchemy[1]	25
Hand repeater	Mechanical Weapons	18
Light and heavy repeater	Mechanical Weapons	16
Double-barreled repeater	Mechanical Weapons	18
Chain-fed assault repeater	Mechanical Weapons	20

1 You must have the Craft Incendiary feat to craft this item.

Special: Novags get a +2 bonus on Craft (mechanical weapons) checks due to their extensive familiarity with modern weaponry.

Heal (Wis)

In addition to the uses described in the *Player's Handbook*, the Heal skill can be used to identify medical conditions. Such identifications are especially useful in the course of investigations and the acquisition of spell components.

Check: The DC and effect depend on the task you attempt.

Task	Heal DC
Determine cause of death	25
Determine time of death	25

Determine Cause of Death: You can determine the cause of a creature's death. If your check succeeds, you can tell if the creature died as a result of natural causes, injury, poison, disease, or due to a special effect such as a spell. If you beat the DC by 10 or more, you can determine the exact cause of death, such as the type of weapon used or what specific disease the creature died from (if magic was the cause, you cannot determine the specific spell used unless you know the spell or have previously witnessed its effects). If the check fails by 4 or less, you cannot determine the cause of death. If it fails by 5 or more, you incorrectly deduce a cause of death.

Determine Time of Death: You can infer the approximate time of death for a corpse. If your check succeeds, you determine if the creature died within the last 24 hours, the last week, or longer. If the check fails by 4 or less, you cannot determine the time of death. If it fails by 5 or more, you incorrectly deduce a time of death.

Action: Determining cause or time of death requires 30 minutes for each.

Try Again: Varies. If you have only attempted to determine cause or time of death in the field, you may make one more attempt with the same body in a lab.

Special: If you have access to a healer's kit, you get a +2 circumstance bonus on the check. If you have access to a medical lab, you get a +4 circumstance bonus to the check. These bonuses do not stack.

Knowledge (Int; Trained Only)

Knowledge encompasses a number of unrelated skills. Knowledge represents a study of some body of lore, regional information, or a scientific discipline. Listed below are typical fields of study.

- Architecture and engineering (buildings, infrastructure, fortifications)
- Demonism (demons, demon cults, demonic glyphs, tainted locales)
- Dungeoneering (caverns, spelunking, subterranean life)
- Geography (lands, terrain, climate, people)
- History (the Reversion, wars, migrations, founding and fall of cities)
- Industry (advanced technology, steam power, manufacturing techniques)
- Local (guilds, legends, personalities, inhabitants, laws, customs, traditions)
- Magic (arcanism, arcane symbols, cryptic phrases, demonic items of power)
- Military tactics (formations, logistics, strategy, siege engines)
- Monsters (rare monsters and legendary creatures)
- Nature (animals, plants, seasons and cycles, weather)
- Nobility and royalty (lineages, heraldry, family trees, mottoes, personalities)
- Religion (factions, scripture, ecclesiastic tradition, rites and rituals, holy items of power)

Most fields are broad enough to represent general competence with all of that field's topics. Some fields however are too general and require focus on a specific topic within that field. When acquiring ranks in Knowledge (local), Knowledge (geography), or Knowledge (religion) you must apply them to a specific topic of focus within that field.

When acquiring ranks in Knowledge (local), apply them instead to a specific city or localized region, such as Knowledge (Pelleton) or Knowledge (county of Braile). When acquiring ranks in Knowledge (Geography), apply them to a specific country or geographic region, such as Knowledge (Precaea) or Knowledge (Deadlands). When acquiring ranks in Knowledge (religion), apply them instead to one or more of the following denominations of the Faith: Knowledge (Beyella Divinity), Knowledge (Church of Deihass), Knowledge (Despinus Chapter), or Knowledge (Prelacy of the Divine Adjudicator); demon cults are covered by Knowledge (demonism).

Check: Answering a question within your field of study has a DC of 10 (for very easy questions), 15 (for basic questions), or 20 to 30 (for very tough or obscure questions).

In many cases, you can use this skill to identify various creatures as specified in each field of study, and their special powers or vulnerabilities. In general, the DC of such a check equals 10 + the creature's HD. A successful check allows you to remember or extrapolate a bit of useful information about that creature.

Knowledge (magic) and Knowledge (religion) can be used to identify demonic and holy items of power, respectively. A successful DC 30 check reveals basic information about the item. In the case of demonic items, you must also be able to read Demon Cuneiform, as all demonic items are inscribed with glyphs that give a hint to their purpose and use during the binding process. When identifying a holy item, the Knowledge (religion) subgroup matching the denomination that consecrated the item must be used, otherwise, you suffer a −5 circumstance penalty on your skill check.

Whether identifying a monster or item, the GM can give another useful piece of information for every 5 points by which your check result exceeds the DC.

Action: Usually none. In most cases, making a Knowledge check does not require an action – you know the answer or you don't.

Try Again: No. The check represents whether you know the answer or not.

Synergy: If you have 5 or more ranks in Knowledge (architecture and engineering), you get a +2 bonus on Search checks made to find secret doors or hidden compartments.

If you have 5 or more ranks in Knowledge (demonism), you get a +2 bonus on Sense Motive checks made against cultists and demon worshipers.

If you have 5 or more ranks in Knowledge (dungeoneering), you get a +2 bonus on Survival checks made while underground.

If you have 5 or more ranks in Knowledge (geography), you get a +2 bonus on Survival checks made to keep from getting lost or to avoid natural hazards for the regions in which you have those ranks.

If you have 5 or more ranks in Knowledge (history), you get a +2 bonus on ecclesiastic knowledge checks (see the Priest class in Chapter 2: Classes).

If you have 5 or more ranks in Knowledge (industry), you get a +2 bonus on Craft (mechanical weapons) and Craft (steam tech) checks.

If you have 5 or more ranks in Knowledge (local), you get a +2 bonus on Gather Information checks for the locales in which you have those ranks.

If you have 5 or more ranks in Knowledge (magic), you get a +2 bonus on Spellcraft checks made to decipher and learn spells and to create a binding circle.

If you have 5 or more ranks in Knowledge (military tactics), you get a +2 bonus on attack rolls made when firing or directing the fire of a siege weapon.

If you have 5 or more ranks in Knowledge (monsters), you get a +2 bonus on Survival checks made to track all creature types, excluding animals, humanoids, and demons.

If you have 5 or more ranks in Knowledge (nature), you get a +2 bonus on Survival checks made in aboveground natural environments (desert, forest, hill, marsh, mountain or plains).

If you have 5 or more ranks in Knowledge (nobility and royalty), you get a +2 bonus on Diplomacy checks.

If you have 5 or more ranks in Knowledge (religion) for your own denomination, you get a +2 bonus on Preach checks.

If you have 5 or more ranks in Survival, you get a +2 bonus on Knowledge (nature) checks.

Special: A priest with the Knowledge dominion can use his ecclesiastic knowledge ability to identify a demon or item of power. If he also has the corresponding skill, he can attempt to acquire knowledge through either means, or through both if one check or the other fails.

Preach (Cha; Trained Only)

You are skilled at reciting scripture with righteous zeal and improvising sermons based on the tenets of your faith.

Check: You can impress the faithful and the skeptical alike with your dictation.

Action: Varies. Preach checks may be used to perform daily duties before a congregation. Opposed preach checks may be used to settle disputes on matters of theology and the interpretation of scripture. The priest's Preach-based sermonize ability is described in that class's description (page 42). Priests can also make Preach checks to recite litanies that empower another priest's Voice.

Perform Empowering Litany: You can recite powerful, repetitive prayers that bolster a priest's effectiveness whenever he is required to make a Voice check. In order to perform the litany, you must have the corresponding holy dominion. Thus, you must have the Consecration dominion to assist in the creation of holy items of power and the Sanctity dominion to aid in the sanctifying (sealing or unsealing) of demonic items of power.

An empowering litany requires the participation of at least four priests, in addition to the priest who is actually using the Voice. For every hour that the priest is assisted, he gains a +1 circumstance bonus to his Voice check. This bonus increases by +1 for every four additional priests, to a maximum bonus of +3 per hour with twelve priests supporting and a maximum total bonus of +10, regardless of how many priests are involved and for how long they pray. Each priest involved must make a single Preach check (DC 10) at the end of each hour to have an effect; extra priests are often assigned to critical rituals in case one or more of their brethren falter in their prayers. If the ritual is interrupted to the point that less than four priests are available to preach simultaneously, the accumulated bonus is lost and the ritual must begin anew for a benefit to be imparted. An empowering litany is the only manner in which a Voice check can be bolstered.

Retry: Retries are allowed, but they don't negate previous failures. A creature that saves against your sermonize ability is immune to any further sermons from you for 24 hours.

Special: A priest must have at least 3 ranks in Preach to recite Binding Rapture, Courage of the Blessed, and Violent Reclamation. A priest needs 6 ranks in Preach to recite Heretic's Distress, 9 ranks to recite Purity of Thought, 12 ranks to recite Divine Might of the Righteous, 15 ranks to recite Fear of God, 18 ranks to recite Tide of the Masses, and 21 ranks to recite True Faith. See Sermonize in the priest's class description, page 42.

Synergy: If you have 5 or more ranks in Knowledge (religion) for your current religion, you get a +2 bonus on Preach checks.

Speak Language (None; Trained Only)

Speak Language functions as described in the *Player's Handbook*, though not all races can read and write their own racial language (see Chapter 1: Races). The following table lists common languages and their alphabets.

Language	Typical Speakers	Alphabet
Abyssal	Demons, arcanists	Demon Cuneiform
Assyric	Assar	Assyric
Bralish	Humans	Ilfernese
Briggan	Briggs	Dwerkant[1]
Dwerkant	Dwerofs	Dwerkant
Eldraamik	Eldrin	Eldraamik
Ilfernese	Humans	Ilfernese
Low Common	Humans, nonhuman immigrants	Ilfernese
Novska	Novags	Novska
Precaean	Humans	Ilfernese
Sarlesse	Humans	Ilfernese

1 Written Briggan uses only one third of the Dwerkant character set.

Spellcraft (Int; Trained Only; Armor Check Penalty*)

All aspects of magic, from learning to casting, require the Spellcraft skill. See Chapter 6: Magic for complete rules on using magic.

Spellcraft DC	Task
15 + spell level	Decipher a spell from a spellbook, scroll, or other medium, so that it can be learned. Retry is allowed the following day. Requires a number of hours equal to the spell's level, minus your Intelligence modifier (if positive); minimum 1 hour required.
15 + (2 × spell level)	Learn a previously deciphered spell from a spellbook, scroll, or other medium. No retry for that spell after two consecutive failures until you gain at least 1 rank in Spellcraft. Requires a number of days equal to twice the spell's level, minus your Intelligence modifier (if positive); minimum 1 day required.
15 + spell level	Identify a spell being cast. (You must know the spell being cast. You must also hear the spell's verbal component or see the spell's material or focus components being used.) No action required. No retry.
20 + spell level	Identify a spell that is already in place and in effect. (You must know the spell that is in place. You must also be able to see or detect the effects of the spell.) No action required. No retry.
20	Create a binding circle, which holds a called demon for an additional 1d4 rounds when casting *call demon*. No retry. The GM makes this check.
10 + (spell level squared)[1]	Cast a spell. Time required varies. No retry.

1 Additional modifiers may exist. See page 97.

Check: You can decipher the basic purpose and functioning of written spells, learn those deciphered spells, identify spells that you know as they are being cast or that are already in place, and cast spells. The DCs for Spellcraft checks relating to various tasks are summarized in the table above. The entries in this table replace all entries for the Spellcraft skill found in the *Player's Handbook*.

Action: Varies; as noted above.

Try Again: See above.

Special: You must have Speak Language (Abyssal) in order to use the Spellcraft skill. Your armor check penalty only applies to Spellcraft checks when using the skill to cast a spell. You cannot Take 10 or Take 20 with the Spellcraft skill.

Synergy: If you have 5 or more ranks in Knowledge (magic), you get a +2 bonus on Spellcraft checks made to decipher and learn spells and to create a binding circle.

Feats

The low-magic nature of DARK LEGACIES necessitates changes to the list of available feats found in the *Player's Handbook* and in third party material. Generally speaking, the following types of feats are not suitable for use in a DARK LEGACIES campaign: feats that simplify or empower magic; feats that relate to concepts not present in DARK LEGACIES, such as scribing scrolls and schools of magic; feats that are specific to druids and clerics; and feats that enable generic magic item creation. Create Demonic Item is a new feat required to create demonic items. The *Dark Legacies Campaign Guide* contains complete rules on creating demonic and holy items of power.

Specifically, the following feats should not be used in a DARK LEGACIES campaign: Augment Summoning, Brew Potion, Craft Magic Arms and Armor, Craft Rod, Craft Staff, Craft Wand, Craft Wondrous Item, Empower Spell, Enlarge Spell, Eschew Materials, Extend Spell, Extra Turning, Forge Ring, Greater Spell Focus, Greater Spell Penetration, Heighten Spell, Improved Counterspell, Magical Aptitude, Maximize Spell, Natural Spell, Quicken Spell, Scribe Scroll, Silent Spell, Spell Focus, Spell Mastery, Spell Penetration, Still Spell, and Widen Spell. Combat Casting is a permissible feat.

New Feats

The following feats supplement those found in the *Player's Handbook* and follow all of the normal rules for feat acquisition and use.

Battle Preaching

You are adept at sermonizing in the thick of combat.

Prerequisite: Priest level 1st.

Benefit: You get a +4 bonus on Concentration checks made to sermonize standard or referenced sermons while on the defensive or while you are grappling or pinned.

Craft Incendiary

You can create alchemical compounds with various violent effects.

Prerequisite: Int 15, Craft (alchemy) 8 ranks.

Benefit: You can use the Craft (alchemy) skill to create any of the incendiaries detailed in Chapter 4: Equipment.

Create Demonic Item

You can reconstruct a deconstructed demon (see *deconstruct into spell form*, page 116) in such a way that only specific qualities materialize rather than the whole demon. These qualities can then be bound into an item, thus creating a demonic item of power.

Prerequisite: Int 15, Knowledge (magic) 8 ranks, Spellcraft 8 ranks.

Benefit: You can create a demonic item of power with one quality.

Special: You can gain Create Demonic Item up to four times. Each time you take the feat, you can implant one more quality into a demonic item when you create it.

Dominion Focus

Your focus on a particular holy dominion grants you with a superior Voice.

Prerequisite: Priest level 2nd.

Benefit: Choose one of your holy dominions for which there is an associated application of the Voice (Consecration, Dominance, Forbiddance, Purity, or Sanctity). When using the Voice for this application, you are considered to be one priest level higher than normal.

Special: You can gain Dominion Focus multiple times. Its effects do not stack. Each time you take the feat, it applies to a new holy dominion.

Extra Sermonizing

You can sermonize more often than normal.

Prerequisite: Sermonize ability.

Benefit: Each time you take this feat, you can use your sermonize ability three more times per day than normal.

Normal: Without this feat, you can use the sermonize ability once per day per priest level.

Special: You can gain Extra Sermonizing multiple times. Its effects stack. Each time you take the feat, you can sermonize an additional three times per day.

Extra Voice

You can use the Voice more often than normal.

Prerequisite: Ability to use the Voice.

Benefit: Each time you take this feat, you can use the Voice one additional time per day.

Normal: Without this feat, you can use the Voice a number of times per day equal to half your priest level + your Charisma modifier.

Special: You can gain Extra Voice multiple times. Its effects stack. Each time you take the feat, you can use the Voice an additional time per day.

Greater Battle Preaching

An undeterred focus while in combat along with considerable improvisational mastery allows you to recite essential sermons while attacking.

Prerequisites: Battle Preaching, priest level 1st, War dominion.

Benefit: You can sermonize Courage of the Blessed and Heretic's Distress as move actions rather than standard actions, and are thus free to sermonize and attack on the same turn.

Normal: A character without this feat must spend a standard action to sermonize.

Special: Assisted sermons still require a full-round action each turn, and cannot be combined with this feat.

Greater Dominion Focus

Your continued focus on a particular holy dominion to which you have already applied the Dominion Focus feat grants you with an even greater Voice.

Prerequisites: Dominion Focus with selected holy dominion, priest level 2nd.

Benefit: Choose one of your holy dominions for which there is an associated application of the Voice (Consecration, Dominance, Forbiddance, Purity, or Sanctity). When using the Voice for this application, you are considered to be one priest level higher than normal. This bonus stacks with the bonus from Dominion Focus.

Special: You can gain Greater Dominion Focus multiple times. Its effects do not stack. Each time you take the feat, it applies to a new holy dominion to which you already have applied the Dominion Focus feat.

A.Smith

Improved Dodge

Your considerable grace and precise awareness of your opponents' positions allows you to dodge blows especially well.

Prerequisites: Dex 15, Wis 13, Dodge.

Benefit: During your action, you may either designate one opponent against whom you receive a +2 dodge bonus to Armor Class, or two opponents against both of whom you receive a +1 bonus to Armor Class. You can select new opponents on any action. This bonus replaces the bonus from Dodge.

A condition that makes you lose your Dexterity bonus to Armor Class (if any) also makes you lose dodge bonuses. Also, dodge bonuses stack with each other, unlike most other types of bonuses.

Special: A fighter may select Improved Dodge as one of his fighter bonus feats.

Last Breath

Your fundamental stubbornness and abject terror of an uncertain afterlife allows you to cling to your current life with greater tenacity than most.

Prerequisite: Con 13, Diehard, Endurance.

Benefit: You do not die until your hit points reach 10 less than normal. The effects of the Diehard feat do not apply when reduced to this range.

Normal: A character without this feat normally dies when his hit points reach –10 minus his Con modifier (if positive).

Prodigy

You were born to greatness with a skill of your choice.

Benefit: You get a +4 bonus on all skill checks with the chosen skill.

Special: You may only take this feat as a first level character. This bonus stacks with all other bonuses to the chosen skill, including Skill Focus. If applied to a skill that has subgroups, such as Craft, the Prodigy feat only counts against a single subgroup rather than the entire group. Knowledge skills cannot be chosen with the Prodigy feat.

Secret Lore

You have uncovered and consumed a rare or forbidden body of lore, rich in dark secrets.

Prerequisite: Priest level 1st, Knowledge dominion.

Benefit: You get a +2 bonus on all Ecclesiastic Knowledge checks.

Special: You can gain Secret Lore multiple times. Its effects stack.

Seductive

Your powers of seduction help you to get your way when the lights go out.

Prerequisite: Cha 13.

Benefit: You get a +4 bonus on all Charisma-based checks when employing intimate contact with an intelligent humanoid, whether they are normally receptive to your race and gender or not.

Signature Weapon

Choose a specific weapon in your repertoire that you have used for at least one month. You have become so intimate with this particular weapon's quirks and qualities that you can wield it with especially formidable skill.

Prerequisite: Proficiency with selected weapon, base attack bonus +1.

Benefit: You gain a +1 bonus on attack and damage rolls you make using the selected weapon.

Special: You can gain Signature Weapon multiple times. Its effects do not stack. Each time you take the feat, it applies to a new weapon. This feat cannot be transferred to a new weapon if you lose your signature weapon. At the GM's discretion, a signature weapon that has been destroyed can be reforged so that your bonus still applies when using it.

A fighter may select Signature Weapon as one of his fighter bonus feats.

Street Smart

You have learned how to get around and in the know when in urban environments.

Benefit: You get a +2 bonus on all Bluff, Gather Information, and Knowledge (local) checks when in an urban environment at least as large as a small town.

Upper Class

You were born into an upper-class family, and thus gifted with the privileges of wealth and education.

Prerequisite: Human.

Benefit: When creating your character, you start with twice the maximum starting gold for your class. Additionally, all Knowledge skills are class skills.

Special: You may only take this feat as a first level character.

Chapter 4: Equipment

"You could feel the ground shake before they even came into view – a column of the Divinity's holy guard, escorting some religious procession. Dressed in their finest plate, fierce maces rising from their hands like a divine hand reaching to Heaven, they looked unstoppable. What enemy of the Faith, be they demon or mortal, wouldn't be cowed at such a sight?"

- Janus Duversal, citizen of Montrey

The world has been plagued by conflict since the dawning of known history; it was war that reclaimed the Earth from the demons, and it is war that continues to drive mortals against one another. In the midst of this savage environment are industrious cities and proud nations, where the bloodied tools of war are perpetually resold and manufactured, to the benefit of any adventurer that is willing to pay.

This chapter details the equipment available to characters in Dark Legacies as well the setting's system of commerce and a technological overview. The weapons and armor presented herein replace those found in the *Player's Handbook*. In addition to these standard armaments, there are expanded rules for superior weapons and armor, new rules for piecemeal armor, and a section with adventuring and specialty gear.

Starting Equipment

Use the values below to determine the starting gold for a character at 1st level according to his class. Hybrids begin play with less gold than other races, as indicated.

TABLE 4-1: RANDOM STARTING GOLD

Class	Amount (average)[1]
Arcanist	4d4 × 10 (100 gp)
Barbarian	3d4 × 10 (75 gp)
Fighter	6d4 × 10 (150 gp)
Lurker	5d4 × 10 (125 gp)
Priest	5d4 × 10 (125 gp)
Rogue	5d4 × 10 (125 gp)
Soldier	2d4 × 10 (50 gp)

1 Hybrid characters multiply their starting gold dice by only ×2 rather than ×10.

When creating a character above 1st level, refer to Table 4-2: Character Wealth By Level to determine available resources. In addition to mundane and masterpiece equipment (see Masterpiece Armaments, page 77), contacts, and property, this wealth can be used to "purchase" spells and items of power (see Chapter 6: Magic). Rather than actually buying these items, however, exchanging gold for them represents time spent acquiring exotic goods over the course of the character's career, and a preference for unconventional reward over conventional treasure hunting.

TABLE 4-2: CHARACTER WEALTH BY LEVEL

Character Level	Wealth	Character Level	Wealth
2nd	900 gp	12th	44,000 gp
3rd	1,350 gp	13th	55,000 gp
4th	2,700 gp	14th	70,000 gp
5th	4,500 gp	15th	90,000 gp
6th	6,500 gp	16th	115,000 gp
7th	9,500 gp	17th	150,000 gp
8th	13,500 gp	18th	195,000 gp
9th	18,000 gp	19th	250,000 gp
10th	24,500 gp	20th	320,000 gp
11th	33,000 gp		

Items of power cost 3,500 gp per quality for demonic items and 5,000 gp per quality for holy items. Regardless of how much gold a character has, however, he cannot purchase more than 1 item of power quality for every two full character levels. Thus, an 8th-level character can purchase multiple items of power, but there can be no more than a total of 4 qualities between them.

Spell cost is based on the spell's rarity as well as its level. Uncommon spells have a base cost of 250 gp per spell level, rare spells have a base cost of 500 gp per spell level, legendary spells have a base cost of 1,500 gp per spell level, and lost spells have a base cost of 6,000 gp per spell level. A complete matrix listing spell cost by level and rarity is shown on Table 4-3: Spell Cost By Level and Rarity. A character should always have more uncommon and rare spells than he has legendary spells, and he should only possess lost spells at the GM's discretion since such spells are so exotic and powerful.

TABLE 4-3: SPELL COST BY LEVEL AND RARITY

Spell Level	Uncommon	Rare	Legendary	Lost
1st	250 gp	500 gp	1,500 gp	6,000 gp
2nd	500 gp	1,000 gp	3,000 gp	12,000 gp
3rd	750 gp	1,500 gp	4,500 gp	18,000 gp
4th	1,000 gp	2,000 gp	6,000 gp	24,000 gp
5th	1,250 gp	2,500 gp	7,500 gp	30,000 gp
6th	1,500 gp	3,000 gp	9,000 gp	36,000 gp
7th	1,750 gp	3,500 gp	10,500 gp	42,000 gp
8th	2,000 gp	4,000 gp	12,000 gp	48,000 gp
9th	2,250 gp	4,500 gp	13,500 gp	54,000 gp

When spells are purchased at character creation, the character is in possession of an actual copy of the spell and has also learned it if his Intelligence is high enough. It should generally be assumed that all spells in the character's possession have been cast at least once, including those that inflict ability drain or other permanent effects (GM's discretion). Additionally, a character acquires taint (see Chapter 7: Grit & Consequences) relative to the number of spells purchased and his level, representing corruption from the learning and casting of those spells over his career. Treat the resulting taint threshold as the maximum threshold that the character has reached when determining recovery potential. Characters with arcanist levels always have more taint than dabblers, due to their increased reliance on and addiction to magic. The amount of taint acquired is determined by the following formula:

Taint = number of spells purchased +
      number of spells purchased × ¼ character level +
      number of spells purchased × ½ levels in arcanist or arcanist-based
        prestige class

Thus, a 10th-level rogue that purchases 13 spells has 45 points of taint: 13 + (13 × 2.5) + (0); a 5th-level rogue/5th-level arcanist that purchases the same quantity of spells has 78 points of taint: 13 + (13 × 2.5) + (13 × 2.5); and a 10th-level arcanist with those same spells has 110 points of taint: 13 + (13 × 2.5) + (13 × 5).

Currency

In rural communities and distant colonies, where essential goods are hard to come by, barter is as common as the trading of coins. But in civilized lands, the hard currencies of gold, silver, copper, and occasionally platinum and steel are the standard. A dizzying array of coins, varying in shape and origin, changes hands each day. Moneychangers exploit this chaos, exchanging foreign coins for a lesser quantity of local coins, seemingly identical in weight but bearing a favored religious symbol or crest. Commonly traded coins are listed in Table 4-4: Common Currencies (names listed in brackets are nicknames for the given coin). Also traded are various precious gems and raw ores, retrieved or stolen from the Crimson Reach and other rich regions.

Ilfernese coins, octagonal in shape and emblazoned with the nation's crest on one side and a portrait of the current king on the other, find heavy use in the Corelands, especially in former provinces of the Ilfernac Empire: Precaea, Sarlat, and Ilfernac itself. Precaea and Sarlat maintain their own unique currencies, minted as a symbol of national strength and pride. Precaean coinage is square, with a depiction of the Prelate Ascendant and the phrase "prosperity by law through Deihass" on one side, and the national crest along with year of production on the reverse. Sarlat only presses prestigious metals – platinum, gold, and silver – shunning coppers as the currency of lesser nations. Its coins are circular with the national symbol on one side, and the Divinityhead, symbol of the Beyella Divinity, on the reverse along with the year of mint. Even the chaotic Eastern Ridge has a unique currency – coins of various shapes, sizes, and value, many of which have the heads of long-deposed warlords or governors stamped upon them; the names of these coins change so frequently that they are usually simply called by value, and that value drops sharply outside of the Eastern Ridge.

Adding to the chaos is assar and dwerof currency and the coins of nations destroyed during the Great War. Assar currency, unlike most others, makes heavy use of precious gems with a wide range of values, as well as triangular gold pieces that are pierced at the base, much like their jewelry, so that they can be worn on a belt or necklace. These gold pieces are fashioned in two sizes: a full-size piece is worth 1 gp and is called an "eethchass," meaning full-piece in Assyric; smaller, 5 sp value pieces are called "sethchass," meaning half-piece. Dwerof currency consists of delicate but precisely molded rectangular bricks of varying size, minted from gold and steel, with the flag of Dwer Zotha stamped on both sides. Like the currency of the Eastern Ridge, dwerof currency bricks are referred to only by value.

Paper money, unique to the Corelands, is less common than coinage, but far more practical in the case of large monetary values. Private, heavily guarded banks print bills of varying design, from plain to ornate depending on value and the bank's prestige. These banks make considerable profit from surcharges levied against transactions, and use seals of authenticity, multiple signatures, and dated records as controls against forgery. In addition to such markers, they often require supporting proof of ownership, such as a matching seal or password, before exchanging large quantities of coins back for bills. All banks are local to a particular city, thus paper currency has questionable value outside of the city of issue. It is all but worthless outside of the Corelands, except among those that travel there frequently and are assured of possessing the necessary articles of ownership.

Table 4-4: Common Currencies

Coins	Value[1]	Composition
Ilfernac		
Royal (king-piece)	5 gp	Gold
Crown (castle)	1 gp	Gold
Half Crown (half-piece, halfer)	5 sp	Silver
Lark (wailer)	1 sp	Silver
Double (fifth)	2 cp	Copper
Penny (bit, cougher, copper)	1 cp	Copper
Precaea		
Trine (triple)	3 gp	Gold
Shield (flag)	1 gp	Gold and silver
Quarter (fourth)	2.5 sp	Silver
Single (platter)	1 sp	Silver
Penny (bit, cougher, copper)	1 cp	Copper
Sarlat		
Figurehead (bitch)	10 gp	Platinum
Throne (thorn)	5 gp	Gold
Standard (stem)	1 gp	Gold
Trade-piece (petal)	1 sp	Silver

1 1 gp = 10 sp = 100 cp

Technology

The technology found across the Earth is as diverse as the races and classes who make up its populace, and a history of near-constant war and conflict has had considerable effects on its advancement. Military demands have pushed advances in engineering through the ages, which has filtered down to civilian applications. At the same time, the sheer destructive impact of so many wars has left many regions and cultures in practically primitive states.

Technology levels vary from early industrialization, including the limited use of steam power and factory-based manufacturing, to primitive cultures that fashion a life from stone and hide. Complex alchemy is still considered an exotic science in most cultures, and is often maligned as the purview of arcanists. Regardless of the actual level of technology available in a region, the general population has little access to it save for the most basic devices or advancements. Thus, though steam-powered armored transports shuttle prestigious emissaries between megacities in the Corelands, common citizens rely on walking and conventional horse-driven transportation. Exposure to higher levels of technology is generally limited to the workplace, where overworked laborers coated in sweat and grime tend to machines that fill the purses of powerful guilds.

Novags are recognized as the most technologically advanced race on Earth, though a great deal of that expertise was lost when Novdy Ottor fell during the Great War. Many of their most fantastic inventions, such as the steam-powered battle-suits of their fabled Combat Inventioneers, are now mostly a myth, found only in bits and pieces among the ruins of their homeland. Still, most of the world's steam engines, towering buildings, and sophisticated systems of infrastructure owe their creation to novag engineers, who traded extensively with humans during their foundation years and directly contributed to the establishment of the Corelands megacities.

Humans have been careful to study the sciences of their nonhuman neighbors, matching or surpassing them in recent years. Precaea is the most advanced human nation, but this technological drive frequently comes at the expense of the country's natural resources and population. Regardless of the actual nation, all human megacities share the common markers of a drive forward without consideration to the consequences. They are frequently subject to choking waves of coal smoke, which diminishes the all-important sun to a tiny red orb; sewage conduits spill over from the strain of so many citizens; and rivers disgorge tons of waste while simultaneously being used for bathing and the drinking supply, leading to frequent outbreaks of disease and stunted life spans. The growth of the human population and further industrialization has also resulted in a steady depletion of resources throughout the Corelands.

The remainder of the world's regions is subject to a similar amount of diversity. The Eastern Ridge consistently falls behind the Corelands, due to the lack of strong governorship and a generally haphazard attitude toward expansion. The dwerofs of Dwer Betha learned much from the novags during early conflicts between the two races, but much of that technology was left behind when they fled to Dwer Zotha. The same loss of technology and knowledge follows for the assar, who once populated the world in massive cities the likes of which have yet to be duplicated by human or novag achievement. The assar are now relegated to a single city in the southern deserts and the meager resources accorded them by such harsh climes. Ban Got is clearly the most primitive region of the world, where the brigg race is trapped in a perpetual rut of basic survival.

Advanced technology is detailed in the *Dark Legacies Campaign Guide*.

Weapons

Many new weapons are available in DARK LEGACIES while some old weapons have been removed, replaced, or adjusted. See Table 4-5: Weapons for a complete list of available weapons and their characteristics.

Ranged Weapon Considerations

Evolving trends in warfare and the rapid proliferation of novag technology have changed the disposition of ranged weaponry in DARK LEGACIES. Crossbows are the most common ranged weapon available, by virtue of their ease of use and mass production; even adventurers without specific martial training can use all single shot crossbows, from small handheld units to heavy crossbows. Repeaters – mechanically loaded repeating crossbows – are by and large a military weapon, and are less common among the general populace. The use of conventional bows has dwindled to the point where they are considered exotic weapons, used only by barbarian cultures and by lurkers.

Weapon Descriptions

All new weapons found on Table 4-5: Weapons are described below, along with any special options the wielder ("you") has for their use. Any weapons not listed function as described in the *Player's Handbook*.

Assassin's Fan: This subtle weapon is employed exclusively by the Daughters of Beyella: secret police of the Beyella Divinity. A casual glance betrays nothing more than an ornate fan, popular in Sarlat and eastern Ilfernac. But closer observation reveals strong steel vanes and razor-sharp blade edges that can slice through flesh with ease. You can open an assassin's fan (expanding it from its sealed state) as a free action.

Blowgun: The blowgun is a simple weapon, consisting of a long hollow tube through which you blow tiny needles. It is popular among assassins for its ability to deliver poisons quietly and with minimal motion. Blowgun needles deal minimal damage but they can deliver injury and contact poisons. Additionally, you only take a –15 penalty rather than a –20 penalty on Hide checks when sniping with a blowgun. Normally, firing a blowgun requires two hands. However, you can shoot, but not load, a blowgun with one hand at a –2 penalty on attack rolls. Loading a blowgun is a move action that provokes attacks of opportunity.

Blowgun Needle: Blowgun needles are tiny 2-inch long metal projectiles. A needle that hits its target is destroyed; one that misses has a 75% chance of being destroyed or lost. Needles are often packaged in ornate cases that are designed to protect the carrier from any poison that may have been applied to them. Blowgun needles cannot be crafted with masterpiece qualities.

Cleaver and Heavy Cleaver: The cleaver is a vicious weapon, only slightly longer than a short sword but much heavier, with a deep curved blade. The heavy version is about the length of a longsword but must be wielded two-handed due to its size and weighting. Cleavers are popular among militias, demon armies, and adventurers that prefer brutality to grace. It has high wounding potential, and can inflict grievous injuries when wielded by a skilled warrior.

Crossbow, Assault: The assault crossbow is a very large heavy crossbow – essentially a mini-ballista – with damage and penetration capabilities far superior to standard-sized crossbows. It is rarely seen outside of the military, due to its considerable expense, weight, and long reload time. Assault crossbows use oversized bolts that function identically to standard crossbow bolts, though the two cannot be used interchangeably. You must use two hands to fire an assault crossbow. Loading an assault crossbow involves winding back a heavy winch and requires two full-round actions. If two people reload the assault crossbow, it instead takes each of them one full-round action. Reloading an assault crossbow provokes attacks of opportunity.

Crossbow, Wrist: This weapon consists of a precise crossbow mechanism that is strapped under the forearm and fired with a measured hand movement. It is a favorite among assassins and spies for its invisibility to casual onlookers, but the length of time required to reload it relegates it to use as a one-shot surprise weapon. You shoot a wrist crossbow with one hand. You can shoot a wrist crossbow with each hand, but you take a penalty on attack rolls as if attacking with two light weapons. You must reload a wrist crossbow with the opposite hand. Loading a wrist crossbow is a full-round action that provokes attacks of opportunity. You get a +2 bonus on Sleight of Hand checks to conceal a wrist crossbow on your body.

Dagger, Retractable Punching: This easy to conceal weapon is favored by rogues and by those who wish to retain some measure of defense in cities where weapons are peace-bonded or confiscated. Normally concealed under the forearm of the wearer, a sharp flick of the wrist activates a spring mechanism that pushes the punch dagger forward on a guiding rail and into the hand. Deploying a punch dagger is a free action. Retracting the dagger requires you to push it back into place and is a move action that provokes attacks of opportunity. You get a +2 bonus on Sleight of Hand checks to conceal a retractable punching dagger on your body; this bonus stacks with the +2 bonus to conceal a normal dagger, resulting in a total bonus of +4. Retractable punching daggers cannot be worn with armor heavier than light.

Gauntlet, Clawed: Clawed gauntlets are metal gauntlets with wicked, razor-sharp claws fixed onto the fingertips or above the knuckles. An attack with clawed gauntlets is considered an armed attack. An opponent cannot use a disarm action to disarm you of clawed gauntlets. The claws are designed in such a way that they do not restrict the wielding of weapons but they do prevent you from employing skills that require the use of your hands, such as opening a lock or manipulating spell components; the gauntlet or gauntlets must first be removed. The cost and weight given are for a single gauntlet.

Greathammer: The greathammer is a mighty two-handed version of the warhammer, favored by the dwerof military. It has a large, heavy head and counterweight on opposite ends of a metal or reinforced shaft, which usually has molded handgrips to help the wielder negotiate the weapon's considerable weight.

Gutter: The gutter, named for its tendency to gruesomely disembowel an enemy with a well-placed stab, is the last-ditch weapon for many ranged combatants. It consists of a pair of short blades that mount on a special harness, which in turn is affixed to the end of a repeater. Thus, the wielder uses the force of both hands to drive it home. The gutter cannot be wielded as a weapon if detached from a repeater. It cannot be crafted with masterpiece qualities and does not benefit from any qualities present in the attached repeater. An attached gutter does not impose any attack penalties on the firing of a repeater. Attaching or removing a gutter is a full-round action that provokes attacks of opportunity.

Longarm: The longarm, so named because it extends a warrior's reach, is a standard military weapon normally wielded on wide-open battlefields where there is sufficient room to maneuver. You can strike opponents 10 feet away with it, but you cannot use it against an adjacent foe.

Mace, Spiked: The spiked mace is a versatile weapon, consisting of a mace shaft topped with a metal sleeve and ball, which is riveted through with sharp spikes. Though it is heavier than a standard mace and does not have the piercing capability of the spiker, the spiked mace is a practical weapon nonetheless and extremely intimidating.

Maul, Dwerof: This weapon is the most popular among combat-trained dwerofs both within and beyond the protected walls of their insular homeland. It has a long handle and a heavy head, both of which make it too unwieldy to use in one hand; thus, it is an exotic weapon. A medium-sized character can use a dwerof maul two-handed as a martial weapon, or a large-sized creature can use it one-handed in the same way. Dwerofs, however, are trained in the use of the weapon from adolescence and always treat it as a martial weapon even when using it in one hand.

Repeaters: Repeaters are mechanically loaded crossbow weapons, invented by the novags and refined many times since by novag and human craftsmen. They represent the ultimate evolution of warfare and have been adopted as the standard ranged weapon of all civilized militaries. Many variants of repeater exist: the hand repeater for sidearm duty, the light and heavy repeater for battlefield use, the double-barreled repeater for maximum intimidation, and the chain-fed assault repeater for unparalleled carnage.

Repeaters are crafted from steel and superior materials, making them sturdy but very expensive; they regularly outlive their owners. Standard repeaters utilize a quick-loading bolt clip and a mechanical lever that simultaneously draws the bowstring while loading a bolt from the clip into the barrel of the bow. When the lever is fully articulated, a trigger is depressed and the string is released, firing the bolt, or bolts in the case of the double-barreled variant. Chain-fed repeaters use an ammunition belt rather than a clip, and a heavy winding lever to load and fire the bolts from the belt while passing it through to the other side. This mechanical action allows repeaters to be fired at an incredible rate, permitting the wielder to use a full attack to fire as many bolts as he has attacks (and ammunition remaining), or a standard attack to fire a single bolt.

All repeaters use the same size and type of bolts regardless of actual clip or belt size. Normally, repeaters are reloaded by swapping out a spent ammunition clip or belt for a full one. Alternately, spent clips can be refilled at a rate of one bolt per move action; doing so does not require that the clip be removed, and thus circumvents standard reloading procedure. Ammunition belts can also be refilled but discharging and refeeding the belt requires that you perform the normal reloading procedure (see below).

The only significant drawback to repeating weapons is lower reliability than can be found with conventional crossbows. When a natural attack roll of 1 is made with a repeater, the weapon jams, unless it is faultless (page 78), and it cannot be fired again until the jam is cleared. Clearing a jam requires a Craft (mechanical weapons) check. See the Craft skill (page 59) for complete rules on clearing a repeater jam.

The specific attributes for each repeater variant are listed below.

Repeater, Hand: The hand repeater is a convenient weapon that is normally worn as a backup sidearm rather than depended upon as a primary weapon. It utilizes a mini-clip that holds six bolts. Swapping out a mini-clip is a move action that provokes attacks of opportunity. You must use two hands in order to use the reloading lever (and therefore to get multiple attacks), and to reload. However, you can shoot, but not load, a hand repeater with one hand at no penalty. You can shoot a hand repeater with each hand, but you take a penalty to attack rolls as if attacking with two light weapons.

Repeater, Light and Heavy: These repeaters are very common, and are the weapon of choice for anyone that can handle martial ranged weapons. Though heavy repeaters have superior range and damage capabilities, light repeaters are much more commonplace due to lower cost and the practicality of their lower weight. Light and heavy repeaters both utilize a standard-size clip that holds twelve bolts. Swapping out a standard clip is a full-round action that provokes attacks of opportunity. You must use two hands in order to fire and reload a light or heavy repeater. They cannot be fired or reloaded with one hand.

Repeater, Double-Barreled: The double-barreled variant of the repeater is an imposing weapon and the least common of the variants. It can deal considerably more damage than even a heavy repeater but this advantage is offset by inferior range and accuracy. It is slightly larger than the heavy repeater and utilizes a special double clip that holds two sets of twelve bolts (it cannot use two standard clips in place of a double clip). Swapping out a double clip is a full-round action that provokes attacks of opportunity. You must use two hands in order to fire and reload a double-barreled repeater. It cannot be fired or reloaded with one hand. A single attack roll with a −2 penalty is made for both bolts each time it is fired, though damage is rolled separately for each bolt.

Repeater, Chain-Fed Assault: The assault repeater is the largest of the repeaters, devastating in its potential, and rarely seen outside of the military. It must normally be fired from the ground on a built-in retractable tripod due to its bulk, but it can be fired while standing if attached to a novag-engineered assault harness (page 81). Regardless, you must use two hands to fire an assault repeater. Unlike the assault crossbow, which deals greater damage than standard crossbows by firing oversized bolts, the assault repeater's effectiveness is based on a higher rate of fire than clip-fed repeaters while using standard-sized ammunition. It utilizes an ammunition belt that can vary in size, though 48-bolt belts are the standard. Swapping out an ammunition belt requires three full-round actions. If two people reload the assault repeater, it instead takes each of them two full-round actions. Reloading an assault repeater provokes attacks of opportunity.

When using a full attack action, you can opt to fire the assault repeater in burst mode to gain more attacks than you can normally make in a round with a standard repeater. Burst mode involves loading and firing the repeater with the hand crank at extreme speed so that additional bolts are fired, albeit with lesser accuracy. While attacking in burst mode, you can make a total number of attacks equal to up to twice your normal number; if you have the Rapid Shot feat this number increases by 1. Extra attacks are made at your highest base attack bonus, but all attacks made in that round (the extra ones and the normal ones) take a cumulative −2 penalty for each extra attack. You cannot take advantage of the Precise Shot feat while firing in burst mode.

Thus, a 9th level soldier (BAB +9/+4) can make up to four attacks in burst mode (two normal, two extra), with attack bonuses of +5/+0/+5/+5 (−4 penalty on all attacks from two extra attacks). That same soldier with the Rapid Shot feat can make up to five attacks in burst mode (two normal, two extra, plus one for Rapid Shot), with attack bonuses of +3/−2/+3/+3/+3 (−6 penalty on all attacks from three extra attacks).

Repeater Clip: Repeater clips are available in mini-, standard-, and double-capacity form factors and are usually constructed of strong wood reinforced with metal strips or entirely from steel. Mini clips hold six bolts, standard clips hold twelve bolts, and double-capacity clips hold two sets of twelve bolts. Normally, different clip sizes cannot be interchanged between repeater variants: hand repeaters must use mini-clips, light and heavy repeaters must use standard clips, and double-barreled repeaters must use double clips. The single exception is with light and heavy repeaters, both of which can use a mini-clip if desired.

Repeater Ammunition Belt: Ammunition belts are custom-designed rolls of fabric and leather that are lined with special metal

TABLE 4-5: WEAPONS

Simple Weapons	Cost	Dmg (S)	Dmg (M)	Critical	Range Increment	Weight[1]	Type[2]
Unarmed Attacks							
Gauntlet	2 gp	1d2	1d3	×2	-	1 lb.	Bludgeoning
Unarmed strike	-	1d2[3]	1d3[3]	×2	-	-	Bludgeoning
Light Melee Weapons							
Dagger	2 gp	1d3	1d4	19-20/×2	10 ft.	1 lb.	Piercing or slashing
Dagger, punching	2 gp	1d3	1d4	×3	-	1 lb.	Piercing
Gauntlet, clawed	10 gp	1d3	1d4	×2	-	1 lb.	Slashing
Gauntlet, spiked	5 gp	1d3	1d4	×2	-	1 lb.	Piercing
Sickle	6 gp	1d4	1d6	×2	-	2 lb.	Slashing
One-Handed Melee Weapons							
Club	-	1d4	1d6	×2	10 ft.	3 lb.	Bludgeoning
Mace	12 gp	1d6	1d8	×2	-	6 lb.	Bludgeoning
Mace, spiked	15 gp	1d6	1d8	×2	-	8 lb.	Bludgeoning and piercing
Pick	4 gp	1d3	1d4	×3	-	3 lb.	Piercing
Shortspear	1 gp	1d4	1d6	×2	20 ft.	3 lb.	Piercing
Two-Handed Melee Weapons							
Gutter	10 gp	1d3	1d4	×3	-	3 lb.	Piercing
Longspear[4]	5 gp	1d6	1d8	×3	-	9 lb.	Piercing
Quarterstaff[5]	-	1d4/1d4	1d6/1d6	×2	-	4 lb.	Bludgeoning
Spear	2 gp	1d6	1d8	×3	20 ft.	6 lb.	Piercing
Ranged Weapons							
Crossbow, hand	75 gp	1d4	1d6	19-20/×2	30 ft.	2 lb.	Piercing
Crossbow, heavy	40 gp	1d8	1d10	19-20/×2	120 ft.	8 lb.	Piercing
Crossbow, light	30 gp	1d6	1d8	19-20/×2	80 ft.	4 lb.	Piercing
Dart	5 sp	1d3	1d4	×2	20 ft.	½ lb.	Piercing
Javelin	1 gp	1d4	1d6	×2	30 ft.	2 lb.	Piercing

sleeves. These sleeves hold repeater bolts firmly in place when at rest and then release them when manipulated by a chain-fed repeater's loading mechanism. Ammunition belts are typically bunched into compact rolls or left to hang loose so that they can be draped over an arm or shoulder. Their price and weight varies depending on how many bolts they hold, based on a value of 5 sp and ¼ lb. per bolt sleeve. 48-bolt belts, also known as "twelve packs", are the standard size, at 24gp and 12 lb.

Repeater Bolt: Repeater bolts are typically fashioned of wood and tipped with a steel head. They are shorter than standard crossbow bolts and have no feathers, so that lateral movement is not impeded when the bolt is fired. Repeater bolts cannot be used interchangeably with crossbow bolts. A repeater bolt that hits its target is destroyed; one that misses has a 50% chance of being destroyed or lost.

Spiker and Heavy Spiker: The spiker is a fearsome piercing weapon designed to concentrate the entire force of its blow on a small area. It is composed of a metal shaft or metal-reinforced wooden shaft and a heavy metal spike that protrudes from both sides of the head. The standard spiker is a popular weapon among war priests and mercenaries, while military personnel favor the much longer two-handed heavy spiker.

Spiker, Hooked: This slightly longer two-handed variant of the standard spiker utilizes a curved blade edge on one end of the head and a sharpened metal spike on the other, rather than two uniform spikes. This asymmetrical head design makes the hooked spiker an extraordinarily versatile and deadly weapon. If attacking with the spiked end, the hooked spiker has a critical multiplier of ×4. If attacking with the slashing end, it only has a critical multiplier of ×2 but it can be used to make trip attacks. If you are tripped during your own trip attempt, you can drop the hooked spiker to avoid being tripped.

Whip, Barbed: Barbed whips function identically to normal whips except that they are crafted of thicker leather and are sewn through with metal barbs so that they deal lethal rather than nonlethal damage.

TABLE 4-5: WEAPONS CON'T

Martial Weapons	Cost	Dmg (S)	Dmg (M)	Critical	Range Increment	Weight[1]	Type[2]
Light Melee Weapons							
Axe, throwing	8 gp	1d4	1d6	×2	10 ft.	2 lb.	Slashing
Hammer, light	1 gp	1d3	1d4	×2	20 ft.	2 lb.	Bludgeoning
Handaxe	6 gp	1d4	1d6	×3	-	3 lb.	Slashing
Sap	1 gp	1d4[3]	1d6[3]	×2	-	2 lb.	Bludgeoning
Shield, light	special	1d2	1d3	×2	-	special	Bludgeoning
Spiked armor	special	1d4	1d6	×2	-	special	Piercing
Spiked shield, light	special	1d3	1d4	×2	-	special	Piercing
Sword, short	10 gp	1d4	1d6	19-20/×2	-	2 lb.	Piercing
One-Handed Melee Weapons							
Battleaxe	10 gp	1d6	1d8	×3	-	6 lb.	Slashing
Cleaver	15 gp	1d4	1d6	18-20/×2	-	6 lb.	Slashing
Flail	8 gp	1d6	1d8	×2	-	5 lb.	Bludgeoning
Longsword	15 gp	1d6	1d8	19-20/×2	-	4 lb.	Slashing
Spiker	15 gp	1d4	1d6	x4	-	8 lb.	Piercing
Shield, heavy	special	1d3	1d4	×2	-	special	Bludgeoning
Spiked shield, heavy	special	1d4	1d6	×2	-	special	Piercing
Warhammer	12 gp	1d6	1d8	×3	-	5 lb.	Bludgeoning
Two-Handed Melee Weapons							
Cleaver, heavy	30 gp	1d6	2d4	18-20/×2	-	8 lb.	Slashing
Flail, heavy	15 gp	1d8	1d10	19-20/×2	-	10 lb.	Bludgeoning
Greataxe	20 gp	1d10	1d12	×3	-	12 lb.	Slashing
Greatclub	5 gp	1d8	1d10	×2	-	8 lb.	Bludgeoning
Greathammer	20 gp	1d10	1d12	×3	-	14 lb.	Bludgeoning
Greatsword	50 gp	1d10	2d6	19-20/×2	-	8 lb.	Slashing
Longarm[4]	10 gp	1d6	2d4	×3	-	12 lb.	Slashing
Spiker, heavy	30 gp	1d8	1d10	x4	-	12 lb.	Piercing
Spiker, hooked	25 gp	1d6	2d4	x4/×2	-	10 lb.	Piercing or slashing
Ranged Weapons							
Repeater, hand	100 gp	1d4	1d6	19-20/×2	25 ft.	3 lb.	Piercing
Repeater, light	120 gp	1d6	1d8	19-20/×2	70 ft.	6 lb.	Piercing
Repeater, heavy	200 gp	1d8	1d10	19-20/×2	100 ft.	12 lb.	Piercing
Repeater, double-barreled	400 gp	1d6×2	1d8×2	19-20/×2	90 ft.	15 lb.	Piercing

TABLE 4-5: WEAPONS CON'T

Exotic Weapons	Cost	Dmg (S)	Dmg (M)	Critical	Range Increment	Weight[1]	Type[2]
Light Melee Weapons							
Assassin's Fan	50 gp	1d4	1d6	×3	-	3 lb.	Slashing
Dagger, retractable punching	50 gp	1d3	1d4	×3	-	1 lb.	Piercing
One-Handed Melee Weapons							
Maul, dwerof	30 gp	1d8	1d10	×3	-	8 lb.	Bludgeoning
Sword, bastard	35 gp	1d8	1d10	19-20/×2	-	6 lb.	Slashing
Whip[4]	1 gp	1d2[3]	1d3[3]	×2	-	2 lb.	Slashing
Whip, barbed	5 gp	1d2	1d3	×2	-	4 lb.	Slashing
Two-Handed Melee Weapons							
Chain, spiked[4]	25 gp	1d6	2d4	×2	-	10 lb.	Piercing
Flail, dire[5]	90 gp	1d6/1d6	1d8/1d8	×2	-	10 lb.	Bludgeoning
Sword, two-bladed[5]	100 gp	1d6/1d6	1d8/1d8	19-20/×2	-	10 lb.	Slashing
Ranged Weapons							
Blowgun	5 gp	1	1	×2	10 ft.	2 lb.	Piercing
Bolas	5 gp	1d3[3]	1d4[3]	×2	10 ft.	2 lb.	Bludgeoning
Crossbow, assault	300 gp	2d6	2d8	18-20/×2	120 ft.	25 lb.	Piercing
Crossbow, wrist	100 gp	1d3	1d4	19-20/×2	10 ft.	1 lb.	Piercing
Net	10 gp	-	-	-	10 ft.	6 lb.	-
Repeater, assault	1,000 gp	1d8	1d10	19-20/×2	100 ft.	35 lb.	Piercing
Shortbow	50 gp	1d4	1d6	×3	60 ft.	2 lb.	Piercing
Shortbow, composite	100 gp	1d4	1d6	×3	70 ft.	2 lb.	Piercing
Longbow	100 gp	1d6	1d8	×3	100 ft.	3 lb.	Piercing
Longbow, composite	150 gp	1d6	1d8	×3	110 ft.	3 lb.	Piercing

Ammunition	Cost	Weight[1]
Arrows (20)	1 gp	3 lb.
Blowgun needles (10)	1 gp	1 lb.
Crossbow bolts (10)	1 gp	1 lb.
Crossbow bolt, assault (1)	3 gp	2 lb.
Repeater bolts (12)	2 gp	1 lb.

Ammunition Cases[6]	Cost	Weight[1]
Repeater ammunition belt	special	special
Repeater clip, double	8 gp	3 lb.
Repeater clip, mini	2 gp	1 lb.
Repeater clip, standard	4 gp	2 lb.

1 Weight figures are for Medium weapons. A Small weapon weighs half as much, and a Large weapon weighs twice as much.

2 When two types are given, the weapon is both types if the entry specifies "and," or either type (player's choice at time of attack) if the entry specifies "or."

3 The weapon deals nonlethal damage rather than lethal damage.

4 Reach weapon.

5 Double weapon.

6 The cost and weight given for ammunition cases does not include the cost and weight of the actual ammunition.

Armor

DARK LEGACIES presents two options to characters that wish to wear armor: standard armor, as described in the *Player's Handbook*, and piecemeal armor. Standard armor provides protection for the entire body or an area large enough to be considered comprehensive, while piecemeal armor represents a hobbled-together assortment of armor pieces or junk; a medium "suit" of piecemeal armor may consist of no more than scavenged shoulder guards and a scrap metal breastplate, fastened together with loose leather straps or chain.

Standard armor is superior to piecemeal armor in most regards, and provides better reliability, Armor Bonus potential, fit, and mobility. Piecemeal armor's advantages are quick donning and removal, low initial cost, and ease of assembly and upgradeability in remote locations. Often, scavenged piecemeal armor is all that is available to those who drift a long way from civilization and to others living within its shadow, with no means to obtain properly fitted goods. Unless noted otherwise in the armor description, standard armor and piecemeal armor cannot be combined.

Armor, Encumbrance and Spellcasting

Spells in DARK LEGACIES do not have somatic components but they all require material components or focuses that must be handled and combined with care. When casting a spell in armor, apply the armor check penalty of the armor to your Spellcraft roll, rather than using the armor's arcane spell failure value. If you are carrying a shield (and can still conceivably cast the spell considering the required material components), the shield's armor check penalty is also applied. Likewise, apply any check penalty due to encumbrance to your Spellcraft roll when casting a spell.

Standard Armor Descriptions

All new or modified armor found on Table 4-6: Armor is described below, along with any special options the wielder ("you") has for their use. Any armor not listed functions as described in the *Player's Handbook*. Table 4-7: Donning Armor shows the time required to don and remove all standard armor types found in DARK LEGACIES.

Ceremonial: Ceremonial armor includes a variety of light armor types that are worn for show as much as for protection. Such suits of armor are normally made up of a light breastplate or steel gorget, shoulder guards, and other elements that enhance the wearer's presence. Priests, in particular, are fond of ceremonial armor, for its protective and aesthetic qualities. The price of ceremonial armor can vary greatly, depending on its workmanship and decorative elements.

TABLE 4-6: ARMOR

Armor	Cost	Armor/Shield Bonus	Maximum Dex Bonus	Armor Check Penalty	Speed 30ft	Speed 20ft	Weight[1]
Light Armor							
Padded	5 gp	+1	+8	0	30 ft.	20 ft.	10 lb.
Leather	10 gp	+2	+6	0	30 ft.	20 ft.	15 lb.
Studded leather	25 gp	+3	+5	−1	30 ft.	20 ft.	20 lb.
Ceremonial	50 gp	+3	+4	−2	30 ft.	20 ft.	25 lb.
Medium Armor							
Hide	15 gp	+3	+4	−3	20ft.	15 ft.	25 lb.
Scale mail	50 gp	+4	+3	−4	20 ft.	15 ft.	30 lb.
Chainmail	150 gp	+5	+2	−5	20 ft.	15 ft.	40 lb.
Heavy Armor							
Composite	250 gp	+6	+1	−7	20 ft.	15 ft.	45 lb.
Plate	600 gp	+7	+1	−7	20 ft.	15 ft.	50 lb.
Heavy plate	1,200 gp	+8	+0	−8	20 ft.	15 ft.	60 lb.
Siege plate	5,000 gp	+9	+0	−9	20 ft.	15 ft.	75 lb.
Shields							
Buckler	+15 gp	+1	-	−1	-	-	5 lb.
Shield, light wooden	3 gp	+1	-	−1	-	-	5 lb.
Shield, light steel	10 gp	+1	-	−1	-	-	6 lb.
Shield, heavy wooden	7 gp	+2	-	−2	-	-	10 lb.
Shield, heavy steel	30 gp	+2	-	−2	-	-	15 lb.
Shield, tower	50 gp	+4	+2	−10	-	-	45 lb.
Extras							
Armor spikes	+50 gp	-	-	-	-	-	+10 lb.
Gauntlet, locked	8 gp	-	-	Special	-	-	+5 lb.
Shield spikes	+10 gp	-	-	-	-	-	+5 lb.

1 Weight figures are for armor sized to Medium characters. Armor fitted for Small characters weighs half as much, and armor fitted for Large characters weighs twice as much.

Composite: Composite armor is a novag design, consisting of a combination of overlapping metal plates, reinforced leather, and rubber that is easy to adjust and fit to diverse body types. It was adopted by human armies during the Kingdoms War, where it proved itself as a versatile armor type that had protective capabilities almost as good as expensive plate armor but that could be mass-produced at low cost; it has since become a favorite for mercenaries and adventurers as well. Composite armor includes gauntlets.

Plate, Heavy Plate, and Siege Plate: These armor types represent the best personal protection available to a combatant, and are the preference of armed forces everywhere. The heavier suits are generally intended for persons of high rank or importance, as well as individuals that must undertake missions and quests without the backing of an entire army. Siege plate in particular is cautiously guarded by anyone lucky enough to procure a suit; it is usually reserved for specific missions or ceremonial functions rather than prolonged wear. Most suits of heavy and siege plate are beautifully detailed affairs with a long and glorious legacy of battle or a dull history of dusting and polishing on the wall of a general's war room.

All plate variants provide comprehensive protection to the wearer, by way of layers of riveted steel plates and accoutrements (helm, gauntlets, etc.) worn over thick padding and leather supports. Advances in armor design and manufacturing have long since eliminated the need for plate armor to be individually fitted to its owner. Still, all suits are built to a general body size and height and captured suits must be refitted if the new owner is of a moderately different height or weight (GM's discretion). Plate armor cannot be refitted to a character of a different size category than the original wearer or to a character that is the same size category but still significantly larger or smaller than the original wearer (humans, assar, hybrids, and eldrin have compatible body shapes but briggs, dwerofs, and novags can only wear plate that is made for a member of their own race). Refitting must be performed by a master armorsmith or available foundry and costs 100 to 400 (2d4 × 50) gp.

Table 4-7: Donning Armor

Armor Type	Don	Don Hastily	Remove
Shield	1 move action	n/a	1 move action
Light	1 minute	5 rounds	1 minute[1]
Medium	4 minutes[1]	1 minute	1 minute[1]
Heavy	4 minutes[2]	4 minutes	1d4 +1 minutes[1]

1 If the character has some help, cut this time in half. A single character doing nothing else can help one or two adjacent characters. Two characters cannot help each other don armor at the same time.
2 The wearer must have help to don this armor. Without help, it can only be donned hastily.

Piecemeal Armor

Since one "suit" of piecemeal armor rarely has anything in common with another, piecemeal armor qualities are based on the armor's Armor Bonus rather the armor's specific description. See Table 4-8: Piecemeal Armor for piecemeal armor characteristics by effective armor type. Generally, piecemeal armor is only bought during character creation, and is scavenged thereafter.

Piecemeal armor has limited protective potential and cannot be created with an Armor Bonus higher than 6. Since piecemeal armor is of inherently inferior quality, it cannot be crafted with masterpiece qualities. Bonuses and penalties from shields stack with those from piecemeal armor, just as they do with standard armor. All normal considerations regarding effective armor type apply, including armor proficiency and reduced speed in the case of medium and heavy effective armor types.

Getting Into and Out of Piecemeal Armor

Piecemeal armor can be donned and removed faster than standard armor. The reduced time required represents its haphazard nature and a lesser dependence on precise fit. Because it is already being donned hastily in effect, piecemeal armor cannot be donned even more hastily at penalty. Refer to Table 4-9: Donning Piecemeal Armor for the time required, based on the effective armor type of the piecemeal armor worn.

Table 4-8: Piecemeal Armor

Armor	Cost	Armor Bonus	Maximum Dex Bonus	Armor Check Penalty	Speed 30ft	Speed 20ft	Weight[1]
Light Armor							
Piecemeal Armor AB1	1 gp	+1	+6	0	30 ft.	20 ft.	7 lb.
Piecemeal Armor AB2	4 gp	+2	+5	−2	30 ft.	20 ft.	14 lb.
Medium Armor							
Piecemeal Armor AB3	9 gp	+3	+4	−4	20 ft.	15 ft.	21 lb.
Piecemeal Armor AB4	16 gp	+4	+3	−6	20 ft.	15 ft.	28 lb.
Heavy Armor							
Piecemeal Armor AB5	25 gp	+5	+2	−8	20 ft.	15 ft.	35 lb.
Piecemeal Armor AB6	36 gp	+6	+1	−10	20 ft.	15 ft.	42 lb.
Extras							
Armor spikes	+5 gp	-	-	-	-	-	+10 lb.

1 Weight figures are for armor sized to Medium characters. Armor fitted for Small characters weighs half as much, and armor fitted for Large characters weighs twice as much.

TABLE 4-9: DONNING PIECEMEAL ARMOR

Effective Armor Type	Don	Remove
Light	5 rounds	5 rounds
Medium	1 minute	5 rounds
Heavy	2 minutes	1 minute

Piecemeal Armor Deterioration

Piecemeal armor is not as well put together as standard armor, and is thus susceptible to damage in combat. Whenever a critical hit is scored against a character wearing piecemeal armor, his armor loses 1 point of Armor Bonus; this lost armor cannot be reintegrated, but damaged piecemeal armor can be upgraded again at a later time from a new armor source (see Scavenging and Assembling Piecemeal Armor, below). Damaged piecemeal armor acquires all of the traits of piecemeal armor with the lower Armor Bonus value.

Scavenging and Assembling Piecemeal Armor

Piecemeal armor can be assembled with minimal tools, from actual armor sources or other materials that may be suitable as armor, such as a metal plate salvaged from an industrial ruin. It can also be continually upgraded to a higher Armor Bonus as more parts are found. See the Craft skill (page 59) for complete rules on scavenging and assembling piecemeal armor.

Masterpiece Armaments

Set apart from the abundance of mediocre, mass-produced armaments are finely crafted masterpieces of superior quality and function. These masterpiece weapons, ammunition, and armor are rare and expensive, sold at a considerable premium by specialized arms manufacturers and legendary master craftsmen. In a world where holy armaments are closely guarded by the church that consecrated them, and where demonic armaments demand a higher and fouler cost than mere gold, masterpiece armaments are the best tools that an adventurer could hope for and therefore well worth the price.

Creating Masterpiece Armaments

A masterpiece armament is a weapon, a round of ammunition, or a suit of standard armor that has been crafted with one or more special qualities. A masterpiece armament must be crafted from scratch, thus extra qualities cannot be added to an item later. Creating a masterpiece armament requires at least 10 ranks in the relevant Craft skill: Craft (weaponsmithing) for most conventional weapons, Craft (bowmaking) for bows, Craft (mechanical weapons) for repeaters, and Craft (armorsmithing) for armor. Each masterpiece quality is created as if it was a separate item in addition to the base item. Each quality has its own price listed in the descriptions below and a Craft DC of 20. Once both the base item and all of the desired qualities are completed, the masterpiece armament is finished.

Masterpiece weapons can be crafted with any qualities allowed for that weapon type (such as the wounding quality for slashing weapons); weapon qualities cannot be added to improvised weapons. Ammunition qualities can be added to all arrows and bolts, regardless of the type of weapon that is firing them. Armor qualities can be added to standard armor but not to piecemeal armor. Weapon qualities cannot be applied to armor that can be used as a weapon (such as a spiked shield). Masterpiece weapon and armor qualities can be combined, unless otherwise noted in their descriptions; the bonuses, effects, and penalties (such as weight increase) of multiple qualities stack. Masterpiece ammunition qualities cannot be combined.

Adding a masterpiece quality to a double weapon costs twice the normal price for the quality, but the bonuses and effects of the quality are not also doubled. A weapon with two attack types (such as a dagger or hooked spiker) can be enhanced with any qualities available to the weapon's modes, but each quality only applies to the relevant attack type. Thus, if a hooked spiker is crafted with the wounding quality, that quality only comes into play when the slashing end is used. Because the masterpiece qualities are still effectively crafted into the same weapon, qualities that cannot normally be combined remain exclusive; a weapon that deals damage of multiple types (such as a spiked mace) can only be crafted with qualities that are available to both attack types.

Masterpiece Bonuses

Masterpiece qualities provide an item with craftsmanship bonuses or special effects, which stack with the enhancement bonuses and effects of demonic and holy items of power. Thus, a precise demonic spiker +1 confers a +2 bonus to attack rolls. The effects of ranged weapon qualities stack with those of masterpiece ammunition. Masterpiece ammunition is damaged (effectively destroyed) when used.

Masterpiece Armaments and Masterwork Items

The rules for masterpiece weapons and armor supersede those for masterwork weapons and armor, and the two properties should not be combined. However, the rules for masterwork tools remain unchanged.

Masterpiece Quality Descriptions

Each masterpiece quality entry begins with the name of the quality and a descriptor that indicates what kind of item the quality can be applied to. Following that is a brief description that explains the quality. Next is the price; double this price when creating a quality for a double weapon. Prices for ammunition qualities are for a single unit of ammunition only. Listed after the price is the quality's benefits and effects, then any relevant notes, including restricted combinations.

Masterpiece Weapon Qualities

Faultless [all repeaters]

A faultless repeater is precision-engineered to never jam.

Cost: 300 gp for hand, light, and heavy repeaters; 450 gp for double-barreled repeaters; 750 gp for assault repeaters.

Benefit: When a natural attack roll of 1 is made with a faultless repeater, there is only a 25% chance that it will jam.

Fierce [all melee weapons]

A fierce weapon is larger and more brutal in all respects than a conventional weapon of its type.

Cost: 300 gp.

Benefit: +1 bonus on damage rolls.

Notes: A fierce weapon is 50% heavier than normal and has 25% more hit points. Cannot be combined with precise quality.

Hardened [piercing and slashing melee weapons]

A hardened weapon combines unparalleled cutting ability with increased resiliency.

Cost: 900 gp.

Benefit: Critical multiplier increases by 1. Thus a hardened longsword has a critical range of 19–20/×3 instead of 19–20/×2.

Notes: A hardened weapon has 25% greater hardness than normal. Cannot be combined with wounding quality.

Precise [all weapons]

A precise weapon is crafted for accuracy, through superior weighting, materials, or firing mechanisms.

Cost: 300 gp.

Benefit: +1 bonus on attack rolls.

Notes: Cannot be combined with fierce quality.

Wounding [slashing melee weapons]

A wounding weapon is serrated, increasing the potential to inflict critical damage at the cost of fragility.

Cost: 600 gp.

Benefit: Critical range increases by 1. Thus a wounding long-sword has a critical range of 18–20 instead of 19–20.

Notes: A wounding weapon has 25% less hardness than normal. Cannot be combined with hardened quality.

Masterpiece Ammunition Qualities

Armor-Piercing

Armor-piercing ammunition utilizes a special head design that penetrates armor better at the cost of ultimate damage inflicted.

Cost: 8gp.

Benefit: 2 points of worn or natural armor on the target are ignored, but damage decreases by one step. Thus a Medium light repeater loaded with armor-piercing ammunition only does 1d6 damage instead of 1d8 damage.

Barbed

Barbed ammunition does not have the penetrating power of standard ammunition, but has a greater chance to inflict grievous injury.

Cost: 8 gp.

Benefit: Damage die decreases by one step, critical range increases by 1. Thus, a Medium light crossbow loaded with barbed ammunition deals 1d6 damage and has a critical range of 18–20/×2.

Note: Barbed ammunition cannot be used with repeaters.

Disabling

Disabling ammunition uses a blunt rubber end rather than a piercing tip and is used to disable rather than kill.

Cost: 8 gp.

Benefit: Disabling ammunition provides no inherent bonus; instead it deals nonlethal damage rather than lethal damage.

High-Impact

High-impact ammunition is heavier and deals more damage in exchange for accuracy and range.

Cost: 8 gp.

Benefit: Damage increases by one step, attack roll penalty of –2, and range increment decreases by 25% (rounding down to the closest 5 ft. increment). Thus a Medium light repeater loaded with high-impact ammunition deals 1d10 damage instead of 1d8 damage, and has a range increment of 50 ft. instead of 70 ft.

Note: High-impact ammunition weighs twice as much as normal ammunition.

Masterpiece Armor Qualities

Articulated [all armor]

Articulated armor is designed with superior clearance and sophistication in key joints to provide improved mobility over standard armor.

Cost: 150 gp.

Benefit: Armor check penalty is lessened by 1.

Note: Articulated armor cannot also be fortified.

Extra Plating [heavy armor]

By integrating extra plating into a suit of armor, the wearer is afforded greater protection at the cost of added weight and bulk.

Cost: 300 gp.

Benefit: Armor bonus increases by +1.

Note: Extra plating increases the armor's weight by 20%, reduces its maximum Dexterity bonus by 1 (to a minimum of 0) and worsens its armor check penalty by –1.

Fortified [metal armor]

Fortified armor is reinforced with layered plates and guarded joints that protect vital areas of the wearer more effectively.

Cost: 500 gp.

Benefit: When a critical hit or sneak attack is scored on the wearer, there is a 25% chance that the critical hit or sneak attack is negated and damage is instead rolled normally.

Note: Fortification increases the armor's weight by 20%, reduces its maximum Dexterity bonus by 1 (to a minimum of 0) and worsens its armor check penalty by –1. Thus, a suit of fortified heavy plate weighs 75 lbs., has a maximum Dexterity bonus of 0, and an armor check penalty of –9. Fortified armor cannot also be articulated.

Hardened [all shields]

This shield has been reinforced against breakage.

Cost: 100 gp.

Benefit: A hardened shield has 50% higher hardness and hit points than normal.

Note: Hardening a shield increases its weight by 25%.

Specialty Equipment

The following new equipment is suitable for play in a DARK LEGACIES campaign, and supplements the specialty and adventuring supplies found in the *Player's Handbook*.

Incendiaries

Incendiaries are alchemical compounds that produce a violent, generally explosive reaction, which is triggered by exposure to fire. Such compounds are rare, both because the processes involved in creating them are complex and because these processes are similar to those required to prepare the material components of spellcasting, earning alchemists the enmity of religious authorities. The prices on Table 4-10: Incendiaries are base prices where there is reasonable access to such items; prices often range from two to ten times the listed value when such items are purchased on the black market. Creating incendiaries requires the Craft Incendiary feat (page 63).

Incendiaries come in a number of varieties. The simplest is flashpowder, which is simultaneously thrown at an enemy and ignited in order to blind them. The more complex varieties are crafted constructs four to eight inches in diameter, consisting of the alchemical compound, a fuse, and a casing designed to burst apart when the compound erupts. Incendiaries with short fuses are generally thrown while long fuses are used for planted (usually hidden) incendiaries. Once an incendiary has been created, swapping out its fuse for a shorter or longer one requires a Craft (alchemy) check (DC 8). If this check fails, the incendiary is damaged and must be repaired. Fuse length can be set to instantaneous (detonating when it lands) or as long as desired, but for each round of delay longer than 2 rounds, there is a cumulative 10% chance that the fuse fails and the incendiary does not detonate.

When throwing an incendiary, all of the standard rules for throwing splash weapons apply. Unless otherwise stated, the full effect of the incendiary is applied against a single target, with lesser effects suffered by all creatures within 5 feet of the target. Before an incendiary can be thrown, it must be lit. Lighting an incendiary is a move action that provokes attacks of opportunity. If you are disrupted while lighting an incendiary, there is a 50% chance that it is actually lit but dropped, rather than not lit at all. Once an incendiary is lit, it must be thrown at the target or target area. Treat this attack as a ranged touch attack with a range increment of 10 feet. A natural 1 on the attack roll indicates faulty handling of the incendiary or a defective fuse and subsequent detonation in your hands, dealing damage as described in each incendiary's description, or 1d6 points of fire damage for incendiaries that do not normally deal damage (such as smoke bombs).

Fire Bomb: These incendiaries are deadly, spewing fire and shrapnel over the target. Depending on the formula used, their explosive core may consist of a bag of reactive powder or a suspension of volatile gel and particulates. Regardless of the actual substance used, the core is encased in a lattice that is in turn attached to a casing of small, spiked metal plates. When the incendiary ignites, the construct bursts, dealing 2d8 damage to everything within the affected square, and 1d8 splash damage to everything within 5 feet of the point where the explosive lands. Half of this damage is fire damage and the other half is slashing (shrapnel) damage. Characters within the area of effect may make

a DC 15 Reflex save to take half damage; prone characters receive a +2 bonus on this save.

Flash Bomb: Flash bombs are essentially large quantities of flashpowder packed into an explosive shell, that when detonated have the potential to blind any creature within the target square, and all creatures within the splash radius. The creature occupying the square in which the flash bomb detonates must make a DC 15 Reflex save or suffer 1d4 points of fire damage and be blinded (see Flashpowder, below). All creatures within 5 feet of the point where the explosive lands must make DC 12 Reflex saves or suffer the same blinding effect (but no damage).

Flashpowder: This red grainy powder erupts into a blinding flash when ignited, singeing and blinding the target. Flashpowder is only effective against a single creature that is adjacent to you and that you are facing. Using flashpowder is a standard action, during which you simultaneously throw it into the air and ignite it, generally with a lit torch or match. When you use flashpowder, you must make a DC 5 Reflex save or suffer 1 point of fire damage. The target, in turn, must make a DC 12 Reflex save or suffer 1 point of fire damage and be temporarily blinded. If the target fails its Reflex save by 5 or more or rolls a natural 1, it is blinded for 2 rounds; otherwise, it is blinded for only 1 round. When it recovers from the blindness, the creature suffers an ongoing −1 penalty to attack rolls and sight-based skill checks, such as Search and Spot, for 1 minute. The listed cost is for one application of flash powder, which fills a small pouch.

Rocket Flare: Rocket flares are delicate tubes filled with alchemical blasting powder, launched into the air from the ground and exploding 1 round later. Rocket flares must be lit like other incendiaries, but they immediately launch themselves thereafter. Where they are permitted, rocket flares are generally used in military applications, as a means of signaling distant allies to transpiring events. Different alchemical combinations can produce different colored explosions and thus different messages to the recipient. The explosion itself does not have significant damage potential, nor does it make a great deal of sound, but it can be seen from up to a mile away. If constrained to the ground, a rocket flare has the same effect as a flash bomb when it detonates.

Smoke Bomb: These types of incendiaries leverage specific smoke-producing qualities of the alchemical compound rather than a flash or explosion. When detonated, a smoke bomb creates thick, opaque yellow smoke that fills a 10-foot cube. The smoke obscures all sight, including deepsight and darksight, beyond 5 feet. A creature within 5 feet has concealment (attacks have a 20% miss chance). Creatures farther away have total concealment (50% miss chance, and the attack can't use sight to locate the target). A moderate or greater wind disperses the fog in 1 round, otherwise it dissipates in 1d4 + 1 rounds.

Smoke Bomb, Expanding: These rare variants of the smoke bomb incorporate the mysterious black fog that plagues Novdy Ottor, captured near the ruined novag capital where it is most dense. An expanding smoke bomb acts in all regards like a regular smoke bomb except that 1 round following the detonation, the smoke (which is black rather than yellow) expands out from its 10-foot cube into a 20-foot cube.

TABLE 4-10: INCENDIARIES

Item	Cost	Weight
Fire bomb	60 gp	2 lb.
Flash bomb	40 gp	2 lb.
Flashpowder	10 gp	-
Rocket flare	70 gp	1 lb.
Smoke bomb	50 gp	2 lb.
Smoke bomb, expanding	100 gp	2 lb.

Miscellaneous Gear

Ammunition Harness: This harness consists of two belts that are either worn vertically over the chest or in a crisscross fashion, and a belt worn around the waist, all of which have compartments for repeater ammunition. Each of the three belts can hold one double-clip, two standard clips, or three mini-clips, and they are configured to the desired clip size when purchased. Ammunition harnesses can be worn over any type of armor, and under a coat or cloak, but cannot be combined with an assault harness.

Assault Harness: This novag invention was developed as a mobility solution for soldiers in the field equipped with bulky assault repeaters. It consists of a specially fitted cage, braces, reinforced joints, and metal plates that distribute and balance the ungainly assault weapon so that it can be fired and reloaded while standing. An assault harness can be worn over any type of armor but imposes a maximum Dex bonus of +1 and a −5 armor check penalty. Additionally, mobility is decreased while wearing an assault harness as though you were wearing heavy armor. Treat an assault harness as heavy armor when calculating donning and removal time.

Lantern, Barrel-Mounted: This smaller version of a bullseye lantern is designed to mount under the barrel of a repeater, so that a combatant can illuminate the area directly in front of him while having both hands free to fire and load his weapon. The lantern illuminates a cone 30 feet long and 10 feet wide at the end, and it burns for 3 hours on 8 ounces (half a pint) of oil. While attached, a barrel-mounted lantern imposes a −1 penalty on attack rolls with the repeater (and with an attached gutter). Attaching or detaching the lantern is a full-round action that provokes attacks of opportunity.

Lock Breaker: Lock breakers are sophisticated mechanical bypass devices, used to circumvent locks that incorporate a keyhole. By inserting a lock breaker into the keyhole and clamping down on the handle, you can make a Strength check with a +2 circumstance bonus rather than an Open Lock check against the normal DC for opening the lock. If the check succeeds, the lock breaks open; if it fails, the lock does not budge and cannot thereafter be picked or opened with a lock breaker. If a natural 1 is rolled, the lock breaker breaks off inside the lock and is destroyed.

Longcoat: Longcoats are typically three-quarter length jackets made of cotton, wool, or leather. Those worn only for fashion or warmth come in varying degrees of quality and cost and can be worn over or under any type of armor. Longcoats made of heavy leather provide a marginal armor bonus while permitting a large range of movement, but can only be combined with light armor (standard or piecemeal). When combining a leather longcoat with light armor, it provides an additional +1 Armor Bonus and −1 armor check penalty; the combination is still treated as light armor. Donning or removing a longcoat is a full-round action.

Matches: Matches are small wooden sticks coated on one end with an alchemical compound that ignites when struck against a rough surface. The listed price is for a package of eight matches, encased in a wooden or metal box with one rough side for striking. Lighting an incendiary fuse with a match is a move action, lighting a torch with a match is a standard action, and lighting any other fire with one is at least a standard action. Matches remain lit for 1d4-1 rounds (minimum 1 round) and leave behind a distinctive (and unpleasant) odor for 2d10 minutes. If a match becomes wet, it is ineffective for 24 hours. Thereafter, it has only a 25% chance of working and is destroyed if it does not ignite.

Medical Lab: In addition to various containers and chemicals similar to those found in an alchemist's lab, a medical lab contains surgical gear, stitches, braces, and various diagnostic tools. A medical lab provides a +4 circumstance bonus on Heal checks but cannot be combined with a healer's kit.

TABLE 4-11: MISCELLANEOUS GEAR

Item	Cost	Weight
Ammunition harness	15 gp	2 lb.
Assault harness	200 gp	15 lb.[1]
Lantern, barrel-mounted	15 gp	2 lb.
Lock breaker	60 gp	1 lb.
Longcoat	5 gp	4 lb.[1]
Longcoat, leather	20 gp	8 lb.[1]
Matches	5 gp	-
Medical lab	500 gp	40 lb.

1 Weight figures are for items sized to Medium characters. Wearable items fitted for Small characters weigh half as much, and those fitted for Large characters weigh twice as much.

Chapter 5: Religion

"Bow before the Divinity. Show your obedience and be content with the life that we have given you. Or find yourselves thrust from the grace of the Under Matriarch, damned to be devoured by demons then vomited up and devoured again, each day for all eternity in the Abyss!

- Pristine Claudette Grotine,
Beyella Divinity

Religion plays an important role in DARK LEGACIES campaigns, particularly within the Corelands where human religious institutions hold great sway over the lives of all, regardless of station, and where each nation is subject to some measure of theocratic rule. The foundation of religion on Earth is rooted in two divine figures: Deihass, commonly referred to as the Day Father or simply as God, and Azrae, who is often called the Adversary.

The religion founded upon the worship of Deihass is known simply as the Faith, and is largely a human phenomenon, though the gradual integration of nonhumans into human culture has seen them too adopting roles within the clergy and among congregations of the faithful. The Faith is divided into four powerful denominations, whose relationships with one another range from barely tolerant to extremely antagonistic. Each denomination is further divided into factions, with their own agendas and extremely specific interpretations of the Faith.

Predating and opposing the Faith are a seemingly infinite number of demon worshippers. These followers of Azrae, or of lesser demons in her stead, are organized only in so far as they need to be in order to practice their religion. Demon cults, secret cabals, and arcanist circles that pledge themselves to Azrae exist wherever they can be sustained – from underground chapels, behind false storefronts, and within the very hearts of the institutions that oppose them.

There are no religions of note beyond these two institutions. Briggs and novags are nonreligious to the core. The eldrin abandoned religion long ago, and whatever remains of an eldrin church and its faithful is buried under the ruins of their decimated homeland. The assar are an enigma, recognizing both Deihass and Azrae as gods in their own right, yet worshipping neither and adhering to no religion based around their worship. Dwerof society is entirely secular.

The Faith

Humans were a godless people prior to the Reversion, all vestiges of religion and culture lost to the basic struggle for survival in a dark Earth that had been swallowed by the Abyss. This all changed with the Reversion, when the world tore itself halfway from the demonic realm and the sun lifted from the horizon for the first time in millennia. With the sun came an emissary, known as the First Priest, who spoke of Deihass. He claimed this god was responsible for producing the miracle of the sun and that through worship of Deihass, one could command supernatural power – the Voice – against the forces of Azrae, so that the Earth might be reclaimed. He spoke with the Voice and all were commanded by it. So began the Faith, three thousand years ago.

In the years since, it has evolved from a religion for the priesthood to a religion for all humanity, but not without challenge. The Faith has become divided along political and spiritual lines, into four denominations – the original Church of Deihass, the matriarchal Beyella Divinity, the militant Prelacy of the Divine Adjudicator, and the much-maligned Despinus Chapter. These denominations are divided into factions, and broken down further by the growing proliferation of arcanism, which threatens to tear down the foundations of theocratic rule that have stood for so long.

Foundations of Belief

Humanity's reclamation of the Earth was undeniably facilitated through the return of the sun, the subsequent appearance of the First Priest, and his teaching of the Voice to a human ministry. The Faith is firmly entrenched in human society in the form of powerful institutions that have grown out of that original ministry. These institutions are founded on tradition, force of numbers, political influence, supernatural power in the form of the Voice, and not in small part upon the efficient quashing of any controversy or questioning that may compromise their power base. Virtually all humans – and a growing number of nonhumans – count themselves as members of the Faith and worshippers of Deihass, whether out of true conviction or convenience. Those that do not subscribe to the Faith are known as the Unbidden, for the Covenant of the Faith – its written testament – states that one must worship Deihass in order to gain entrance into Heaven.

Despite the considerable strength of the Faith, its churches are not infallible. That a divine force exists and plays a part in the affairs of mortals is preached as sacrosanct truth by the priesthood, but among the common people, a lack of absolute proof winds its way through doubtful circles like a weed that grows with the passing years, compounded by the nonreligious influence of nonhuman races, the spread of arcanism, and the physical manifestation of Azrae upon the Earth while Deihass remains elusive. The Eastern Ridge, in particular, is a hotbed for dissent. Though the Faith is still practiced there, historical resistance to imperialism from the Corelands has also meant an absence of powerful religious institutions. This, along with the chaotic region's reputation as a breeding ground for arcanist guilds and demonic cults, sees the Faith losing ground in a large quarter of humanity.

Debate in the absence of a manifest God has also grown since the Great War, during which Azrae undeniably tread upon the mortal plane. Though many high priests of the Faith, zealots, and madmen claim to have seen Deihass, no undisputed records exist. As a means of countering this disturbing disparity, priests of the Faith uniformly decry Azrae's worshippers as simple malcontents and arcanists rather than agents of a true divine power. This refusal of Azrae's divinity, as well as her worshippers' lack of the Voice, secures the parishes of all denominations against crises of faith where they would otherwise be vulnerable to physical proof of the enemy's god where none exists for their own.

Not all doubt comes from outside of the Faith, however – a great deal of debate originates from within the clergy itself. Throughout the Faith's difficult history of schism and divergence, belligerent denominations have discounted one another's miraculous events as fiction, contesting each other's credibility in a relentless competition for converts to their church and to their interpretation of the Faith. Even within their own denominations, priests butt heads when discussing the legitimacy of such events. Arguments between extremist factions have led, in the past, and continue to result in mass conversions from one denomination to another, the establishment of entirely new denominations, and the excommunication of entire factions on grounds of heresy.

Stirring further speculation are the findings of the modern age of adventure and exploration. Exposure to ancient ruins and cultures breathes life into dead history, revealing mysterious and contradictory facts about the beings that are worshipped as gods, and the validity of institutions of the Faith. The legends of the assar – in particular, those that claim Deihass and Azrae are connected by their creation of the assar race – are of great interest and concern to these institutions. Consequently, religious institutions spend a great deal of resources acquiring and confiscating such knowledge, and compete vigorously with private, political, and arcanist organizations to control as much of this dangerous information as they can.

Holy Texts

The beliefs, traditions, and historical accounts of the Faith are cemented in holy books, some ancient and others comparatively new. The oldest of these is the Covenant of the Faith, which retells the events immediately following the Reversion, from the time that the First Priest appeared in Year 1 until his ascension into Heaven three hundred years later. There are numerous interpretations of the miracles and events portrayed in the Covenant, argued about ad infinitum by theologians and historians. Regardless of varying interpretation, the Covenant is the foundation text for all denominations of the Faith. It lays out the basic tenets of religion, foremost of which is the rejection of Azrae and of magic, and describes in detail the eight precepts of priestly power, otherwise known as holy dominions. Both the Church of Deihass and Despinus Chapter regard the Covenant as the Faith's only sacred text.

Among the Covenant's most contested chapters are those that detail the Prophecy of Return. This prophecy states that when all demons and demonic influences are purged from the Earth, Deihass will descend with his legions, bringing Heaven to the Earth. Striving toward such a day was considered a core responsibility of priesthood in the early years of the Faith, but the prophecy has been neglected since. While orthodox factions continue to work toward the Return, urging their fellows to do the same and acting on their own regardless of the complacency of others, the controlling cores of most religious institutions are content with the current balance of power, and

dismissive of the prophecy as being a metaphor for the current state of civilization as it exists under ecclesiastic rule.

The second-oldest holy text is the Beyella Dictate. More of an elitist sociopolitical treatise than a holy text, it describes the foundation of the Beyella Divinity, the specific beliefs of that denomination, and contains the denomination's tenets on society, social classes, and the ascendance of a female church as the ultimate institution of divinity on Earth. Numerous sections of the Beyella Dictate refute important events in the Covenant, recasting incidental female figures as influential icons, creating a clear lineage that peaks with the Matriarch Beyella and her subsequent founding of the Beyella Divinity. The somewhat fanatical nature of the Beyella Dictate is conducive to extremist and paranoid interpretation. Such interpretations have resulted in an increasing number of edicts that distance the Beyella Divinity further from the Faith's other denominations. The most recent, and also the most far-reaching of these is the Purity Edict, which bans the teachings and practice of all other denominations from Divinity-controlled Sarlat on penalty of death.

Most recent among humanity's holy texts is the Second Chronicling, a series of three testaments penned by consecutive Prelate Ascendants of the Prelacy of the Divine Adjudicator. This trilogy continues where the Covenant leaves off, and combines historical accounts with orthodox interpretations of the Faith. These latter passages simultaneously enforce strict adherence to the basic foundational tenets of the Faith while also elevating key denominational figures to near godhood. A good deal of the Second Chronicling deals with war, conflict, and brutal moral lessons, painting such events as the necessary purification of humanity and the Earth.

Religious Iconography

Prior to the Reversion and the subsequent appearance of the First Priest, humans were damned to the perpetual night of the Abyss, which had swallowed the Earth completely. The Covenant states that when the world lifted out of the darkness and the sun appeared once more in the sky, it did so at the beckoning of Deihass – this is the preeminent event that marks the ascension of humanity to its rightful place as rulers of the Earth. The image of a fiery sun rising from the horizon is consequently the basis for all icons of the Faith, and is also found in a great number of political, military, and civic crests.

Sun-based imagery is often combined with symbols denoting the eight holy dominions of the Faith – the foundation of a priest's power and what truly distinguishes the priesthood from the general populace. Holy dominions are generally represented as flames affixed to the sun (or a generic sphere) or as spokes on a circle. One of the oldest symbols of the Faith is the "octafex," a circle with eight intersecting spokes, each of which represents a particular dominion. Senior members of the Synod of the Church of Deihass carry scepters bearing an octafex, as do the renegade priests of Despinus Chapter, the latter using it as a symbol of empowerment and ongoing protest against those that excommunicated them. Occasionally, the octafex is altered so that certain spokes are omitted, to emphasize the importance of the remaining dominions, or as a method for demon cults to intentionally corrupt a symbol of the Faith.

The "fiery crown" is the official icon of the Church of Deihass, consisting of a rising sun with eight rays. The Beyella Divinity's "Divinityhead" glorifies that church's first matriarch Beyella, by showing her lifting her hands to a similar crown and thus claiming divinity. The primary symbol of the militant Prelacy of the Divine Adjudicator is the "armor cross," crossed gauntlets surrounded by a wreath of flame. There are uncounted variations of these icons within each denomination's factions, accompanied by other symbols specific to their ideological focus. The wearing or possession of holy symbols of the Faith is exclusive to priests and forbidden to lay worshippers, with the exception of the Beyella Divinity, which promotes the possession of idols of the Matriarch Beyella.

Less commonly seen in religious circles, but often used on political and military insignia, as well as in more mystical circles are the Saenadi, the servants of the First Priest. These mysterious twin beings, often simply called "the twins", are spoken of in the Covenant as being the First Priest's administrators and protectors, never leaving his side all the while he shepherded humanity in the foundation years of the Faith. They are portrayed as regal, winged, vaguely humanoid creatures with large beaks and bird-like legs. When characterized as protectors, they are often depicted wielding crossed swords over the subject of their protection. Less orthodox representations have them bearing a flame or other symbol of divine power in each hand. Regardless of the manner in which they are portrayed, the twins are never separated. Ironically, the Saenadi appear almost demonic in many of these portraits. Ecclesiastic academics dismiss such claims as absurd, if not outright heretical, but the twins have fallen out of favor nevertheless, and are rarely seen in modern religious iconography.

Cosmology

Death is permanent and irreversible. Not even the most powerful priest of his fold has the ability to bring back departed souls. Only with magic can the dead be animated, though such monstrosities are possessed by demonic energy rather than a soul. As for a tangible existence after death, each denomination has its own assurances and paths to attaining happiness beyond the grave. Most commonly, these paths involve a life lived according to the dogma of the church for both lay followers and the clergy themselves, promising reward or punishment as a measure of success.

The Covenant describes the domain of Heaven as a realm of eternal happiness, populated by the righteous and lorded over by Deihass and his legions. It is said to exist beyond the stars, inaccessible until after death. The sun is traditionally viewed as a conduit to Heaven, hence the longstanding practice of burning the dead, so that they may be sped on their way by fire and flame. Burial is generally shunned, excluding cases where a priest is preserved in state so that his spirit might remain to guard the Earth, and graveyards are generally intended as a final resting place only for the Unbidden. Tales exist in the Covenant and throughout history of righteous priests granted a view of Heaven, or of lay folk claiming to glimpse its enormity near death, but the Blessed Realm is wholly out of the reach of mortal hands.

The same cannot be said of the Abyss, whose physical presence upon the horizon overshadows all the promises of Heaven and the hopes of the faithful. This realm of torment and terror, in such visible proximity to the mortal plane, is the native home of Azrae and all demonkind. Powerful magic can call demons from one plane to the next and even banish living mortals to unknown torture there. The Abyss is also the ultimate destination of deceased mortals that paid homage to demons in life, according to the Faith, whether through actual worship or magical practice. The list of lesser crimes that might warrant such a fate is endless, shifting with new ecclesiastic administrations and debated constantly among factions within the clergy – they range from committing palpable crimes against humanity to simply living a life as an Unbidden.

Church Services

Representatives of the Faith preside over a wide array of services and functions, from birthing ceremonies to marriage to the consecration of monarchs to funerals. Few events of importance are free from the purview of a religious institution. The true supernatural power of priests, however, is notably reserved and has been since the founding of the original Church of Deihass. Strict edicts and punishments restrict the use of the Voice so that it is used only in the direct interests of a priest's church or that church's political, military, or economic allies. Even in instances where the Voice might be a practical solution, conventional methods are preferred and promoted; for instance, a religious authority might participate in the quarantine and wholesale burning of a town that is in the throes of a highly infectious plague, rather than allowing priests to endanger the church by exposing themselves to a contagion while purifying the diseased citizens with the Voice. This reluctance to use the Voice has resulted in many black marks upon the history of the priesthood. Ironically, it is the reviled priests of Despinus Chapter that break this mold. They operate out of adventurer guilds and back alleys, where they provide for their customers in a completely mercenary capacity, unfettered by the status quo that established institutions perpetuate. It is to these dark priests that most independent adventurers flock.

Divinity & Rank

The Faith in all its denominational guises is based upon a consistent hierarchal foundation. Deihass is recognized as the solitary divine figure, represented on Earth by the authority of a high priest or ruling council. Beneath this figurehead is a rigid hierarchy, the ranks of which are as often based on politics and patronage as they are defined by measurable power. Even at the highest levels of the hierarchy, what was once a position achieved through mastery of the True Voice has shifted over the centuries to one of political achievement. This does nothing, however, to affect the pomp and ritual that accompanies their ascension ceremonies, edicts, and funerals. These events are laden with heady ritual as a means of deification, attracting hundreds of thousands of worshippers and curious onlookers.

This trend of representing high priests as living gods increases with each passing year. The Beyella Divinity and the Prelacy of the Divine Adjudicator, in particular, have taken to deifying their leaders more so than any other denomination. The Matriarch Beyella has always been worshipped within her denomination as an equal counterpart to Deihass himself, while Under Matriarchs enjoy unmatched privilege and adoration. In death, these glorified priestesses are immortalized through idols and statuary. The Prelacy preserves their deceased Prelate Ascendants and accomplished priests in state, naming them as saints to whom prayers are directed and dedications are made in the Second Chronicling.

Far below these icons, cemented in the mortal realm, is the rank and file of the Faith. Just as the hierarchies above it, political influence determines position and privilege in the churches as much as actual power does. A priest with fifty years of experience in the service of his church can easily find himself under the authority of a much younger, though better-connected or higher-born priest. His accomplishments are generally recognized only within factional hierarchies and specialized organizations attached to the denomination's ruling body. Finding the least favor within church hierarchies are nonhumans that have converted to the Faith. These outcast priests are universally given the title of Convert, regardless of the denomination that they practice, and are generally barred from attaining positions of authority. Only the Church of Deihass and Despinus Chapter accept nonhuman clergy.

The specific hierarchal structure for each denomination is detailed in The Four Denominations, below. Table 5-1: Titles By Dominion is a listing of generalized titles attributed to priests depending on the holy dominion in which they specialize. These titles are usually given as honorifics rather than a designation of rank. For the Consecration, Dominance, Forbiddance, Purity, and Sanctity dominions, these titles are acquired through acquisition of the related Dominion Focus feat. Priests that acquire the Secret Lore feat are generally distinguished with a Knowledge-related title, and priests that possess Battle Preaching or a large assortment of combat-oriented feats earn a War-related title. Where a priest is especially accomplished with one or more dominions, such as through the Greater Dominion Focus, Greater Battle Preaching, or multiple Secret Lore feats, they may acquire the additional title of Master, Chief, or Prime, though such prestigious titles are often withheld if they would seem to contradict actual rank.

TABLE 5-1: TITLES BY DOMINION

Dominion Focus	Titles
Consecration	Consecrator
Dominance	Compeller
Forbiddance	Exorcist
Knowledge	Librarian
Purity	Purifier
Sanctity	Warden
War	Battlepriest

Factions

Factions are niche religious societies and cults that exist within a denomination, but have an ideology or motivations that differ from the standard teachings or methods. Although priests are officially united by their denomination, factional infighting can set them at each other's throats. A moderate faction may have harmless views that deviate slightly from the denomination proper, such as a unique interpretation of an innocuous event portrayed in the Covenant, while an extreme faction may diverge drastically, such as by attaching esoteric rituals to their services or even adopting arcanism as a weapon against their enemies. Some factions are entirely focused on (and sometimes obsessed with) one or more holy dominions, orienting themselves to the teachings of those dominions and nothing else. The most insidious of factions are often political in nature, working toward inserting themselves into the power center of their denomination as a means of gaining wealth or enacting policy change. A faction may be as loosely organized as a small number of priests thinly spread over a region, who meet only when the need warrants, or so pervasive that its influence extends to the highest levels of the ecclesiastical hierarchy. Bloody internal purges and sweeping policy changes are typical signs of an extreme faction becoming dominant in a denomination's ruling body.

The Four Denominations

The Faith is represented by four denominations that emerged from the original ministry of Deihass, birthed during years of chaos and schism: the Church of Deihass, the first and longest lived institution that once stood as the solitary foundation of human spirituality; the Beyella Divinity, a priesthood made up entirely of women and the first institution to formally divorce itself from the Church; Despinus Chapter, an underground organization of rogue priests that were excommunicated for their controversial views a thousand years ago, which continues to thrive in the nether regions of society; and the Prelacy of the Divine Adjudicator, a militant institution that emerged from the Church's own military wing during the Unification Wars. Each of these denominations follows the same basic tenets of the Faith, but they are irreconcilably divided by specific interpretations, varying recognition of hierarchal authorities, and bitter disputes along political lines and borders.

Church of Deihass

The Church of Deihass, also simply called the Church, is the oldest surviving institution of the Faith. Though its influence has dwindled over history, weakened by schism and political upheaval, it is still the majority religion of humanity and the divine will behind the throne of Ilfernac. Many grand cathedrals in Precaea and Sarlat, bearing symbols of the Prelacy of the Divine Adjudicator and the Beyella Divinity respectively, are converted temples of the Church of Deihass, standing as monuments to the once mighty reach of the Mother Church.

In addition to the uncontrollable divisions that have rent the Church into its current form, its governing body has voluntarily instituted an increasing number of reformations and reorganizations throughout history, as a means of intentionally divorcing the Church from its offshoots. While some historians commend these changes as a step towards renewed vitality, others mark it as an admission of defeat and a precursor to the complete dissolution of the Church.

Power Center: The Church of Deihass is centered in the nation of Ilfernac, with its headquarters located in Vience alongside the monarchy. The will of the Church has been intertwined with state interests since time immemorial, and it is embraced as the soul of the nation. The highest stations of power under the king (or arguably above him) belong to senior members of the Church. This power does not extend beyond the borders of Ilfernac, however. Loyalty to the Church of Deihass subsists there only on the tenuous faith of old loyalists and grows weaker with each passing year. Families that have traditionally practiced the Faith under the Church of Deihass do so with a weak resolve, detached from their religious leaders and under increasing pressure to convert to the local denomination. The Church's influence in the Eastern Ridge, slight even during the glory days of the empire, has all but faded entirely.

Hierarchy: The head of the Church of Deihass is the Synod, a ruling body that sets and controls the Church's administrative, doctrinal, liturgical, and canonical norms. The Synod is comprised of priests that have ascended to the rank of bishop, and the Archus, the supreme spiritual leader of the Church. The Archus is an ascended bishop, elected to his position by the collected bishops of the Synod, obligated to lead the Church until his death or invalidity. The Archus sits alongside the king upon the throne of Ilfernac, where he serves as the monarch's adviser and confessor, in addition to being responsible for consecrating new bishops. Though the Archus is officially titled the most powerful priest of the Church, the role is often filled by a weak figurehead with little actual authority, carefully placed by political or factional interests at the highest levels of the Church hierarchy. This is especially apparent where an invalid Archus is retained and manipulated to the will of powerful members of the Synod long after senility or sickness overcomes him. In these cases, the Archus is carefully attended to by trusted priests so that he does not diverge from the path that has been set forth for him.

There is a single bishop within the Church of Deihass for every county within Ilfernac. There have been no bishops assigned to regions outside of Ilfernac since the Kingdoms War, thus the Synod has no direct representation beyond the borders of its home nation. New bishops are consecrated only when an old one dies, retires, or is excommunicated. Because of the considerable power accorded bishops, voluntary resignation is rare; when a bishop does resign, he is permitted some say in his replacement, though the Archus makes the final decision. Each bishop is accountable for his designated region, where he is the ecclesiastical counterpart to a feudal lord or governor. Bishops are responsible for all of the temples and agents of the Church within their realm of influence, and possess the authority to delegate to and override the actions of these subordinates. Priests that operate in foreign lands are obligated to defer to the head of whatever jurisdiction they arrive in when returning to Ilfernac.

Curates are next in rank below bishops. These high-ranking priests are appointed by the regional bishop to oversee a single church and its attached priests. Posturing is common among prospective curates as each struggles to prove his worth, in hopes of promotion to a distinguished cathedral and its associated political and financial benefits, or even to the rank of bishop. Common priests typically communicate with the higher levels of the ecclesiastical hierarchy through their curate rather than speaking directly to a bishop or the Synod.

Beneath curates are a plethora of ordained priests, clerks, and lay administrators, designated by a dizzying array of titles that are the legacy of thousands of years of expansion, division, and distant isolation from the Synod. While this chaotic structure persists outside of Ilfernac, efforts to reestablish a proper sense of order among the clergy within Ilfernac have resulted in a newly laid foundation for the Church. Consequently, all priests that serve under curates officially share identical privilege, and specific titles are used only to designate a priest's dominion focus or are an honorific to their length of service. These priests do the bulk of the Church's work, ministering to the populace and fulfilling duties related to their respective holy dominions, both within and outside of Ilfernac.

The lowest rank of priest, regardless of experience or proficiency with the Voice, is the convert. These nonhuman priests are tasked with assisting and protecting human priests and are wholly responsible for missionary work in nonhuman districts; it is only within these districts that a convert can attain the rank of curate. The Church of Deihass is second only to Despinus Chapter in the extent to which it accepts a nonhuman clergy, citing waning influence in the Corelands and the need to grow in whatever manner possible. Novags, long since integrated into human society, have worn the vestments of faith for centuries, though in exceedingly small numbers due to the nonreligious nature of the race as a whole. True controversy has arisen however with recent edicts that permit dwerofs and eldrin entrance into the clergy. Open-minded priests – and forgiving ones as regards the eldrin – view this development as not only natural but crucial for the continued survival of the Church, but an equal number are antagonized by it and veer closer to the camp of the human-centric Prelacy of the Divine Adjudicator, cementing division in the ranks all the way up to the Synod.

The Church remains cohesive however, thanks to strict enforcement of hierarchy and protocol. This vigilance has increased steadily since the end of the Kingdoms War, as the Synod becomes increasingly paranoid of defections and any further dissolution of their institution. Priests of low rank are closely monitored, and those that ascend to positions of authority within the hierarchy are subject to even greater scrutiny. The Synod employs its own elite division of priests known as the Baeus Bissancti that serves it directly and can be dispatched in the event of an internal crisis. These priests are accommodated rare privilege, are accountable only to the Synod, and are immune to accusation and prosecution from secular authorities within Ilfernac. The division is entrusted with the reigning in of heretic and separatist factions within the Church, all the while it furthers its own agendas – like the Synod itself, this secretive sect is subject to no small measure of their own political and factional influence.

Relationships: The Church's relations with its offshoot denominations are at a crossroads. Despite the denominational bloodshed of the Kingdoms War, the Church of Deihass remained relatively intact, as a matter of tradition and respect from the other denominations toward the Mother Church. But as these empowered denominations continue to grow, and the memory of a ruling Synod recedes along with the memory of the Ilfernac Empire, passive resentment is turning into active contempt. The Prelacy of the Divine Adjudicator moves ever closer to completely eliminating the legacy of the Church from Precaea, rededicating icons, statuary, and cathedrals in a methodical, barely diplomatic purge. And the Beyella Divinity, the eldest and most embittered offshoot of the Church, has declared war on all denominations by enacting the Purity Edict, which bans all foreign religious entities from its cities; temples dedicated to Beyella are built over the demolished ruins of Church temples, forcing their curates underground. This

predicament has produced unique relationships within the nation of Sarlat, where the dispossessed clergy of the Church of Deihass have taken up quarters with priests of Despinus Chapter, who are normally disdained by their counterparts. Outside of such extenuating circumstances, Despinus Chapter is uniformly decried as a heretic division of the Church.

Beyella Divinity

The Beyella Divinity is the oldest and also the most unique of the Church's offshoots. It is a relatively small denomination, which has survived through the political manipulation and eventual domination of the monarchy in Sarlat. Rather than positioning itself as an institution to which the general populace can relate, it takes the position of an elite priesthood, granted the divine right to dictate policy and be worshipped for it. Centered in a country where class division is extreme, the Beyella Divinity exists as an accepted extension of the upper class. Of all the denominations, it caters the least to the needs of the general populace, but a combination of high pomp and visibility along with the efficient suppression of dissent has cemented the superior status of the priesthood in the minds of those that worship them.

Power Center: Sarlat is without a doubt the stronghold of the Beyella Divinity. While Deus is recognized as the denomination's holiest city, the Office of the Under Matriarch – its spiritual headquarters – is located in the affluent capital of Nalterei. Worship of Beyella is rare outside of Sarlat's borders and falters without a greater support network. Scores of decadently embellished cathedrals populate the nation's largest cities, and even the poorest and most pitiful outcroppings of civilization are home to temples that have as much gold invested in their maintenance as is spent on the entire surrounding town. Temples are consistently built on or near the grounds of each city's governing district, so that they share political visibility with the local leadership. But where the Prelacy of the Divine Adjudicator lords over the nation of Precaea as a theocracy, the Beyella Divinity officially serves as the spiritual body of Sarlat, much like the Church of Deihass in Ilfernac. It is no secret, however, that the leaders of the denomination have had the royal family under their thumbs since even before the nation's secession from the greater empire of Ilfernac. With a king in tow, the will of the Under Matriarch has become the will of the nation, establishing the Beyella Divinity as a force to be reckoned with despite having far fewer numbers than any other denomination.

Hierarchy: The Beyella Divinity is comprised entirely of human women, with most of its key members drawn from the ranks of nobility and wealth. While lower class women are present in the Divinity, they cannot attain the same rank as their better-mannered counterparts. Men do exist within the institution's hierarchy, but most are simple clerks or assistants while those of higher breeding are recruited as holy temple guards.

The supreme ruler of the denomination is the Under Matriarch, traditionally a noble-blooded figure with a terrifying command of the Voice and an unequaled mastery of the Dominance dominion. Under Matriarchs derive their title from the founder of the Beyella Divinity, the Matriarch Beyella, and are forbidden from calling themselves by that title. The Under Matriarch, or Holy Mother as she is also known, has singular authority over the entire denomination and can dictate denominational policy, judgment, promotion, and demotion with impunity. She vacates the office only upon her death, which usually comes as a result of assassination rather than natural causes. Because the position is so vulnerable to sudden evacuation, the Holy Mother is guarded at all times by a significant retinue of conventional and unconventional bodyguards and secret police.

Well beneath the Under Matriarch are the Pristine. Each pristine is a high priestess of noble blood, promoted to the position of overseer of a church, whether through deeds glorifying the Divinity or the ousting of the previous overseer through vicious politicking. Pristines collectively form a congregation called the Under Council, convening regularly at the Office of the Under Matriarch to receive instructions from and deliver status reports to the Holy Mother. The Under Council is also a forum for recommendations to the Under Matriarch, though such requests are made with a good deal of care and genuflection for fear of appearing too ambitious.

Parallel to the Pristine but barred from the Under Council are the Pristine Exemptat. These priestesses have achieved the same distinctions as their counterparts but are limited by being born of common blood. "The Exempt," as they are also called, are placed in lower profile temples adjacent to laborer districts or in backwater towns. Despite being of considerably high station in the Divinity, they often find themselves unsupported by the Under Council and the Under Matriarch when challenged by a lower ranking but higher born priestess.

The core of the Beyella Divinity is made up of dilectates, who serve under pristines and pristine exemptats. They form the bulk of the clergy and are responsible for pacification of the local citizenry and dominion duties. Dilectates often juggle responsibilities between their home church and estates or government outposts to which they have been assigned, or are assigned roaming duties in the service of the Divinity; most adventuring priestesses of the Beyella Divinity are dilectates.

Servitors form the bottom tier of the clergy. All new priestesses in the Beyella Divinity begin as servitors, and lowborn priestesses that do not possess the capacity or confidence to elevate themselves can remain trapped in the position for their entire lives. As their name suggests, servitors serve a higher-ranking priestess, generally a pristine or pristine exemptat, to whom they are fully accountable. They may also be assigned to a dilectate, but only on the orders of a higher-ranking priestess. A servitor has no rights and can voice no complaint against her superior or any other member of the clergy. Servitors can only be promoted by their superior or by direct order of the Under Matriarch; the latter typically only occurs as a matter of patronage to upper class initiates with influential families.

Adherence to the established hierarchy is enforced without exception. Strict internal policing and threats of severe punishment enforce deference to one's superiors. The presence of the Daughters of Beyella – the feared secret police of the denomination, accountable only to the Under Matriarch – weighs heavily on every parish no matter how remote. These powerful priestesses are placed within the normal hierarchal structure, where they act for all intents and purposes as standard members of the priesthood while reporting back to the Under Matriarch. Still, accomplished priestesses of the Beyella Divinity are cunning and the edict against outright violence does nothing to allay their more insidious and political maneuverings. Pristines are especially infamous for having gained their positions at the expense of another's falsely tarnished reputation.

Relationships: The Beyella Divinity was the first institution to formally divorce itself from the Church, triggering the Unification Wars in the process, as the Church and Ilfernac sought to reign in all of the Corelands. Beyella's execution by the Church and subsequent oppression under the heels of the Fist of Deihass, once the Church's military wing and now the independent Prelacy of the Divine Adjudicator, has cemented a deep history of resentment between the Beyella Divinity and the Prelacy in particular. The standing enmity between them and the nations they control is vicious, and to this day peace between them subsists on weak ceasefires. The Divinity's policies toward the other denominations has followed suit with the recent introduction of the Purity Edict, which bans all other denominations from Sarlat. Temples formerly belonging to the Church of Deihass are routinely converted or demolished, and priests of both the Church and Despinus Chapter are persecuted to the extreme where they are found guilty of defying the edict. Simply wearing an article of allegiance to the Prelacy of the Divine Adjudicator is grounds for imprisonment or execution.

Despinus Chapter

Despinus Chapter, also called the Dark Church, is a renegade offshoot of the Church of Deihass, characterized most by its rejection of the Synod and the belief that the Voice should be used to the benefit of all society. The bishop Despinus founded the denomination after the Fifty Year Blight – a brutal plague that claimed the lives of a third of the Corelands population in humanity's middle years. Advocating the indiscriminate sale of the Voice to counteract the disease, and also considering the possibility of leveraging magic to combat it, Despinus was instead accused by the Synod of creating the blight, excommunicated, and his faction nearly obliterated by the Church's military wing, the Fist of Deihass. It has existed since in a state of exile, subsisting on secrecy and commercial sales of the Voice.

Power Center: Despinus Chapter has no official base of operations, due to being branded as a renegade faction in the Corelands, and adhering to a moderate level of discretion even in the Eastern Ridge. As such, shrines, temples, or any other hard proof of membership is rare in the Corelands. Most regular cities and all megacities have small shrines scattered throughout the dark places where customers from all walks meet to partake of spiritual nourishment and the Voice. Some standing churches do exist within the Eastern Ridge, though many are nothing more than extensions attached to a thieves' guild or mercenary barracks. The only sizable cathedral belonging to the Dark Church – and, in fact, the only cathedral of any sort in the Eastern Ridge – is located in Falldrake, where the ruling council often meets under heavy guard.

Hierarchy: Despinus Chapter's sordid history of exile and persecution has molded it into a unique institution, whose hierarchal structure borrows as much from its religious roots as it does from organized crime. Though the Dark Church rejects the authority of the Synod, and the entire notion of a single supreme denominational leader, it relies on the authority of a similar council of bishops called the Synod In Exile, or "Exsilium." This secretive council meets only when it is convenient and safe to do so, to pass edicts, settle disputes, and share news and events, which each attending bishop is responsible for disseminating to his individual network of priests.

Bishops themselves mark the highest rank of priest in the Dark Church, ascended to their rank either by invitation into the Synod or their own claim to the rank. Like bishops of the Church of Deihass, Despinus Chapter bishops are distinguished by their territorial power. But unlike the Mother Church, numerous small territories may exist within a single city, let alone province or county, resulting in hundreds of bishops, some legitimate and others self-titled. Territorial disputes are common, especially where no single bishop has complete control over a region. When such disputes cannot be settled through a council vote, the outcome is usually determined by secret wars fought through the disputing bishops' proxies. Though the Synod is officially a council of equals, bishops with larger territorial influence exert disproportionate influence amongst their peers, and can therefore sway the Synod vote to their favor.

Outside of Synod politics and the constant shift of power within the Dark Church are its populous clergy. Where a priest makes his living in bishop-controlled territory, he must submit to that bishop's authority, usually being absorbed into a micro-hierarchy established by the controlling bishop, replete with varying ranks, responsibilities, and rewards. Outside of these jurisdictions, he is accountable only to himself, to the Faith, and ultimately to the collective Synod In Exile should he partake in crimes against Despinus Chapter. Roaming priests are accorded considerable freedoms, but acts of heresy and collaboration with the forces of Azrae do not go overlooked. Punishment for such indiscretions ranges from simple admonitions to execution at the hands of hired assassins. The Dark Church Synod maintains no official policing service, but individual bishops regularly rub shoulders with the criminal underworld, granting them a long reach and access to considerable muscle and resources.

For every actual priest of the Dark Church, there are many more functionaries that are not priests at all, but rather rogues or commoners under contract. Additionally, Despinus Chapter is home to the largest population of nonhuman clergy of any denomination. Though it remains predominantly human, especially within the Synod, there are no edicts that specifically limit the potential authority of nonhuman priests.

Relationships: To this day, priests of the Dark Church suffer scathing accusations of heresy from the Church of Deihass and contempt from both the Prelacy of the Divine Adjudicator and the Beyella Divinity. It is no surprise, however, that the denomination's adherence to most of the original tenets of the Covenant, its humanisitc views, and the commercial access they offer to the Voice makes them a popular choice amongst the common populace. Of the four denominations, Despinus Chapter is the widest spread with priests dispersed across the entire human dominion. Its official status as a criminal division of the Church of Deihass, however, demands vigilant secrecy, forcing discretion in the Corelands. Much of the priesthood was displaced or killed during the Cleansing, leaving few of their kind in Prelacy-controlled territory. Those that do remain are extremely bitter and antagonistic toward their former oppressors and forego some of their mercenary neutrality when given an opportunity to strike back. Likewise, Dark Church priests in Sarlat's underworld have recently come under attack by the Daughters of Beyella as a result of the Beyella Divinity's devastating Purity Edict. Only in the stubborn Eastern Ridge, where the influence of the Corelands is weak, do priests of Despinus Chapter walk openly.

Prelacy of the Divine Adjudicator

The Prelacy of the Divine Adjudicator represents the most orthodox denomination of the Faith, characterized by a militant perspective and a black and white approach to the world. As the only denomination that cites the Return as a key motivator, is infamous for an unrelenting crusade against the "heretic threat" – a title given to anyone that opposes it, traditionally practitioners of magic and worshippers of demons. It labels the complacency of the other denominations as an indicator of corruption and failure to responsibly deliver the Faith. The Prelacy is also the most human-centric of the religious institutions, painting humans as the original and only children of Deihass.

Power Center: The Prelacy of the Divine Adjudicator is not only a massive and militarily significant denomination, but also a theocracy that controls the nation of Precaea. The Ascendancy, the denomination's ruling body, is located in Pelleton and simultaneously serves as the nation's spiritual, political, and military headquarters. A great number of cathedrals cement the Prelacy's dominance throughout Precaea, and extend into Eastern Ilfernac where traditional elements of the Prelacy remain embedded in Ilfernese society.

Hierarchy: The Prelacy hierarchy has two distinct components: a leadership that possesses ultimate and unquestioned authority, and a subservient supporting structure organized into subsections of equal rights and privilege, where positions of power are regularly rotated as a means of staving off corruption and factional influence. The head of the Prelacy is the Prelate Ascendant, a powerful leader who traditionally has a strong military and political background in addition to considerable mastery of the Voice. The Prelate Ascendant chooses his own successor as well as the seven members of his advisory council, the Septem Ordinis.

Each member of this council is an ordained priest that has mastered a single holy dominion, completing a circle of eight with the Prelate Ascendant representing Piety. Septem members exist outside of the standard denominational hierarchy, neither subject to an external authority nor able to dictate orders to any other priest. Rather, their power comes from the influence that they exert on the decisions of the Prelate Ascendant and the selective dissemination of information to him from common priests of the denomination, who generally address the Prelate Ascendant through them rather than directly.

Below the Prelate Ascendant and his council are the middle prelates. Each middle prelate is assigned a single church and its parish, for whom he is the representative to the Prelate Ascendant by proxy of the Septem Ordinis. Within Precaea, where most cities run under theocratic law, the jurisdiction of a single church extends into a ward. These cities are divided into numerous such wards so that each middle prelate is accorded equal power. The Prelate Ascendant designates one middle prelate in each city as a consul, who oversees all of its wards. Consuls share their ecclesiastic duties with governorship and call their fellow middle prelates to council in civic matters on behalf of the Ascendancy.

The last rung of the hierarchy is the ordained priest. The Prelacy has the largest clergy of any denomination, including the Mother Church, due to its triple role as spiritual body, governing body, and armed forces. These priests take their duties seriously, and minister to the populace as di-

rected. Priests that take on roaming duty in the service of the Prelacy are forbidden from increasing in rank, but their exploits may garner them an even greater station under the wing of the Prelate Ascendant, where they can acquire the title of Inquisitor. Modeled after both the Church's Baeus Bissancti and the Beyella Divinity's Daughters of Beyella, the Ascendancy Inquisitori are tasked with internal policing and investigation of external threats, particularly as regards arcanism and demons. Each inquisitor answers only to the Prelate Ascendant, though they are encouraged to respect the standard chain of command. Unlike their counterparts within the other denominations, inquisitors act openly and in full regalia, so as to present consistently visible representation from above in all quarters.

Despite the external appearance of this hierarchy as a well-oiled machine, discord brews beneath the calm surface, particularly in the periphery of the nation beyond the Ascendancy's immediate reach. Strong differences of opinion have emerged regarding the Prelacy's relationship with the Mother Church and the continued persecution of the heretic threat. Fiercely devout elements of the church advocate a policy much like Sarlat's Purity Edict that bans all religions other than the state sanctioned faith, and a renewed inquisition against suspected agents of Azrae as well as all practitioners of arcane magic – a position that extremist factions have long held and impressed upon consecutive Prelate Ascendants. Others view this as needlessly fanatical and warn that such a path would lead only to renewed chaos and strife, and possibly even to a civil war within Precaea. Both sides quietly mold subordinates in their interpretation of the Faith, and a quiet but growing schism chisels at the foundations of another human church.

Relationships: Of all the Faith's denominations, the Prelacy is the youngest and also the most ironic in its origin. It is a direct descendant of the Mother Church's Fist of Deihass, a militaristic faction that was tasked with bringing all denominations back into the fold. It exists today as the strongest of these offshoots, though paranoia and an unyielding obsession with order threatens its foundations. Its position as a political entity has left it on shaky terms with its neighbors, particularly its old enemy Sarlat, which was originally annexed into the Ilfernac Empire by the Prelacy itself when it was still the Fist of Deihass, and then warred against a second time during the Kingdoms War. Priests of the Prelacy and of Sarlat's Beyella Divinity are not easily tolerated in each other's domains and small-scale skirmishes continue across their borders in the absence of a meaningful truce. Though relations with Ilfernac have settled somewhat since the Kingdoms War, the seizure and conversion of many Church facilities during and after the war has not gone unnoticed by the Mother Church. Relations with Despinus Chapter are extremely hostile on account of so many of their priests persecuted and killed during the Cleansing, the Prelacy's bloody crusade against hybrid and heretic.

Chapter 6: Magic

"With my ritual and my words, spoken in the dark and most holy tongue, I can embrace you wherever you be – more tender than the lustiest of imaginings, or so tight that your head might burst. The choice is mine. The power is mine. Fear me, for I am the new God."

- Liette Drus, human arcanist, fallen of the Beyella Divinity

This chapter contains all the rules and information necessary for using magic in a DARK LEGACIES campaign, replacing the Magic chapter in the *Player's Handbook* in its entirety.

Overview

The following sections provide information on the flavor of magic in DARK LEGACIES as well as an overview of how the magic system differs from that in the core rules. Refer to Learning Spells, Casting Spells, and Spell Descriptions following this overview for complete rules on using magic in your campaign.

Nature of Magic

The origin of all magic on Earth is Azrae and the Abyss. It is said that magic is the soul of Azrae, and that each demon is given life by being invested with a portion of that soul. Demons and their subtypes have an inherent ability to wield magic in the form of spell-like abilities. Mortals gain access to magic through the science of arcanism, whereby they transmute demonic energy into spells through incantation and alchemy; this science is dangerous, often vile, used sparingly, and then only when the desired result could not be achieved through mundane means.

Unlike the Voice, which is specific to priests, arcanism is accessible to all characters, regardless of class. It is an unrestricted power, the practice of which has grown steadily since the Great War, much to the horror of the churches of humanity. Those that use it do so knowing that they practice a forbidden science that exists in violation of the laws of Deihass and the Faith, but among those that travel the dark road, the promise of unrestricted personal power outweighs all concerns of retribution for heresy.

Spell-like Abilities

The spell-like abilities of monsters – specifically demons – in a DARK LEGACIES campaign represent those creatures' intrinsic ability to summon and command magical effects mentally. Spell-like abilities are unchanged from the core rules, and are not subject to any of the requirements for casting a spell as an arcanist. Thus, Spellcraft checks are unnecessary, components are not required, spell failure due to lost concentration results in no further consequences, spellcasting strain and damage from the casting process are not suffered, and taint is not accrued. The resulting effect of a spell-like ability may still cause damage or other consequences, however, such as the damage taken when changing form via *shapeshift*.

Unless otherwise noted in a creature's spell-like ability description, using a spell-like ability requires a standard action. A creature may have a combination of spell-like abilities and spells that have been learned through arcanism. In this case, it must adhere to all of the rules and trappings involved when casting a spell as an arcanist; likewise, a creature cannot cast a spell-like ability as an arcanist spell unless the spell equivalent has been properly learned and the components are available.

Arcanism

The science of arcanism is the means by which all spells are learned and cast in DARK LEGACIES. Any character with Speak Language (Abyssal), at least 1 rank in Spellcraft, and who possesses the requisite materials can learn and cast spells by making a Spellcraft check. Dedicated arcanists receive a bonus to their Spellcraft checks along with other special abilities that facilitate greater spellcasting mastery (see the Arcanist, page 29). Failing a check to learn a spell can result in years passing before a character is able to cast it; failing a check to cast a spell often results in brutal side effects. Arcanism is a difficult, unforgiving, and inherently corrupting science, the product of which does not come naturally to mortals: when a character learns or casts a spell, he accrues taint, which represents the gradual degradation of his sanity and morals in the pursuit of limitless power; when he casts a spell, a character suffers ill effects in the form of nonlethal damage, ability damage, ability drain, or worse.

Casting a spell requires that a character know the spell he is to cast and that he possess the necessary components. The first component of a spell is incantation, read aloud from passages of demon cuneiform. The second component is a material – usually a set of chemical reagents that act as a mundane catalyst for the desired effect, and a specific or symbolic object that is offered as a sacrifice in order to lure energy from the Abyss. The process is long, involved, and prone to failure; all spells have a casting time of at least one round in DARK LEGACIES, thus most spells are better suited to a controlled environment than the chaos of battle. When the two components are combined, demonic energy is channeled into the caster's body. It is willful but chaotic, and surges through the blood and organs of the caster until it is finally given shape by the parameters of the spell and then channeled outward. More powerful spells require more energy, and therefore increased physical exertion on the part of the caster. If the spell parameters are incorrect or are poorly delivered, the channeled energy rejects the spell and continues to violate the body of the caster until expended, with the potential to inflict suffering, and even death, upon him and anyone near him.

Power of Magic

DARK LEGACIES is a low-magic campaign setting. As such, magic is rare, difficult to use, and extremely difficult or impossible to neutralize once invoked. There is no metamagic with which to increase a spell's effectiveness, no spell resistance to guard against magic, no counterspelling, and no easy dispelling of magic. The same spell is rarely cast repeatedly within a short period of time, due to the extreme physical and mental cost of spellcasting and the obscure components required.

The power of a spell is in the spell itself; range, duration, effect, and saving throw are all determined by the spell or the spell's level, rather than the caster of the spell or his level. A caster's power instead comes from the ability to actually cast the spell – no easy feat in DARK LEGACIES. Most high-level spells demand such extreme precision and control of their summoned demonic energies that multiple characters are required in their casting, so as to minimize the risk of catastrophic spell failure. Some extremely accomplished arcanists can cast spells up to 7th level on their own, but dabblers are generally limited to 5th-level spells. Attempting to cast an 8th-level spell on one's own is tantamount to suicide, and 9th-level spells are impossible to cast individually regardless of a caster's expertise.

Even demons are limited in the scope of their spell-like abilities. Spells with open-ended effects, such as *teleport* and *wish* do not exist in DARK LEGACIES. Likewise, no creature, mortal or otherwise, has the ability to return a soul to its body after death; rather, similar spells result in the creation of mindless automatons, neither dead nor alive. Refer to Environmental Considerations, below, and the Spells section at the end of the chapter to assist in determining whether a given spell is suitable for inclusion in a DARK LEGACIES campaign.

Environmental Considerations

Earth has the unique condition of existing halfway between the mortal realm and the Abyss, with the latter located beyond the impassable coasts, behind a ridge of perpetual storm cloud that seethes on the horizon. There are no other planes of existence as far as the people of Earth are concerned, except for the paradise of Heaven that is promised to faithful worshippers of Deihass, unattainable until after their death. Because the Earth and the Abyss are effectively on the same plane, all creatures of the Abyss (demons) are considered to be on their home plane; they can still be called and dismissed from and to the Abyss with specific spells, but if they are killed on either plane, they are destroyed completely. Additionally, summoned creatures always originate from the Abyss, and they do not return there when the summoning spell's duration expires; they must be manually dismissed with another spell. This second consideration is especially relevant to arcanists that mistakenly believe demons to be a disposable tool rather than the horrific threat they truly are. Lastly, plane-based concepts such as positive and negative energy, and travel through the astral or ethereal plane do not exist. There are some spells in DARK LEGACIES that behave in a similar fashion as spells that normally depend on these concepts, but they do so as unique entities with specialized effects.

Divine Magic

Priests use the Voice, rather than magic, to produce miraculous effects. This unique power, specific to priests, grants them supernatural abilities associated with their holy dominions, as well as the ability to augment their normal voice beyond human limits. Though priests have used the Voice freely for three thousand years, new questions as to the roots of this power have emerged as a result of a growing awareness of arcanism among the general populace. Similarities are drawn between the two powers, suggesting that the Voice is perhaps just a different kind of magic: "divine magic". Such controversial views are generally kept private, however, as they attract vicious retribution from religious authorities.

Regardless of the fact that the Voice and magic both produce fantastic effects, the two are dissimilar in the manner in which they affect the world: magic manifests often-chaotic changes or circumstances that could not occur naturally, while the Voice is usually reactive, invoked to maintain or impose order. Likewise, each has their strengths and weaknesses: magic is generally more diverse, able to produce appallingly far-reaching effects, but it cannot in any way disrupt the Voice; the Voice, on the other hand, has limited potential compared to magic, but can disrupt both magical effects and the magical abilities of demonic items of power.

Magic Items

Generic magic items do not exist in DARK LEGACIES. Rather, there are items of power, identified as either demonic or holy. All items of power are extremely rare and generally of lower power than standard magic items found in the core rules. Items of power have a maximum of four qualities, where a quality is a specific ability or embedded spell-like ability, or a point of bonus, such as an ability score bonus or attack bonus. Additionally, no item of power can have greater than a +2 bonus of any one given type. However, the bonuses and effects of items of power do stack with those of masterpiece qualities.

Demonic items are created by a torturous process of binding a demon into a mundane item through spells and sheer will. Anyone with access to a deconstructed demon (see *deconstruct into spell form*, page 116), the requisite Spellcraft skill, nerves of steel, and the Create Demonic Item feat can create a demonic item of power. However, just as with casting powerful spells, the process of creating a demonic item inflicts temporary and permanent ability drain on the creator. Additionally, all demonic items are cursed with inherent side effects due to the constant struggle of the bound demon to be free. These effects can be localized to the user, who might suffer taint-like effects while wielding the item, or they can affect the world at large, causing severe environmental distortions and mass hysteria.

Holy items of power are free of such side effects and therefore more desirable, but they can only be created by priests – specifically, priests with the Consecration dominion – through the Voice and prayer. The creation of holy items is similar to the creation of demonic items, however, in that it requires a permanent sacrifice on the part of the creator. Experienced consecrators retire from service as emotional blanks, drained of their personality and the very ability to use the Voice. Holy items are closely guarded by the church that consecrated them, and are almost always loaned rather than given away. When holy items are stolen or not returned in due course, bloody retribution is visited upon the culprits and any presumed accomplices that stand in the way of retrieval.

The creation and qualities of items of power are fully detailed in the *Dark Legacies Campaign Guide*.

Learning Spells

Arcanism is an obscure and difficult science, subject to much personal interpretation and diversity in the transcribing of magic onto the written page. Two identical spells may be structured and written in completely unique formulas regardless of producing the same result. Some spells are scattered into many fragments, unusable until all pieces are found and merged into a single cohesive formula.

When a new spell is discovered, it must be deciphered and then learned before it can be cast. Mundane exposition, diagrams, and so forth may accompany the actual demonic text, but these are often vague or intentionally misleading and cannot be relied upon. In order to truly know what he is dealing with, a character must delve into the cryptic demonic formulas. Only then, and if he is possessed of the requisite Intelligence, can he attempt to cast the spell.

Deciphering Stage

Nothing is known about a newly discovered spell until it has been deciphered. Once deciphered, the spell's level and basic function are established, as well as what components are required for its invocation. Deciphering a spell also reveals whether the spell is complete or a fragment of a greater spell. In the latter case, clues may be provided as to how much of the spell is missing.

Deciphering a spell requires a number of hours equal to the level of the spell (known by the GM) and a successful Spellcraft check (DC 15 + the spell's level) at the end of that study period. A character with 5 ranks in Knowledge (magic) gains a +2 bonus on the Spellcraft check. If the check fails, the character cannot attempt to decipher that particular spell again until the next day. The time required to decipher a spell is reduced by a number of hours equal to the character's Intelligence modifier, with a minimum of one hour required. Thus, a character with an

Intelligence of 16 (+3 bonus) attempting to analyze an 8th-level spell requires only 5 hours to decipher it. If the person that actually transcribed the spell is present and able to help the character, a skill check is not required but the requisite time must still pass.

Learning Stage

If a character possesses a complete spell that has been deciphered (see above) and has a high enough Intelligence score to learn the spell, he may attempt to do so with further study. Learning a spell requires an Intelligence score of 10 plus the spell's level. Once a spell is learned, it can be cast from that same reference, or memorized if the character has the ability to memorize spells. A learned spell does not need to be transcribed to a personal spellbook or scroll in order to be usable, but it can be, if desired, during the learning period at no additional cost of time.

A character must spend a number of days equal to twice the spell's level trying to learn it. (A day is considered to be 12 full hours of uninterrupted study.) The total days required is reduced by his Intelligence modifier, to a minimum of one day. At the end of each day, the character must make a Spellcraft check (DC 15 + twice the spell's level). A character with 5 ranks in Knowledge (magic) gains a +2 bonus on these checks. Circumstance modifiers for poor or favorable study conditions can also be applied to this check at the GM's discretion. If the Spellcraft check fails, that day's study is fruitless and does not count towards the total time required to learn the spell. If the Spellcraft check fails two days in a row, the character has encountered a blocking issue and may not try to learn the spell again until he gains another rank in Spellcraft. (This restriction applies only to the specific manuscript that he is studying. If he acquires a different source for the same spell, he may try to learn it again without gaining additional ranks in Spellcraft). If the actual author of the manuscript assists him, the character receives a +5 bonus to his Spellcraft check each day that he is assisted.

When a spell is learned, a character accrues 1 point of taint, regardless of the spell's level. No taint is acquired if he attempts to learn the spell but is unsuccessful.

Spell Storage & Transcription

There are no restrictions regarding the storage of spells. They can be found and stored upon any medium, including traditional spellbooks, scrolls, stone tablets, cavern walls, or even upon the living flesh of a demon. Scrolls have no special significance or function in DARK LEGACIES – there is no concept of a one-shot spell that is consumed after the casting, with the exception of the *deconstructed demon* spell that is created as a result of casting *deconstruct into spell form* upon a demon (page 116).

A spell only needs to be transcribed onto another medium if the character wishes to make a copy of it, if transporting the original is impractical, or if the character wishes to transcribe a memorized spell after losing the spell's reference. A spell can be transcribed during the learning process for free; thereafter, it takes a character one day to transcribe a learned spell, regardless of its level. If a spell has only been deciphered, but not learned, it can still be transcribed but the transcriber must make a Spellcraft check as though he was casting the spell in order to properly transcribe it. If the check fails, the transcribed spell is worthless. The result of this check is not known until the new spell is deciphered. A spell that has not been deciphered cannot be transcribed.

Casting Spells

Spellcasting works the same for all characters, whether they are devoted arcanists or dabblers with more ambition than sense. The following section describes the process for casting

spells through arcanism. Spell-like abilities are handled in the same manner as they are in the core rules.

How Does Spellcasting Work?

Spellcasting in DARK LEGACIES is an involved process that requires great physical and mental sacrifice on the part of the caster, as well as exposure to additional risk and consequence should his spell fail. The spellcasting flow below outlines the process of casting a spell, and the descriptions that follow explain each step of the process.

- Choose a spell from those that you heave learned, and which you have either memorized or have the spell's formula available to reference.
- While the spell is being cast (but before it has completed) make any Concentration checks necessary to avoid casting interruptions.
- If the spell completed without interruption, make a Spellcraft check to determine whether it was cast successfully or failed. If the spell is terminated prematurely or fails due to a failed Concentration check, make a modified Spellcraft check to determine if there are any additional consequences.
- Check off material components consumed by the spell.
- Apply spellcasting strain (nonlethal damage, ability score damage, ability score drain).
- If the spell was successfully cast, adjudicate the results; otherwise, apply the relevant spell failure consequences.
- Apply taint.

Choosing a Spell

First you must choose which spell to cast. All spells are available to all characters regardless of class, though you can only cast a spell that you have previously learned (see Learning Spells, above). There is no limit to how many times that you can cast any given spell in a day, so long as you have the requisite materials and are conscious.

If you have any spells memorized, you can cast those spells without the assistance of a spell reference; only arcanists can memorize spells. If you do not have a spell memorized, you must cast it with the assistance of reference material – this can be a spellbook, a scroll, an inscription on a tablet, or any other legible medium large enough to contain the complete spell formula.

All spells have verbal and material components and some also require a focus; these arcane reagents are required to produce the desired effect. Therefore you must be able to speak clearly, be able to hear yourself speak, and be able to manipulate the required materials. If you are silenced or deafened, you cannot cast spells. Many material components are alchemical mixtures that require some degree of skill to produce and maintain; if you do not have the skill or facilities to fabricate these components yourself, you must procure them through third parties.

Additionally, you must concentrate to cast a spell, making spellcasting during combat a dangerous endeavor. Spellcasting exacts a physical toll on a caster's body, mind, and soul, meaning that you must carefully consider the need for a spell each time you are tempted to cast one.

The Spellcraft Check

Spellcasting is a difficult and unforgiving science, which demands great skill and concentration on the part of the caster. In order to successfully cast a spell, you must make a Spellcraft check (DC 10 + the spell's level squared), modified by your armor and encumbrance check penalties. An arcanist gains a bonus to Spellcraft checks equal to his arcanist level. When casting a spell that takes a full round or longer to cast, the Spellcraft check is made on the completion of the spell's casting; its imminent success or failure is unknown for the duration of the casting. If your Spellcraft check fails, the spell is lost and you suffer a spell failure side effect (see Spell Failure, below).

The casting of a spell can be terminated prematurely if desired, but you must still make a Spellcraft check as though it had reached completion. The spell does not take effect regardless of the outcome of this check (it effectively fails), but failing a Spellcraft check to terminate a spell triggers a spell failure side effect, just as though the spell was miscast. Terminating a spell is a standard action that requires concentration; failing to terminate a spell due to lost concentration is the same as losing concentration during the normal casting of that spell (see Concentration, below).

Regardless of whether or not a spell completes successfully, is terminated prematurely, or fails for any reason, all components are consumed, and all spellcasting strain and taint is incurred.

Table 6-1: Spellcraft DCs

Spell Level	Spellcraft DC[1]
1st	11
2nd	14
3rd	19
4th	26
5th	35
6th	46
7th	59
8th	74
9th	91

1 Armor impedes the handling of material components. Add your armor's armor check penalty to this DC.

Concentration

To cast a spell, you must concentrate. If something interrupts your concentration while you are casting, you must make a Concentration check or lose the spell and possibly suffer additional consequences. The more distracting the interruption and the higher the level of the spell that you are

trying to cast, the higher the Concentration DC is. If the check succeeds, the spell continues uninterrupted; otherwise, the spell fails. When the casting of a spell fails due to lost concentration, you must immediately make a Spellcraft check as though the casting process completed, adding the difference of the Concentration check DC and the Concentration check result to the Spellcraft DC (losing concentration while casting a spell is always more dangerous than simply miscasting a spell). If this Spellcraft check succeeds, there are no further consequences; if the check fails, you suffer a spell failure side effect (see Spell Failure, below).

If a distraction is so severe that continuing to cast a spell is impossible (such as being deafened, silenced, stunned, paralyzed, or otherwise rendered inert or immobile), a Concentration check must still be made, but the spell fails regardless of the check result. Just as with a normal failed Concentration check, a Spellcraft check must then be made, adding the difference of the Concentration check DC and the Concentration check result to the Spellcraft DC if the Concentration check failed, or using the spell's normal Spellcraft DC if it was successful. If this Spellcraft check succeeds, there are no further consequences; if the check fails, you suffer a spell failure side effect (see Spell Failure, below).

The following situations apply when casting a spell. For consequences of losing Concentration while concentrating on an active spell, directing a spell, or using a spell-like ability, see the Concentration skill (page 57).

Injury: If you take damage while trying to cast a spell, you must make a Concentration check (DC 10 + points of damage taken + the level of the spell you're casting). If you fail the check, the spell fails. The interrupting event strikes during spellcasting if it comes between when you start and when you complete a spell (for a spell with a casting time of 1 full round or more) or if it comes in response to your casting the spell (such as an attack of opportunity provoked by the spell or a contingent attack, such as a readied action).

If you are taking continuous damage, such as from *bone spasm*, half the damage is considered to take place while you are casting a spell. You must make a Concentration check (DC 10 + ½ the damage that the continuous source last dealt + the level of the spell you're casting). If the last damage dealt was the last damage that the effect could deal then the damage is over, and it does not distract you.

Repeated damage does not count as continuous damage. Likewise, damage suffered as a result of the casting process or spellcasting strain does not necessitate a Concentration check.

Spell: If you are affected by a spell while attempting to cast a spell of your own, you must make a Concentration check or lose the spell you are casting. If the spell affecting you deals damage, the DC is 10 + points of damage + the level of the spell you're casting. If the spell interferes with you or distracts you in some other way, the DC is the spell's saving throw DC + the level of the spell you're casting. For a spell with no saving throw, it's the DC that the spell's saving throw would have if a save were allowed.

Sermon: If you are affected by a sermon, you must make a Concentration check or lose the spell you are casting. If the sermon being preached is Purity of Thought, you must win an opposed Concentration check against the Preach check of the sermonizing priest or lose the spell you are casting. Otherwise, the DC is the sermon's normal saving throw + the level of the spell you're casting.

The Voice: If you are adversely affected by a Voice effect (but not a sermon augmented with the Voice) while attempting to cast a spell, you must make a Concentration check or lose the spell you are casting. If the Voice affecting you deals damage, the DC is 10 + points of damage + the level of the spell you're casting. If the Voice interferes with you or distracts you in some other way, the DC is the standard saving throw for that application of the Voice + the level of the spell you're casting.

Grappling or Pinned: The only spells you can cast while grappling or pinned are those whose material components you have in hand, and which require no specific placement of those components that would be impossible under the circumstances. Even so, you must make a Concentration check (DC 20 + the level of the spell you're casting) or lose the spell.

Vigorous Motion: If you are riding on a moving mount, taking a bouncy ride in a wagon, on a small boat in rough water, or simply being jostled in a similar fashion, you must make a Concentration check (DC 10 + the level of the spell you're casting) or lose the spell.

Violent Motion: If you are on a galloping horse, taking a very rough ride in a wagon, on a small boat in rapids or in a storm, or being tossed roughly about in a similar fashion, you must make a Concentration check (DC 15 + the level of the spell you're casting) or lose the spell.

Violent Weather: You must make a Concentration check if you try to cast a spell in violent weather. If you are in a high wind carrying blinding rain or sleet, the DC is 5 + the level of the spell you're casting. If you are in wind-driven hail, dust, or debris, the DC is 10 + the level of the spell you're casting. In either case, you lose the spell if you fail the Concentration check. If the weather is caused by a spell, use the rules in the Spell subsection above.

Component Disrupted: If a spell component is momentarily disrupted, you must make a Concentration check (DC 15 + the level of the spell you're casting) or lose the spell. Generally speaking, a disruption is considered to be momentary if the component is interfered with and restored on the same round, but more leeway may be given in longer rituals. In situations where another circumstance may already interfere with the handling of the component (such as taking damage or being grappled), use only the more difficult Concentration check.

If the Concentration check succeeds but the disruption is so severe that it leaves no conceivable means of completing the spell (such as a vital component being smashed), you must terminate the spell on your next turn (see The Spellcraft Check, above). Refer to each spell's components and casting process to determine the extent of component disruptions.

Casting Defensively: If you want to cast a spell without provoking any attacks of opportunity, you must make a Concentration check (DC 15 + the level of the spell you're casting) to succeed. You lose the spell if you fail.

Entangled: If you want to cast a spell while entangled in a bola, net, or while you're affected by a spell with similar effects, you must make a DC 15 Concentration check to cast the spell. You lose the spell if you fail.

Component Use & Identification

The successful casting of a spell depends in large part upon the authenticity and proper handling of material and focus spell components. Each spell description details what components are necessary and how they must be handled. The actual components themselves may vary between different versions of the same spell (see Spells, below), but it is important that you adhere to whatever demands a given spell has, so that the demonic energy of the spell is properly summoned and shaped.

Some spell components require a skill check, such as the Craft (alchemy) check required to produce a special perfume for *beatific veil*. Most spells, however, have more basic requirements such as minerals, chemicals, or biological matter. It is common to secure components in the course of exploration and investigation, and therefore be confident of their authenticity (in the case of cutting the heart out of a fallen demon, you can be assured of having an authentic demon heart rather than a doctored pig's heart). But if you are acquiring such materials through illicit commercial channels, you may, at the GM's discretion, need to identify that the component is authentic. Some components cannot reasonably be identified, as they are based on circumstance rather than science (such as the tears of a suffering humanoid for *despair*); in these cases, it is incumbent upon the caster to procure such components himself, as relying on the assurances of a supplier in such matters is extremely dangerous.

The Appraise skill can be used to identify gems of specific quality or the value of precious metals. Identifying an organic spell component is generally an average (DC 10) or tough (DC 15) task for common items or a challenging task (DC 20) for exotic items. Identifying organs or biological matter can be achieved with the Heal skill when required for humanoids or the relevant Knowledge skill for other creatures or plants. The Heal skill can also be used to identify cause or time of death (DC 25).

If an incorrect or sabotaged spell component is used in the casting of a spell, the spell fails on completion, regardless of the Spellcraft check result. If the Spellcraft check fails, a spell failure side effect occurs as normal (see Spell Failure, below).

Cooperative Casting

Some spells can be cast cooperatively, allowing more than one character to contribute to the casting process and thereby reducing the difficulty of the spell and the damage incurred. High-level spells, in particular, require extreme skill and control of demonic energies that is generally beyond the capabilities of a single caster. Each spell's description indicates whether the spell can be cooperatively cast or not, or whether it requires a specific number of casters. In the latter case, a single individual cannot cast the spell alone regardless of his skill.

In order for multiple casters to cooperatively cast a spell, each of them must have learned the spell. Characters that have memorized the spell can cast alongside characters that must reference it. Unless otherwise noted in the spell description, spell components need not be replicated for each caster when spellcasting cooperatively. For each additional caster after the first, all casters involved gain a +5 bonus to their Spellcraft checks. Additionally, casting strain for the spell is divided evenly among all casters (rounding up). Each caster still accrues 1 point of taint for casting the spell.

The spell is only successful if all casters involved succeed in their Spellcraft checks. In the event of a failure, each caster uses his own Spellcraft check to determine whether he also suffers a spell failure side effect (see Spell Failure, below). If one or more casters have their casting disrupted, the remaining casters must each terminate the spell (see The Spellcraft Check, above).

Spellcasting Strain

In addition to the components required to cast a spell, the act of summoning and manipulating demonic forces is fatiguing and inflicts casting strain in the form of nonlethal damage upon the caster. The amount of casting strain is equal to 1d4 points of nonlethal damage per spell level of the spell being cast. The spell's effective level for calculating this nonlethal damage is reduced by 1 level for every point of casting resistance gained from the arcanist class, though this effective spell level can never be reduced below 1st-level, meaning you always suffer at least 1d4 points of nonlethal damage when casting a spell. Casters that are immune to nonlethal damage instead take half the rolled amount as regular hit point damage. If you fall unconscious as a direct result of taking nonlethal damage

from spellcasting strain (regardless of any unrelated nonlethal damage previously incurred), all excess damage is applied as regular hit point damage.

Many powerful spells also exact additional strain in the form of temporary ability damage, permanent ability drain, or other effects such as hit point damage. These effects may occur as a direct consequence of channeling particularly powerful energy, to fulfill a requirement for an investment of the caster's essence, or as a result of duress directly related to the nature or effects of the spell. Particularly risky spells also require that the caster suffer some damage or effect during the casting process that is neutralized only if the spell is successfully cast. Ability score damage and hit point damage heals normally but ability score drain suffered in this manner can never be restored. Nonlethal damage, ability damage, ability drain, and any other additional effects are incurred in that order immediately following the completion of the spell (whether or not the spell succeeds) but before the spell result or failure effects. In a situation where the spell's result would reverse a detrimental effect caused by casting strain (such as falling unconscious due to the strain of casting *vitality leech* then acquiring enough hit points to become conscious again) treat the effects as simultaneous so that the detrimental effect is negated.

Taint

Magic is inherently corrupting to mortals. The reckless channeling of demonic energy invariably pollutes the minds and bodies of characters that cast spells too frequently; the promise of ever-greater power draws them down a dark road that is devoid of friends and allies. A character gains 1 point of taint every time he casts a spell, regardless of the spell's level and whether the spell is successfully cast or not. As a character accrues an increasing amount of taint, he suffers the effects of corruption, usually in the form of a loss of control over his own actions. The effects of taint are detailed in Chapter 7: Grit & Consequences.

Spell Failure

Spell failure occurs when a spell is not successfully completed. All of the following conditions result in spell failure:

- Failing your Spellcraft check to cast a spell (whether individually or cooperatively).
- Prematurely terminating a spell.
- Losing concentration for any reason during the casting of a spell.
- Being silenced, deafened, or otherwise losing your ability to proceed while casting a spell.
- Using an incorrect or sabotaged spell component (GM's discretion).
- A failed Spellcraft check from one or more participants of a cooperative casting.
- Trying to cast a spell in conditions where the characteristics of the spell (range, area, etc) cannot be made to conform.

When a spell fails, you immediately suffer any damaging effects incurred during the spell's casting process, which would have been reversed were the spell cast successfully. These effects are described in each spell's description. (Note: some spells, such as *creeping tumors*, inflict damage upon the caster whether they are successfully cast or not.)

Additionally, failing the Spellcraft check to cast a spell, or the recovery Spellcraft check allowed when a spell fails due to premature termination, loss of concentration, or the inability to complete a spell, results in a spell failure side effect. This side effect represents a violent release of the spell's demonic energies in the absence of correct parameters that would normally control them. The specific side effect is determined by rolling d%, modified by the failure threshold (Spellcraft DC – Spellcraft check result) against Table 6-2: Spell Failure Side Effects.

Demons (and creatures that are a subtype of demon) do not suffer spell failure side effects.

Table 6-2: Spell Failure Side Effects

d%[1]	Failure Effect	d%[1]	Failure Effect
01-05	None	71-73	Sickened (catastrophic)
06-10	Harmless Effect	74-76	System Shock (major)
11-13	Sickened (minor)	77-79	Internal Effect
14-16	System Shock (minor)	80-82	Sensory Overload (major)
17-19	Amnesia	83-85	Sensory Overload (catastrophic)
20-22	Sensory Overload (minor)	86-88	Stunned (major)
23-25	Stunned (minor)	89-91	Stunned (catastrophic)
26-28	Area Shock (minor)	92-94	Area Shock (major)
29-31	Unconsciousness (minor)	95-97	Unconsciousness (major)
32-34	Backlash (minor)	98-100	Unconsciousness (catastrophic)
35-37	Cascade (minor)	101-103	Backlash (major)
38-40	Confusion	104-106	Cascade (major)
41-43	Sickened (moderate)	107-108	Broken Bondage
44-46	System Shock (moderate)	109-111	System Shock (catastrophic)
47-49	Opposite Effect	112-114	Area Shock (catastrophic)
50-52	Sensory Overload (moderate)	115-116	Possession
53-55	Stunned (moderate)	117-119	Backlash (catastrophic)
56-58	Area Shock (moderate)	120-122	Cascade (catastrophic)
59-61	Unconsciousness (moderate)	123-124	Abyssal Portal
62-64	Backlash (moderate)	125-126	Permanent Drain
65-67	Cascade (moderate)	127-128	Chain Reaction
68-70	Sickened (major)	129+	Annihilation

1 Add the failure threshold to your die roll.

Spell failure side effects listed without a descriptor produce a consistent result that is independent of the failed spell's level. Variable effects, identified by a minor, moderate, major, or catastrophic descriptor, use a calculated severity rating to determine their result. A minor effect has a severity rating equal to half the failed spell's level (with a minimum rating of 1), a moderate effect has a severity rating exactly equal to the spell's level, a major effect has a severity rating equal to twice the spell's level, and a catastrophic effect has a severity rating equal to five times the spell's level. Depending on the specific side effect, this rating might be used to determine the number of dice rolled for damage, the duration of the effect, etc. Hit point damage caused by a spell failure side effect is not subject to reduction by specific resistances.

Spell failure side effects are detailed below.

None

The spell simply fails and the caster is spared any extra effects.

Abyssal Portal

The spell's Abyssal conduit expands out of control, unleashing a demon just as though the character had cast *call demon*. The called demon has HD equal to twice the spell's level.

Amnesia

The caster forgets all memorized spells.

Annihilation

The caster is overwhelmed by the energies released and is consumed by a wash of arcane fire. He is destroyed utterly along with all of his belongings.

Area Shock [variable]

The area surrounding the caster is drenched with energy released from the spell, dealing 1d4 points of nonlethal damage per severity rating to everyone in a burst radius equal to 5 feet per spell level, except for the caster who only takes half damage. Anyone who falls unconscious as a result of this side effect applies the excess damage as normal hit point damage.

Backlash [variable]

The energy of the spell ruptures within the blood vessels of the caster, causing internal hemorrhaging and subsequent 1d4 points of damage per severity rating. At its mildest, backlash causes a nosebleed or a dribble of blood from the mouth. At worst, blood erupts in a violent explosion from every pore of the caster's body. In addition to the hit point damage taken, the character becomes exhausted. An exhausted character moves at half speed and takes a –6 penalty to Strength and Dexterity checks. After 1 hour of complete rest, an exhausted character becomes fatigued.

Broken Bondage

One demonic item of power worn or wielded by the caster is immediately destroyed. The demon within is reconstituted and attacks him.

Cascade [variable]

Demonic energy explodes from the caster, dealing 1d4 points of damage per severity rating to everything in a burst radius equal to 5 feet per spell level, except for the caster who only takes half damage.

Chain Reaction

Roll twice and apply both spell failure effects. If the character dies as a result of a chain reaction effect, continue rolling until all rolls have been completed, to account for other possible effects.

Confusion

The caster attacks the nearest character on his next round.

Harmless Effect

A harmless effect occurs, subject to the GM's interpretation. Example effects are a shift in temperature, an energy wave that distorts the appearance of everything in its path before dissipating, horrifying sounds or smells from the Abyss, etc.

Internal Effect

The spell is activated but is targeted upon the caster rather than the target. This side effect can only occur if the spell was cast to completion before failing due to a failed Spellcraft check. If the spell effect cannot conceivably be inflicted upon the caster, roll again. Beneficial effects cannot be conferred in this manner.

Opposite Effect

The spell is activated but its effect is reversed. This side effect can only occur if the spell was cast to completion before failing due to a failed Spellcraft check. If the spell has no plausible reverse effect, roll again.

Possession

The spell's energy surges, drawing a gush of power from the Abyss that coalesces into an ethereal demonic entity with HD equal to twice the spell's level. (At the GM's discretion, this demon may be one that was previously encountered and banished to the Abyss through the actions of the caster or his allies.) This entity immediately attempts to possess the caster. Possession is detailed in Chapter 7: Grit & Consequences.

Permanent Drain

All ability score damage suffered by the casting of the spell becomes permanent ability score drain.

Sensory Overload [variable]

The caster loses one sense for a number of rounds equal to the severity rating. Roll on the table below to determine the lost sense. If the lost sense is touch, the character automatically falls prone and is effectively paralyzed.

d20	Lost Sense
1-4	Taste
5-8	Smell
9-13	Hearing
14-18	Sight
19-20	Touch

Sickened [variable]

The caster becomes sickened for a number of minutes equal to the severity rating. A sickened character takes a –2 penalty on all attack rolls, weapon damage rolls, saving throws, skill checks, and ability checks.

Stunned [variable]

The caster is stunned for a number of rounds equal to the severity rating. A stunned character drops everything held, can't take actions, takes a –2 penalty to AC, and loses his Dexterity bonus to AC (if any).

System Shock [variable]

The energy of the spell feeds back into the caster, causing 1d4 points of nonlethal damage per severity rating. If he falls unconscious as a result of this side effect, all excess damage is applied as normal hit point damage. In addition to the nonlethal damage taken, the character becomes fatigued. A fatigued character can neither run nor charge and takes a –2 penalty to Strength and Dexterity. Doing anything that would normally cause fatigue causes the character to become exhausted. After 8 hours of complete rest, the character is no longer fatigued.

Unconsciousness [variable]

The caster is knocked unconscious for a number of rounds equal to the severity rating.

The Spell's Result

If a spell is successfully cast, you can apply whatever result it entails, taking into account which creatures (or objects or areas) are affected, and whether those creatures have made successful saving throws (if any were allowed). These results are applied regardless of whether or not you are still conscious or alive following the casting of a spell.

Special Spell Effects

Attacks: Some spell descriptions refer to attacking. All offensive combat actions, even those that don't damage opponents are considered attacks. All spells that opponents resist with saving throws, that deal damage, or that otherwise harm or hamper subjects are attacks. Spells that summon demons are not attacks because the spells themselves don't harm anyone.

Bonus Types: Usually, a bonus has a type that indicates how the spell grants the bonus. The important aspect of bonus types is that two bonuses of the same type don't generally stack. With the exception of dodge bonuses, most circumstance bonuses, and racial bonuses, only the better bonus works (see Combining Magical Effects, below). The same principle applies to penalties – a character taking two or more penalties of the same type applies only the worst one.

Bringing Back the Dead: No spell, priest, or item of power in DARK LEGACIES has the power to restore a soul to its body after death. Some spells animate the bodies of the dead or affect them in some way, but these shells are empty, possessed by demonic energy rather than a soul.

Combining Magical Effects

Spells or magical effects usually work as described, no matter how many other spells or magical effects happen to be operating in the same area or on the same recipient. Except in special cases, a spell does not affect the way another spell operates. Whenever a spell has a specific effect on other spells, the spell description explains that effect. Several other general rules apply when spells or magical effects operate in the same place:

Stacking Effects: Spells that provide bonuses or penalties on attack rolls, damage rolls, saving throws, and other attributes usually do not stack with themselves. More generally, two bonuses of the same type don't stack even if they come from different spells (or from effects other than spells; see Bonus Types, above).

Different Bonus Names: The bonuses or penalties from two different spells stack if the modifiers are of different types. A bonus that isn't named stacks with any bonus.

Same Effect More than Once in Different Strengths: In cases when two or more identical spells are operating in the same area or on the same target, but at different strengths, only the best one applies.

Same Effect with Differing Results: The same spell can sometimes produce varying effects if applied to the same recipient more than once. Usually the last spell in the series trumps the others. None of the previous spells are actually removed or dispelled, but their effects become irrelevant while the final spell in the series lasts.

One Effect Makes Another Irrelevant: Sometimes, one spell can render a later spell irrelevant. Both spells are still active, but one has rendered the other useless in some fashion.

Multiple Mental Control Effects: Sometimes magical effects that establish mental control render each other irrelevant, such as a spell that removes the subject's ability to act. Mental controls that don't remove the recipient's ability to act usually do not interfere with each other. If a creature is under the mental control of two or more creatures, it tends to obey each to the best of its ability, and to the extent of the control each effect allows. If the controlled creature receives conflicting orders simultaneously, the competing controllers must make opposed Charisma checks to determine which one the creature obeys.

Spells with Opposite Effects: Spells with opposite effects apply normally, with all bonuses, penalties, or changes accruing in the order that they apply. Some spells negate or counter each other. This is a special effect that is noted in a spell's description.

Instantaneous Effects: Two or more spells with instantaneous durations work cumulatively when they affect the same target.

Reversing Spell Effects

Spells, for the most part, must be left to do what they will for their given duration. There are no generic means via magic to prematurely end another creature's spell. Some spells, however, particularly those with permanent or localized effects, can be reversed or nullified by casting the same spell with slightly different parameters or by destroying an effigy or power center, as detailed in the spell's description. Before an existing spell can be dismissed, however, it must be identified with a Spellcraft check (page 62). A priest with the Sanctity dominion can also attempt to use his Voice to disrupt existing magical effects (page 48).

Casting Example

The demented Father Piandantus, Master Librarian of the Church in Agsten, Ilfernac, has succumbed to the wiles of arcanism after too many years of exposure to demonic texts. One of those texts now sits on an altar before him, so recently stolen that it still reeks of incense and the musky body odor of the priest's clerks. He turns the pages gingerly until resting with a satisfied sigh at a *purification by fire* spell, then lifts his gaze to a gagged and bound hybrid prostitute, who he has personally tried and convicted as an Azrae worshipper. His spell reference and components ready, Piandantus begins to cast the spell. But halfway into the incantation – a sphere of phosphorous flaring ever more violently in his hands – the priest is interrupted by the sudden appearance of a repeater bolt protruding from his chest, fired by Inquisitor Weal of the Baeus Bissancti, who was hiding in wait for proof of the priest's heresy.

Piandantus takes 15 points of damage from the attack and must make a Concentration check or lose the spell; the Concentration check DC is 31 (10 + 15 points of damage + 6th-level spell). The priest's player rolls a 26: overwhelmed by pain, Piandantus falters and the spell fails. He must then determine if there is an additional side effect as a result of the spell failure. He makes a Spellcraft check against DC 51 (standard casting DC of 46 for a 6th-level spell + 5 calculated from the difference of Concentration DC and Concentration check result) but only pulls off a 38 – a spell failure side effect has occurred.

Piandantus first applies the spell's casting strain: 6d4 points of nonlethal damage. Next, he takes 2d6 points of fire damage from the failed casting process of the spell. He must then determine the spell failure side effect; Piandantus' player rolls a 90, modified by the failure threshold of 13 (Spellcraft DC of 51 – Spellcraft check result of 38) for a final result of 103: a major backlash effect. The backlash side effect inflicts 1d4 points of damage per severity rating and the severity rating for this spell is 12 (6 for spell level × 2 for major effect), thus Father Piandantus suffers 12d4 points of damage. Piandantus disgorges an explosion of blood, first from this mouth then from his eyes and ears until the chamber is covered with it; in the span of a single round, the corrupt priest is reduced to a bloody, smoldering corpse.

Inquisitor Weal retrieves the book of spells, carefully wiping off Piandantus' blood with his sleeve. He pauses as the smooth demonhide brushes seductively against his palm, suddenly unsure whether to return the stolen volume or hold onto it for "safe keeping". After a long minute of staring open-mouthed at its glyphs and textures, Weal is startled back to his senses by the gurgling of the gagged hybrid. His decision made, he turns and walks toward the only remaining witness…

Spell Descriptions

The spells available to characters in DARK LEGACIES are listed and described at the end of this chapter. The description of each spell is presented in a standard format. Each category of information is explained and defined below.

Name

The first line of every spell description gives the name by which the spell may generally be known. Because the study of magic has been so fractured throughout history and among different cultures, it is more likely that any given spell has many different names in as many languages.

Descriptor

While spells in DARK LEGACIES are not divided into schools or categories (they are all effectively demon-based magic), some have descriptors that categorize the spell in some way. These descriptors, encased in square brackets, appear beneath the spell name. Charm and compulsion, which are part of the Enchantment school of magic in the *Player's Handbook*, are spell descriptors in DARK LEGACIES.

The descriptors are acid, air, charm, cold, compulsion, darkness, death, earth, electricity, fear, fire, force, language-dependent, light, mind-affecting, sonic and water.

Most of these descriptors have no game effect by themselves, but they govern how the spell interacts with other spells, special abilities, unusual creatures, and so on.

A language-dependent spell uses intelligible language as a medium for communication. If the target cannot understand or cannot hear what the caster of a language-dependant spell says the spell has no effect. A mind-affecting spell works only against creatures with an Intelligence score of 1 or higher.

Availability

Spells are hard to come by, some more than others. This line indicates just how rare a particular spell is. Characters that begin play as an arcanist possess either two uncommon spells of up to 3rd-level or one rare spell of up to 2nd-level. Spells with large-scale, far-reaching effects are generally legendary or lost. When creating a character above 1st level, a spell's rarity

determines how much it costs to "purchase" that spell during character creation (page 67).

Uncommon: Those spells that are repeatedly learned and practiced in civilized lands usually fall into this category. They are typically spells with limited duration and effect.

Rare: Most spells fall into this category. Few mortals are in possession of rare spells, excluding those that pay dues to arcanist guilds or demon cults, or agents with special access to restricted libraries.

Legendary: Legendary spells are the rarest of treasures (and curses), found in dangerous and old places fraught with peril. When they are discovered – usually at high cost of life and resources – they are rarely in a complete state. Assembling all of the parts to a legendary spell can easily take months or years of adventuring and research.

Lost: These spells are the most powerful, lost to the world for all intents and purposes. Despite their elusive nature, some ambitious arcanists, desperate for the next level of power, devote their lives to tracking down any scrap of spell formula or evidence of the spell's existence they can find. The discovery, reassembly, learning, and casting of a single lost spell might serve as the conclusion (usually a bad one) to a long, hard fought campaign.

Level

The next line of a spell description gives the spell's level, a number between 1 and 9 that defines the spell's relative power. Any spell that has been learned (see Learning Spells, page 95) can be cast, regardless of the spell's level and the character's level.

Cooperative

Some spells can be cast cooperatively (see Cooperative Casting, page 99), making the casting easier and the process less strenuous by spreading the demonic energy across multiple characters. If "no" is written, the spell cannot be cast cooperatively, "yes" means that it can, and a numeric value is listed for spells that require a specific number of casters. Generally speaking, spells that are centered on the caster cannot be cast cooperatively.

Components

A spell's components are what you must do or possess to cast it. All spells have verbal and material components; some also require a focus (a material component that is not consumed by the spell). Specific requirements and usage guidelines for material and focus components are given at the end of the spell's descriptive text.

Material and focus components serve as arcane reagents and sacrifices that are necessary to summon and command demonic energy; they are absolutely required in the casting of spells. Tracking down a spell component can be as difficult as finding and learning the spell itself. This is as often due to the rarity of the component as it is to the often-vile nature of many spell components. Spells that target specific individuals from afar often also require an effigy or some other construct fashioned from the personal possessions or body of the intended victim.

Verbal (V): A verbal component is an incantation spoken aloud from demon cuneiform. To provide a verbal component, you must be able to speak in a strong voice and hear yourself speak. A spell or effect that compromises your voice or deafens you spoils the incantation (and thus causes the spell to fail).

Material (M): A material component is usually a combination of chemical reagents that act as a mundane catalyst for the desired effect, or a specific object that is offered as a sacrifice in order to lure demonic energy from the Abyss. The material component is annihilated when you cast the spell, whether or not the casting succeeds. You must have the proper material component to cast a spell and are not assumed to possess it by default. You must have at least one hand free to provide a material component.

Focus (F): A focus component is identical to a material component in all respects except that it is not consumed when the spell is cast and can be reused. A focus is usually also more complex than a material component and often requires some combination or crafting together of materials.

Strain

Spellcasting strain (page 99) is made up of nonlethal damage, ability damage, ability drain, and/or other effects that are incurred during the spell's casting process. All strain suffered by casting the spell is listed on this line, in the order in which it is incurred. The actual result of the spell may cause additional damage or effects, such as the damage suffered when undergoing a transformation through the *shapeshift* spell (page 123); these effects are detailed in the spell's description. When casting a spell cooperatively, the listed strain is divided evenly between the casters (rounding up), unless otherwise noted.

Casting Time

The time it takes to cast a spell is partially dependent on whether the spell has been memorized or is being referenced. If a spell has been memorized, it can be accessed instantly and requires the standard amount of time to cast as indicated in the spell's description. If a spell is being referenced, you must locate the desired spell then refer to it over the entire course of the casting attempt. If you have your spell source ready or are reading from a scroll, locating the spell is a free action. Otherwise you have to find the spell first, which is a move action. Spells with a casting time of less than 1 minute have their casting time doubled if being referenced. Spells with a casting time greater than a minute require the same amount of time whether they are memorized or referenced, as such spells generally involve more ritual than direct invocation.

All spells in DARK LEGACIES have a casting time of 1 round or more. A spell that takes 1 round to cast is a full-round action. It comes into effect just before the beginning of your turn in the round after you began casting the spell. You then act normally after the spell is completed.

A spell that takes 1 minute to cast comes into effect just before your turn 1 minute later (and for each of those 10 rounds, you are casting a spell as a full-round action, just as noted above for 1-round casting times). These actions must be consecutive and uninterrupted, or the spell automatically fails.

When you begin a spell, you must continue the invocations, component manipulation, and concentration from the current round to just before your turn in the next round (at least). If you lose concentration after starting the spell and before the casting is complete, the spell fails and you may also suffer a spell failure side effect.

You make all pertinent decisions about a spell (range, target, area, effect, version, and so forth) when the spell comes into effect, unless otherwise specified in the spell's description.

In addition to actual casting time, some spells require additional preparation time, such as *call demon* and *soul offering*. Concentration need not be maintained during this preparation, unless otherwise noted in the spell's description.

If a spell is being cast from memory, you only provoke attacks of opportunity when you begin casting the spell, regardless of the actual casting time. If you are casting a spell from a reference, you provoke attacks of opportunity at the beginning of each turn in which you are casting. While casting a spell, you don't threaten any squares around you.

Range

A spell's range indicates how far from you it can reach, as defined in the Range entry of the spell description. A spell's range is the maximum distance from you that the spell's effect can occur, as well as the maximum distance at which you can designate the spell's point of origin. If any portion of the spell's area would extend beyond this range, that area is wasted. Where a range is variable, the resulting range is not determined until after the spell is successfully cast; therefore your spell may be ineffectual if it falls short of expectations. Standard ranges include the following.

Personal: The spell affects only you.

Touch: You must touch a creature or object to affect it. A touch spell that deals damage can score a critical hit just as a weapon can. A touch spell threatens a critical hit on a natural roll of 20 and deals double damage on a successful critical hit. Some touch spells allow you to touch multiple targets. You can touch as many willing targets as you can reach as part of the casting, but all targets of the spell must be touched in the same round that you finish casting the spell.

Close: The spell reaches as far as 25 + (1d10 × 5) feet away from you.

Medium: The spell reaches as far as 100 + (1d20 × 10) feet.

Long: The spell reaches as far as 400 + (1d20 × 40) feet.

Unlimited: The spell reaches anywhere on Earth or the Abyss, but cannot create an effect from one realm to the next.

Special: Some spells have no standard range category, just a range expressed in feet or miles.

Aiming a Spell

You must make some choice about whom the spell is to affect or where the effect is to originate, depending on the type of spell. The next entry in a spell description defines the spell's target (or targets), its effect, or its area, as appropriate.

Target or Targets: Some spells have a target or targets. You cast these spells on creatures or objects, as defined by the spell itself. You must be able to see or touch the target, and you must specifically choose that target. You do not have to select your target until you finish casting the spell.

If the target of a spell is yourself (the spell description has a line that reads Target: Caster), you do not receive a saving throw. The Saving Throw line is omitted from such spells.

Some spells restrict you to willing targets only. Declaring yourself as a willing target is something that can be done at any time (even if you're flat-footed or it isn't your turn). Unconscious creatures are automatically considered willing, but a character who is conscious but immobile or helpless (such as one who is bound, cowering, grappling, paralyzed, pinned, or stunned) is not automatically willing.

Some spells allow you to redirect the effect to new targets or areas after you cast the spell. Redirecting a spell is a move action that does not provoke attacks of opportunity.

Effect: Some spells create or summon things rather than affecting things that are already present. You must designate the location where these things are to appear, either by seeing it or defining it. Range determines how far away an effect can appear, but if the effect is mobile it can move regardless of the spell's range.

Ray: Some effects are rays. You aim a ray as if using a ranged weapon, though typically you make a ranged touch attack rather than a normal ranged attack. As with a ranged weapon, you can fire into the dark or at an invisible creature and hope you hit something. You don't have to see the creature you're trying to hit, as you do with a targeted spell. Intervening creatures and obstacles, however, can block your line of sight or provide cover for the creature you're aiming at.

If a ray spell has a duration, it's the duration of the effect that the ray causes, not the length of time the ray itself persists.

If a ray spell deals damage, you can score a critical hit just as if it were a weapon. A ray spell threatens a critical hit on a natural roll of 20 and deals double damage on a successful critical hit.

Spread: Some effects, notably clouds and fogs, spread out from a point of origin, which must be a grid intersection. The effect can extend around corners and into areas that you can't see. Figure distance by actual distance traveled, taking into account turns the spell effect takes. When determining distance for spread effects, count around walls, not through them. As with movement, do not trace diagonals across corners. You must designate the point of origin for such an effect, but you need not have line of effect (see below) to all portions of the effect.

Area: Some spells affect an area. Sometimes a spell description specifies a specially defined area, but usually an area falls into one of the categories defined below.

Regardless of the shape of the area, you select the point where the spell originates, but otherwise you don't control which creatures or objects the spell affects. The point of origin of a spell is always a grid intersection. When determining whether a given creature is within the area of a spell, count out the distance from the point of origin in squares just as you do when moving a character or when determining the range for a ranged attack. The only difference is that instead of counting from the center of one square to the center of the next, you count from intersection to intersection. You can count diagonally across a square, but remember that every second diagonal counts as 2 squares of distance. If the far edge of a square is within the spell's area, anything within that square is within the spell's area. If the spell's area only touches the near edge of a square, however, anything within that square is unaffected by the spell.

Burst, Emanation, or Spread: Most spells that affect an area function as a burst, an emanation, or a spread. In each case, you select the spell's point of origin and measure its effect from that point.

A burst spell affects whatever it catches in its area, even including creatures that you can't see. It can't affect creatures with total cover from its point of origin (in other words, its effects don't extend around corners). The default shape for a burst effect is a sphere, but some burst spells are specifically described as cone-shaped. A burst's area defines how far from the point of origin the spell's effect extends.

An emanation spell functions like a burst spell, except that the effect continues to radiate from the point of origin for the duration of the spell. Most emanations are cones or spheres.

A spread spell spreads out like a burst but can turn corners. You select the point of origin, and the spell spreads out a given distance in all directions. Figure the area the spell effect fills by taking into account any turns the spell effect takes.

Cone, Cylinder, Line, or Sphere: Most spells that affect an area have a particular shape, such as a cone, cylinder, line, or sphere.

A cone-shaped spell shoots away from you in a quarter-circle in the direction you designate. It starts from any corner of your square and widens out as it goes. Most cones are either bursts or emanations (see above), and thus won't go around corners.

When casting a cylinder-shaped spell, you select the spell's point of origin. This point is the center of a horizontal circle, and the spell shoots down from the circle, filling a cylinder. A cylinder-shaped spell ignores any obstructions within its area.

A line-shaped spell shoots away from you in a line in the direction you designate. It starts from any corner of your square and extends to the limit of its range or until it strikes a barrier that blocks line of effect. A line-shaped spell affects all creatures in squares that the line passes through.

A sphere-shaped spell expands from its point of origin to fill a spherical area. Spheres may be bursts, emanations, or spreads.

Creatures: A spell with this kind of area affects creatures directly (like a targeted spell), but it affects all creatures in an area of some kind rather than individual creatures you select. The area might be a spherical burst, a cone-shaped burst, or some other shape.

Many spells affect "living creatures," which means all creatures other than constructs and undead. Creatures in the spell's area that are not of the appropriate type do not count against the creatures affected.

Objects: A spell with this kind of area affects objects within an area you select (as Creatures, but affecting objects instead).

Other: A spell can have a unique area, as defined in its description.

(S) Shapeable: If an Area or Effect entry ends with "(S)," you can shape the spell. A shaped effect or area can have no dimension smaller than 10 feet. Many effects or areas are given as cubes to make it easy to model irregular shapes. Three-di-

mensional volumes are most often needed to define aerial or underwater effects and areas.

Line of Effect: A line of effect is a straight, unblocked path that indicates what a spell can affect. A line of effect is canceled by a solid barrier. It's like line of sight for ranged weapons, except that it's not blocked by fog, darkness, and other factors that limit normal sight.

You must have a clear line of effect to any target that you cast a spell on or to any space in which you wish to create an effect. You must have a clear line of effect to the point of origin of any spell you cast. A burst, cone, cylinder, or emanation spell affects only an area, creatures, or objects to which it has line of effect from its origin (a spherical burst's center point, a cone-shaped burst's starting point, a cylinder's circle, or an emanation's point of origin).

An otherwise solid barrier with a hole of at least 1 square foot through it does not block a spell's line of effect. Such an opening means that the 5-foot length of wall containing the hole is no longer considered a barrier for purposes of a spell's line of effect.

Duration

A spell's Duration entry tells you how long the magical energy of the spell lasts.

Timed Durations: Many durations are measured in rounds, minutes, hours, or some other increment. When the time is up, the magic dissipates and the spell ends. If a spell's duration is variable, the duration is rolled secretly (the caster doesn't know how long the spell will last).

Instantaneous: The spell energy comes and goes the instant the spell is cast, though the consequences might be long-lasting. A priest with the Sanctity dominion cannot disrupt such spell effects.

Permanent: The energy remains as long as the effect does. This means the spell is vulnerable to disruption by a priest with the Sanctity dominion, unless otherwise noted in the spell description.

Concentration: The spell lasts as long as you concentrate on it. Concentrating to maintain a spell is a standard action that does not provoke attacks of opportunity. Anything that could break your concentration when casting a spell can also break your concentration while you're maintaining one, causing the spell to end. You can't cast a spell while concentrating on another one. Sometimes a spell lasts for a short time after you cease concentrating.

Subjects, Effects, and Areas: If the spell affects creatures directly, the result travels with the subjects for the spell's duration. If the spell creates an effect, the effect lasts for the duration. The effect might move or remain still. Such an effect can be destroyed prior to when its duration ends. If the spell affects an area then the spell stays with that area for its duration. Creatures become subject to the spell when they enter the area and are no longer subject to it when they leave.

Touch Spells and Holding the Charge: In most cases, if you don't discharge a touch spell on the round you cast it, you can hold the charge (postpone the discharge of the spell) indefinitely. You can make touch attacks round after round. If you cast another spell, the touch spell dissipates.

Some touch spells allow you to touch multiple targets as part of the spell. You can't hold the charge of such a spell; you must touch all targets of the spell in the same round that you finish casting the spell.

Discharge: Occasionally a spells lasts for a set duration or until triggered or discharged.

(D) Dismissible: If the Duration line ends with "(D)," the spell's effects can be dismissed by magical or mundane means. In the case of spell durations based on concentration, simply ceasing to concentrate ends the spell. Otherwise, dismissing a spell generally requires that the spell be cast again, sometimes with different components, or that a specific power center, such as an effigy, be deactivated or destroyed. A spell cannot simply be dismissed with a gesture or change of heart. The descriptive text of dismissible spells details the procedures for ending or reversing their effects.

Saving Throw

Usually a harmful spell allows a target to make a saving throw to avoid some or all of the effect. The Saving Throw entry in a spell description defines which type of saving throw the spell allows and describes how saving throws against the spell work.

Negates: The spell has no effect on a subject that makes a successful saving throw.

Partial: The spell causes an effect on its subject. A successful saving throw means that some lesser effect occurs.

Half: The spell deals damage, and a successful saving throw halves the damage taken (round down).

None: No saving throw is allowed.

Disbelief: A successful save lets the subject ignore the effect.

(object): The spell can be cast on objects, which receive saving throws only if they are items of power or if they are attended (held, worn, grasped, or the like) by a creature resisting the spell, in which case the object uses the creature's saving throw bonus unless its own bonus is greater. (This notation does not mean

that a spell can be cast only on objects. Some spells of this sort can be cast on creatures or objects.) An item of power's saving throw bonuses are each equal to 4 + (number of qualities × 2).

(harmless): The spell is usually beneficial, not harmful, but a targeted creature can attempt a saving throw if it desires.

Saving Throw Difficulty Class: The power of a spell in Dark Legacies is entirely based on the spell itself, rather than the person that casts it. A saving throw against your spell has a DC of 15 + the level of the spell.

Succeeding on a Saving Throw: A creature that successfully saves against a spell that has no obvious physical effects feels a hostile force or a tingle, but cannot deduce the exact nature of the attack. Likewise, if a creature's saving throw succeeds against a targeted spell you sense that the spell has failed. You do not sense when creatures succeed on saves against effect and area spells.

Automatic Failures and Successes: A natural 1 (the d20 comes up 1) on a saving throw is always a failure, and the spell may cause damage to exposed items (see Items Surviving after a Saving Throw, below). A natural 20 (the d20 comes up 20) is always a success.

Voluntarily Giving up a Saving Throw: A creature can voluntarily forego a saving throw and willingly accept a spell's result.

Items Surviving after a Saving Throw: Unless the descriptive text for the spell specifies otherwise, all items carried or worn by a creature are assumed to survive a magical attack. If a creature rolls a natural 1 on its saving throw against the effect, however, an exposed item is harmed (if the attack can harm objects). Refer to Table 6-3: Items Affected by Magical Attacks. Determine which four objects carried or worn by the creature are most likely to be affected and roll randomly among them. The randomly determined item must make a saving throw against the attack form and take whatever damage the attack deals. If an item is not carried or worn and is not magical, it does not get a saving throw. It simply is dealt the appropriate damage.

TABLE 6-3: ITEMS AFFECTED BY MAGICAL ATTACKS

Order[1]	Item
1st	Shield
2nd	Armor
3rd	Demonic or holy headgear
4th	Item in hand (including weapons)
5th	Demonic or holy outerwear (including coat or cloak)
6th	Stowed or sheathed weapon
7th	Demonic or holy bracers
8th	Demonic or holy clothing
9th	Demonic or holy jewelry (including rings)
10th	Anything else

[1] In order of most likely to least likely to be affected.

Descriptive Text

This portion of a spell description details what the spell does and how it works. Also described is the exact process for handling the spell's components as well as any extra effects suffered by the using of those components and other rituals necessary to cast the spell. If one of the previous entries in the description includes "see text," this is where the explanation is found.

Spells

Spells are rare treasures or terrible curses (or both). They do not exist upon store shelves or in any easily accessible location. Finding a spell, especially a rare, legendary, or lost spell, requires time, investigation, and, above all, risk. Though some spells found in this chapter – uncommon spells and rare spells, in particular – can be acquired within the darker corners of civilization, most await rediscovery in dead and haunted lands, beneath the earth or beyond the range of common sense. These spells can be found within musty assar, dwerof, and eldrin texts; upon profane altars and caverns hidden from prying eyes, immobile and retrievable only by transcription; or inscribed upon the very flesh of demons.

The many and sundry origins of spells in a DARK LEGACIES campaign makes for a situation where two instances of the same spell are rarely identical in name and execution, especially when they have been reassembled, reinterpreted, and rewritten by so many different hands. The spell names given in this chapter are intended as generic titles, and should be replaced by names that are more descriptive, with cultural or language-based variances. Thus, *locate* may be transcribed in a found spellbook as *Azrae's all-seeing eye*. To a lesser extent, the nature of a spell's components may vary, often in accordance with a specific cultural context, though the rarity of a component and the challenge that a particularly vile component poses to a caster's conscience should never be lessened in this fashion. The actual effects of a spell may also have slight variances from one to the next, though these variations should be presented as subtle flavor changes rather than game mechanics changes.

Spells from Other Sources

The spells listed within this chapter are not intended as an exhaustive list of all of the spells that are available to a caster. New spells can be created, or existing spells may be drawn from third party sources and modified for use in a DARK LEGACIES campaign. Care must be taken, however, to preserve the mood with the consideration that it is a low-magic setting, and that magic is demonic in nature.

Spells in DARK LEGACIES are generally exotic, deceptive, hurtful, selfish, inconsiderate of collateral damage, and ultimately beneficial only at the expense of an equal or greater pain on the part of another. The majority of spells are intended for use in an indirect manner rather than the thick of battle.

Spell effects are twisted rather than straightforward, cast in a demonic mold, never allowing the caster to forget from where he is drawing his power. 0-level spells or spells with negligible effects do not exist in DARK LEGACIES; likewise, spells with extremely powerful effects also do not exist, or do so only in isolated and campaign-ending circumstances. Additionally, all spells have verbal components and material components that are invariably rare, costly, or vile; somatic components are not used in DARK LEGACIES.

Spells to be avoided are those that provide mundane effects or benefits such as *animate rope* or *mending*; bypass or trivialize conventional investigation, intuition, or a requirement for knowledge or specific information, such as *detect poison* or *detect secret doors*; provide moderate to high curative, restorative, and regenerative effects, such as *cure light wounds* or *restoration*; make magic mundane, easily detectable, identifiable, or dismissible, such as *identify* or *read magic*; circumvent the need for exploration and travel through dangerous routes, such as *teleport* or *wind walk*; base their effect on alignment which does not exist in DARK LEGACIES, such as *detect evil* or *protection from evil*; affect the soul or reverse an effect of death, such as *raise dead* or *speak with dead*; or those that provide extremely powerful open-ended effects, such as *wish* or *time stop*.

When incorporating a new spell into DARK LEGACIES, its rarity, strain parameters, and material components must be added. Refer to the spells in this section as a guide when applying rarity to a spell and determining suitable spell components. Strain above and beyond the standard 1d4 points of nonlethal damage per spell level should be added when the spell has a particularly vile or far-reaching effect or empowers the caster beyond mortal levels; ability damage is common in these cases, while permanent ability drain is typically applicable only to spells that have long-term (months, years, or permanent) or especially destructive effects.

Spells By Level

1st-Level Spells

Uncommon **Black Curtain:** Obscures 10 feet for 1d6 rounds.

Deceptive Shroud: Subject becomes friendly for 2d6 minutes.

Demonic Visage: One creature is shaken for 1d4 rounds.

Sensory Multiplication: +4 on Spot and Listen checks, +2 on Initiative checks.

Spawn Umbilical Guardian: 1d4 tentacles spawn to intercept ranged attacks.

Rare **Spinal Decoder:** Know all languages for 5d12 minutes.

2nd-Level Spells

Uncommon **Brain Sieve:** −4 on Concentration checks.

Shuddering Bowel: One humanoid is sickened for 4d6 hours.

Smothering Embrace: Subject suffocated for 1d6 rounds.

Vitality Leech: Touch steals 4d4 hp from subject.

Rare   **Demonic Augmentation:** Acquire one of several demonic traits for 6d10 minutes.

Gibber: Subject cannot speak for 2d4 rounds.

Vermin Eyes: See through eyes of insect for 2d6 hours.

3rd-Level Spells

Uncommon   **Bone Spasm:** Subject takes Con damage and −2 on attacks and checks for 1d4 rounds.

Explode Corpse: Touched corpse explodes, dealing 2d6 damage within 10 ft.

Rare   **Abyssal Window:** Creatures with 5 HD or less take 2d6 damage and cower.

Beastial Slave: Gain full control over one animal while concentrating.

Beatific Veil: +2 to Cha for 4d6 hours.

Eyes of the Grave: See and hear out of a dead body.

Night Terror: Sends subject nightmares, causing fatigue next day.

Psyche Parasite: Variable Int damage and confused for 1d4 rounds.

Vile Seduction: Distracts creature for concentration + 1d3 rounds.

Legendary   **Shrieking Ward:** Possessed head screams an alarm on given condition.

4th-Level Spells

Uncommon   **Groping Hands:** Demonic hands grapple all within 10 ft. spread.

Rare   **Atmospheric Surge:** Subject takes 5d6 damage.

Bypass Barrier: Opens locked or sealed door.

Intellect Overload: Gain +1 to +4 bonus to Intelligence for 1d4 days.

Locate: Determine general location of a specific creature.

Memory Wipe: Removes one memory from creature touched.

Skin Seal: Makes subject permanently blind, deaf, or mute.

Legendary   **Brain Swell:** Subject takes 3d6 Int damage.

Shapeshift: Assume new form from Diminutive to one size larger than normal.

5th-Level Spells

Rare   **Call Demon:** Summons a demon from the Abyss.

Cardiac Assassin: Deals Con damage each round until subject dies.

Cascade of Spikes: 10d6 slashing damage; half damage to 1d4 secondary targets.

Despair: −1 to −7 on attacks, saves, and checks; 1d3 Cha drain if not disrupted.

Mark of the Pariah: Permanent −4 on Cha checks and negative reaction to target.

Legendary   **Bind Intentions:** Prevents creature from ever harming you.

Consume Mind: Transfer memories and Int from subject for 2d4 minutes.

Listening Pool: Allows casters to communicate over long distance.

Steal Likeness: Permanently assume form of deceased creature.

6th-Level Spells

Rare   **Creeping Tumors:** Subject ages 1 year/day for 10d6 days.

Deconstruct Into Chaos: Transforms subject to shapeless mass.

Dismiss Demon: Sends a demon back to the Abyss.

Noxious Cloud: Kills 3 HD or less; 4-6 HD save or die; 6+ HD takes Con damage.

Purification By Fire: While concentrating, 2d12 fire damage/round, 1 Cha drain/3 rounds.

Soul Offering: Gain long-term +1 bonus to chosen ability score.

Legendary   **Blood Blessing:** Gain long-term DR by consuming own flesh.

Deconstruct Into Spell Form: Transforms demon into a spell.

Undead Proxy: Animate a corpse, through which you can act indefinitely.

7th-Level Spells

Rare   **Flaying Despair:** Touched subject takes 1d6 damage and Cha drain on every action.

Legendary   **Abyssal Transport:** Transports creature to the Abyss.

Living Effigy: Subject is turned into a statue.

Prosthesis: Restores severed appendage to subject.

8th-Level Spells

Rare   **Crippling Blight:** Str and Dex drain over 2d6 days.

Legendary   **Torment Cage:** Imprisons subject in eternal torment; variable ability drain.

Transference: Regain youth by draining Con from victims.

9th-Level Spells

Lost   **Armageddon Device:** Incinerated to 1 mile, 100d6 to 2 miles, 40d6 to 5 miles, 10d6 to 7 miles.

Plague Bearer: Spread highly infectious disease, to which you are immune.

Dark Legacies Spells

Abyssal Transport
Availability: Legendary
Level: 7
Cooperative: Yes
Components: V, M
Strain: 7d4 nonlethal, 2d4 Int damage, 1 Wis drain
Casting Time: 1 minute
Range: Close
Target: One humanoid creature
Duration: Instantaneous
Saving Throw: Will partial

The victim of this spell suffers a misery far worse than simple death: rather than being killed outright, the creature is banished to the Abyss, where it is subjected to presumably eternal torture. The creature is consumed in a black wash of energy that erupts from the ground. If its saving throw fails, it becomes trapped within this ball of energy, which then speeds away toward the Abyss. Nothing of the creature or its possessions remains. Even if the save succeeds, the creature comes away from the experience less than whole: it takes 1d4 points of permanent drain to each ability score, rolled separately.

Material Component: The detached head of a priest who was corrupted by magic; tar.

Casting Process: The caster seals the decapitated head's eyes, mouth, and ears with the tar. As the spell is invoked, the tar expands to cover the entire head, which then disappears into shadow.

Abyssal Window
[Fear, Mind-Affecting]
Availability: Rare
Level: 3
Cooperative: No
Components: V, M
Strain: 3d4 nonlethal, 1 Wis damage
Casting Time: 1 round
Range: Close
Targets: All living, non-demonic creatures with 5 or fewer HD within 30 feet of the caster
Duration: 2d4 rounds
Saving Throw: Will partial; see text

The caster opens a window into the bowels of the Abyss, where the suffering and torment of uncounted souls inflicts terror and scathing pain upon those around him. Any creature that fails its save suffers 2d6 points of damage and cowers for the duration of the spell. A cowering creature is frozen, unable to take actions, takes a −2 penalty to Armor Class, and loses its Dexterity bonus (if any). Creatures that make their saving throw suffer no damage, and are instead shaken for the spell's duration. A shaken creature takes a −2 penalty on attack rolls, saving throws, skill checks, and ability checks. The caster must also make a saving throw against this spell, but he is only shaken, as above, if his saving throw fails, and suffers no ill effect if it succeeds. Creatures with greater than 5 HD, demons, and hybrids are unaffected by this spell.

Material Component: Tears of a child; a shard of stained glass taken from a window.

Casting Process: The caster dribbles tears in the shape of a symbol of Azrae over the glass, then throws it into the air above his head. The glass ruptures, opening the abyssal window.

Armageddon Device
[Fire]
Availability: Lost
Level: 9
Cooperative: 8
Components: V, M
Strain: 9d4 nonlethal, 2d4 Int damage, 1d6 Str drain, 1d4 Wis drain; all casters involved suffer the full spellcasting strain
Casting Time: 1 day
Range: 100 miles
Area: See text
Duration: Instantaneous
Saving Throw: None

The area of effect of the Armageddon Device is spectacular: a black glass crater 100 feet deep and 500 feet wide marks the center of the blast radius and everything within 1 mile is incinerated (1000d6 damage); everything out to 2 miles takes 100d6 damage; everything out to 5 miles takes 40d6 damage; and everything out to 7 miles takes 10d6 damage. Damage inflicted is half fire damage and half regular damage. The affected landscape becomes inert, never again spawning crops or vegetation.

Material Component: The Armageddon Device is an actual construct that must be built. Only after it has been built and placed at the desired target is the rest of the spell cast. The casing of the device is a 3 ft. diameter perfect sphere formed out of pure gold (10,000 gp value), split into two halves. Within each semi-sphere is a central chasm intersected by eight spokes that connect it to an outer ring, which in turn is composed of smaller chasms connected by conduits. The still-beating heart of a newborn demon must be placed in the center chasm. In each of the outer chambers must be placed the heart of a child that was born to one of the casters. When the device has been built and the proper components inserted, the two halves are riveted shut. Additionally, the spell requires a smaller object (6 inch diameter) that exactly matches the Armageddon Device (500 gp value).

Casting Process: Once placed, the Armageddon device can be detonated from 100 miles away. The casters stand in a circle around the smaller device, their position matching that of their children's hearts in the actual sphere. As they continue to recite the spell's invocations, both the ritual device and the actual Armageddon Device begin to generate heat and light. When the spell completes, the ritual device blinks out of existence. If the spell was successful, the Armageddon Device detonates to full effect. If it was cast to completion but failed, the device still explodes, but only deals 20d6 damage out to 500 feet.

Atmospheric Surge
[Air]
Availability: Rare
Level: 4
Cooperative: No
Components: V, M
Strain: 4d4 nonlethal
Casting Time: 3 rounds
Range: Close

Target: One corporeal creature
Duration: Instantaneous
Saving Throw: Reflex half

The demonic energies of this spell whirl around a target, where they alter the atmospheric pressure surrounding it. If the creature fails to dodge the effect, it is caught in a localized effect that causes it to rupture or implode and takes 5d6 points of damage.

Material Component: A hollow ball the size of a palm, composed of sewn triangles of flesh from a sentient creature, with a hole in the bottom.

Casting Process: To create an implosive effect, the caster inserts one finger into the hole, and then crushes the ball with the other hand. To create an explosive effect, he inserts one finger from each hand into the hole and rips outward, so that the stitches tear and the ball bursts apart. The ball disintegrates upon the spell's completion in either case.

Beastial Slave
Availability: Rare
Level: 3
Cooperative: No
Components: V, M
Strain: 3d4 nonlethal
Casting Time: 1 round
Range: Touch
Target: Animal touched
Duration: Concentration
Saving Throw: Will negates

This spell gives the caster full control over an animal. He may command it mentally as he desires, but he cannot see through its eyes, therefore the animal must be kept within range. The demonic energy that possesses the animal pollutes its body and poisons its blood; when the spell ends, there is a 50% chance that the animal dies.

Material Component: A tooth, claw, or other part of an animal that could be used as a natural weapon, taken from the same kind of animal as the target.

Casting Process: The caster must hold the component in his hand while casting the spell and continue to hold it until he has touched the target animal. Once he does, he releases the component and in doing so, also releases the animal's aggression toward him.

Beatific Veil
Availability: Rare
Level: 3
Cooperative: No
Components: V, M
Strain: 3d4 nonlethal
Casting Time: 1 hour
Range: Personal
Target: Caster
Duration: 4d6 hours

Potent demonic energy enshrouds the caster, sharpening both his personality and looks, which results in a +2 enhancement bonus to Charisma for the spell's duration.

Material Component: A special perfume created from the flesh of a beautiful humanoid (Cha 15+), mixed with rose petals and spices, and diluted in alcohol. Creating such a perfume requires a Craft (alchemy) check against DC 20.

Casting Process: The caster sprays the perfume over his naked body while invoking the spell. This spell cannot be cast if the caster is exposed to a heavy wind or inclement weather.

Bind Intentions
[Compulsion, Mind-Affecting]
Availability: Legendary
Level: 5
Cooperative: No
Components: V, M, F
Strain: 5d4 nonlethal, 1 Str drain; see text
Casting Time: 1 hour
Range: Unlimited
Target: One humanoid creature
Duration: Instantaneous; see text
Saving Throw: Will negates

By keeping in his possession an effigy of the victim, the caster prevents that creature from doing him harm through physical violence or indirect methods. The spell is broken if the caster attacks the bound creature, if the creature dies, or if the effigy is destroyed; it cannot be otherwise terminated. When the spell is terminated, whatever the cause, the caster regains his lost Strength. If the spell fails, the caster cannot attempt to bind the same creature again until he gains another rank in Spellcraft.

Material Component: 500 gp worth of fine silver chain.

Focus: An effigy of the creature; this small puppet or doll must incorporate a treasured belonging or organic matter (hair, blood, etc) taken from the creature.

Casting Process: The effigy is wrapped with the fine chain over the course of the casting. When the spellcasting completes, the chain is consumed. The effigy must remain on the caster's person in order for the spell to be effective.

Black Curtain
[Force]
Availability: Uncommon
Level: 1
Cooperative: No
Components: V, M
Strain: 1d4 nonlethal
Casting Time: 1 round
Range: 20 ft.
Effect: An obscuring black curtain of energy, 10 feet in length and height; see text
Duration: 1d6 rounds
Saving Throw: None

The demonic energy conjured by this spell coalesces into a pitch-black curtain, positioned by the caster's will, which completely obscures everything behind it. Such curtains are often used to facilitate a hasty retreat. Passing through the curtain causes 1d4 points of force damage.

Material Component: A swatch of fabric from an actual black curtain; a handful of dust.

Casting Process: As the spell is invoked, the caster tosses the cloth and dust in the direction that he wishes the curtain to materialize. Both components remain suspended in the air, then combine and expand into the spell's effect.

Blood Blessing

Availability: Legendary
Level: 6
Cooperative: No
Components: V, M
Strain: 6d4 nonlethal, 1 Wis drain, variable hit point damage; see text
Casting Time: 1 hour
Range: Personal
Target: Caster
Duration: Instantaneous (see text)

Blood blessing is an exceptionally difficult and grotesque spell, the casting of which is as harmful to the caster's psyche as the results are beneficial. Casting the spell requires the completion of a ritual in which the caster consumes a part of his own body, dedicating it as a sacrifice to the demons of the Abyss. If the spell is cast successfully, he gains damage resistance for 12d6 months (rolled by the GM), the extent of which is commensurate with the value of the sacrifice.

The caster may use a body part that has been previously detached as a result of combat or other circumstances unrelated to the spell, so long as it has been well preserved. Sacrificing a finger, toe, ear, or eye grants him with a minor blessing (DR 3/demonic or holy). Sacrificing a hand, foot, or genitalia grants him a moderate blessing (DR 5/demonic or holy). Sacrificing an arm, leg, or internal organ grants him with a great blessing (DR 10/demonic or holy).

Material Component: Recently removed or well-preserved body part from the caster's own body; the cremated remains of a demon.

Casting Process: The caster must eat the body part during the first half of the incantation, ingesting portions in regular intervals between passages until it has been fully consumed. A Fortitude save is required at the half hour mark to complete this process (DC 15 for a minor blessing, DC 20 for a moderate blessing, or DC 25 for a great blessing). If the save is successful, the sacrifice is fully consumed and the spell proceeds; if the save fails, the spell ends as though the caster terminated it prematurely.

In the second half of the ritual, the caster inflicts damage upon himself (or allows another to inflict it upon him) with one piercing, one slashing, and one bludgeoning weapon, each of which must deal at least 6 points of hit point damage. This damage disappears only if the spell completes successfully.

At the conclusion of the ritual, the caster pours the cremated demon remains over his body. The ash is absorbed into his skin, and in combination with the summoned energies, forms the protective layer.

Bone Spasm

Availability: Uncommon
Level: 3
Cooperative: No
Components: V, M
Strain: 3d4 nonlethal
Casting Time: 2 rounds
Range: Close
Target: One humanoid
Duration: 1d4 rounds; see text
Saving Throw: Fortitude negates; see text

For each round that this spell continues, a bone within a designated humanoid creature spontaneously snaps, inflicting 1 point of temporary Constitution damage. The creature also suffers a −2 penalty on attack rolls, skill checks, and ability checks on that round. It gains a Fortitude save for each round; if a save is successful, it suffers no ill effect and the spell ends.

Material Component: A shard of humanoid bone, fine enough to be snapped in two.

Casting Process: The caster breaks the symbolic bone with the final word of the invocation, triggering the effect.

Brain Sieve

[Compulsion, Mind-Affecting]
Availability: Uncommon
Level: 2
Cooperative: No
Components: V, M
Strain: 2d4 nonlethal
Casting Time: 1 round
Range: Close
Target: One living creature
Duration: 1d6 minutes
Saving Throw: Will negates

With this spell, the caster induces extremely erratic behavior in one creature. The creature becomes so disoriented that it suffers a −4 penalty on Concentration checks for the spell's duration.

Material Component: Small (6 inch diameter) net fashioned from metal wire.

Casting Process: The caster must succeed on a ranged touch attack to hit his target with the wire net. If the attack is successful, the net becomes momentarily affixed to the creature's head before being absorbed through its skin, into the skull and brain.

Brain Swell

Availability: Legendary
Level: 4
Cooperative: No
Components: V, M
Strain: 4d4 nonlethal
Casting Time: 2 rounds
Range: Close
Target: One living creature
Duration: Instantaneous
Saving Throw: Fortitude partial

This spell causes the victim's brain to swell and spasm. The effects begin with bleeding from the nose, followed by extreme pressure in the ears, then brain damage. If the creature fails its Fortitude save, it suffers 3d6 points of Intelligence damage; if the saving throw succeeds, it suffers only 1d6 points of Intelligence damage. A creature that is reduced to 0 Intelligence by this spell falls into a coma and is helpless.

Material Component: The preserved brain of a sentient creature; barbed wire.

Casting Process: The caster wraps the barbed wire around the brain, applying increasing pressure until the completion of the invocation. If the caster is not wearing gauntlets, he takes 1 point of damage and suffers a −2 penalty to attack rolls and to skill and ability checks that require the use of his hands, all for a period of 24 hours.

Bypass Barrier

Availability: Rare
Level: 4
Cooperative: Yes
Components: V, M, F
Strain: 4d4 nonlethal, 1d4 Str damage
Casting Time: 1 hour
Range: Touch
Target: One door, container, or other sealed/barred entrance
Duration: Instantaneous
Saving Throw: None

By invoking a lengthy ritual, the caster can call upon slithering demonic arms to bypass an otherwise impassable barrier. If it is a locked door, they defeat the lock. If the door is barred, they smash it open. Whatever the case, the caster has no control over the manner in which the spell opens the way for him (or the commotion that it causes). It takes the spell 1d4 rounds to bypass the barrier. If an active trap was set to trigger on the door or object being opened, it is triggered normally.

Material Component: Metal spike.

Focus: Hammer.

Casting Process: The caster embeds the spike in the ground next to what he wishes opened. As he invokes the spell, he continues to tap the spike at regular intervals. The spell activates when the spike is fully embedded, marking the spot from which the demonic arms emerge.

Call Demon

Availability: Rare
Level: 5
Cooperative: Yes
Components: V, M
Strain: 5d4 nonlethal, 1d4 Str damage
Casting Time: 1 hour
Range: Close
Effect: One summoned demon
Duration: Instantaneous; see text
Saving Throw: None

This spell opens a one-way conduit from the Abyss, through which a demon is transported. Demons are usually called for a specific purpose, such as immediate deconstruction for use in creating a demonic item of power. Calling a demon with an intention to negotiate some service typically results in deception on the demon's part, followed by the caster's slow and painful death. Each demon reacts differently to being called – some are enraged at being manipulated by mortal hands, while others may be entertained. The final attitude of the called demon is ultimately up to the GM.

In order to bring a creature of the Abyss to Earth, the caster must exchange a living humanoid as trade – one from the Abyss, one to the Abyss, the latter presumably to be tortured, eaten, or beaten about as sport. The type of demon called is directly related to the type of creature sacrificed: if the caster desires a demon for combat, he must sacrifice a warrior; if he wants power, he might sacrifice a priest; if he desires sexual favors, he sacrifices a prostitute. Likewise, the power of a called demon is commensurate with the sacrifice. It has Hit Dice equal to the level of the creature being sacrificed, plus or minus (determined randomly) 1d6 HD, with a minimum of 5 HD. Thus, a caster may not always procure a demon with the power he was expecting.

A demon is disoriented for 1d3 rounds after being called, during which it loses its Dexterity bonus to AC and can take no actions. If it is attacked, however, it automatically gains its bearings. If a binding circle has been set up (see below), the demon cannot affect the world beyond the edge of the circle with attacks, spell-like abilities, or by any other means for an additional 1d4 rounds, but it may communicate normally. After this time has passed, the demon is freed from its bondage.

Material Component: A living humanoid creature; blood and ash if using a binding circle (see below).

Casting Process: If the caster wishes to contain the demon for as long as possible – a necessity when he or another caster wishes to immediately deconstruct it – he can set up a binding circle. Doing so requires that he paint a symbol of Azrae along with specific glyphs of restraining within a perfect circle. The caster must use a brush constructed from a skull and human hair, with paint made from the victim's blood mixed with ash. Constructing a binding circle requires an additional hour of preparation and a Spellcraft check (DC 20), all the while ensuring that the sacrifice does not die of blood loss; a caster with 5 ranks in Knowledge (magic) gains a +2 bonus on this check. The GM makes the check secretly. If it fails, the circle is ineffective. Failing to use the proper materials also renders the circle ineffective.

In order for the spell to take effect, the sacrifice must be incapacitated but alive. If using a binding circle, the sacrifice is placed in the center of the circle. As the spell is cast, a portal opens to the Abyss directly above the sacrifice. Halfway into the casting, the terrified victim is pulled physically into the portal, all the while bellowing out screams of agony. The final note of these screams remains audible until the spell completes, at which point a demon materializes from the conduit and silence descends.

Cardiac Assassin

Availability: Rare
Level: 5
Cooperative: No
Components: V, M
Strain: 5d4 nonlethal, 1 Str damage
Casting Time: 1 round
Range: Medium
Target: One living creature
Duration: Concentration; see text
Saving Throw: Fortitude negates; see text

The caster violates the chest cavity of a single creature from a distance, crushing its heart by proxy of a surrogate heart squeezed within his hand. On the completion of the spellcasting, the creature becomes paralyzed as though suffering from a severe heart attack, and remains paralyzed for 1d6 rounds after the spell ends, if it survives. The creature is allowed a Fortitude save each round including the first; each time it fails, it suffers 1 point of Constitution damage. The spell ends if the creature's saving throw succeeds or the caster loses concentration.

Material Component: A well-preserved heart, extracted, still beating, from a creature of the same race as the target.

Casting Process: The caster crushes the heart with one hand while invoking the spell and for its duration. When the creature dies or the spell ends, the heart is consumed. The caster's crushing hand remains bloody for a number of days equal to the number of rounds that the spell lasted; the blood cannot be washed off by any means.

Cascade of Spikes

Availability: Rare
Level: 5
Cooperative: No
Components: V, M
Strain: 5d4 nonlethal
Casting Time: 1 round
Range: Medium
Targets: One primary target, plus 1d4 secondary targets (each of which must be within 15 ft. of the primary target)
Duration: Instantaneous
Saving Throw: Reflex half

This spell summons a length of spiked chain, which erupts out of the caster's mouth toward the target. The chain deals 10d6 points of slashing damage to the primary target. After it strikes this target, 1d4 new lengths of chain instantaneously spawn from the original to strike secondary targets. These additional chains each strike one target, dealing half as much damage as the primary chain to their target. The caster has no control over who they attack; targets are chosen randomly from creatures within 15 feet of the primary target, and no target can be struck more than once. All targets of this spell can attempt a Reflex saving throw for half damage.

Material Component: A chain link with a spike or hook attached to the end.

Casting Process: The caster threads the chain into his mouth and down his throat after completing the spell's invocation. This chain is fully consumed, but

erupts only if the spell is successfully cast. If the casting of the spell fails, the caster is unable to speak for 24 hours.

Consume Mind
[Mind-Affecting]
Availability: Legendary
Level: 5
Cooperative: No
Components: V, M, F
Strain: 5d4 nonlethal, 1 Wis damage
Casting Time: 5 rounds (30 seconds)
Range: Personal
Target: Caster
Duration: 2d4 minutes

By implanting a demon jawbone into his own head, the caster's mouth is transformed into a hideous, gaping maw, which he can wrap around a creature's head in order to absorb some of its knowledge and memories. The new jaw transforms the lower half of the caster's face into a jagged, bony formation twice the width of his head. While enhanced, he can consume the head of a creature up to one size larger than he is.

In order for the process to work, the intended target must be unconscious, paralyzed, or otherwise unable to move or defend itself. Once the spell has been cast, the caster must spend a full-round action wrapping his mouth around the head of the creature. Following this, he can take no other actions until he detaches himself, thus ending the spell. If the cater loses concentration while attached, his jaw snaps back into its original shape, and the spell ends.

For every full minute that the caster is attached to the victim, he has a 25% chance of recalling a single piece of knowledge possessed by the creature – a location, password, facial memory, etc. He also gains a +1 enhancement bonus to Intelligence per minute; this extra Intelligence provides a bonus to Intelligence-based skill checks, but the caster does not gain any skill ranks because of it. The temporary Intelligence bonus lasts 6d10 minutes following the termination of the spell. The creature, in turn, takes 1 point of Intelligence damage for every full minute the caster

is attached, and 1 point of Constitution damage for every two minutes.

Material Component: A thick paste made from glue, rosemary, and bile, in sufficient quantity to coat the jawbone.

Focus: Demon jawbone.

Casting Process: The caster coats the jawbone with the paste then holds it in front of his mouth while invoking the spell. Once completed, his jawbone cracks, splitting his mouth so that it is wide enough to accept the demon's jawbone, which is then inserted. When the spell ends, the demon jawbone is expelled and the caster's face reverts back to normal except for slight scarring upon the corners of the mouth, and an ache that lasts several days.

Creeping Tumors

Availability: Rare
Level: 6
Cooperative: No
Components: V, M, F
Strain: 6d4 nonlethal, 1d4 Con damage
Casting Time: 3 hours
Range: Unlimited
Targets: One humanoid creature
Duration: Permanent; see text
Saving Throw: Fortitude partial; see text

This spell creates an infestation of demonic tumors in the body of the victim that suck away its vitality, causing rapid aging. The tumors ravage the creature's body for 10d6 days before becoming inert. If the victim's saving throw succeeds, the spell lasts only 1 day. For each day (or portion of a day) that passes, the creature ages one year. If the effect of this spell is disrupted by a priest, the tumors immediately become inert, but the aging is irreversible. A creature suffers all of the physical detriments of aging (such as the −1 to Str, Dex, and Con at middle age) but none of the mental benefits, until the proper number of years have passed before he would have reached that age naturally.

Material Component: A tumor removed from a creature of the same type as the victim; fluids from the actual victim (such as saliva retrieved from a glass, or urine from a toilet).

Focus: The skull of a creature of the same type as the victim, which died at a venerable age. Such focus skulls are normally highly polished, jeweled, and inlaid with gold detailing.

Casting Process: The cancerous flesh is placed in the mouth of the skull. The caster wets his hand with the victim's fluids then places the palm on the top of the skull, which becomes hot with his touch. A deep red glow – dull at first then intensifying as the spell progresses – emanates from the skull's eye sockets then fades entirely when the spell completes. The process burns the tumor away completely and also inflicts mild burners on the caster's hand; he suffers a –1 penalty on attack rolls and to skill and ability checks that require the use of that hand, all for a period of 24 hours.

Crippling Blight
Availability: Rare
Level: 8
Cooperative: Yes
Components: V, M
Strain: 8d4 nonlethal, 1d6 Con damage, 1 Str drain
Casting Time: 1 hour
Range: Unlimited
Target: One humanoid creature
Duration: Instantaneous; see text
Saving Throw: Fortitude partial; see text

With this spell, the caster triggers an effect that causes the victim's body to degenerate over time until it becomes a weak, rotted husk. The victim does not automatically know why its body is failing; only that it is getting steadily worse. The creatures suffers 1 point of permanent Strength and Dexterity drain each day for 3d6 days; if its save is successful, the effect lasts only 1d6 days. A creature that is reduced to a Strength or Dexterity score of 0 cannot move at all and is helpless.

Material Component: A dose of poison that deals Strength or Dexterity damage

or drain; a length of muscle taken from a creature of the same type as the victim.

Focus: A miniature humanoid figurine fashioned from lead.

Casting Process: The poison is placed in a dish or bowl, and then brought to a boil over an open flame while the spell is invoked. As it begins to bubble, the caster tears the muscle into shreds, dropping them into the poison. To complete the spell, he drops the figurine into the mixture. The ingredients flare for a moment before being absorbed totally into the lead.

Deceptive Shroud
[Charm, Mind-Affecting]
Availability: Uncommon
Level: 1
Cooperative: No
Components: V, M, F
Strain: 1d4 nonlethal
Casting Time: 1 round
Range: Close
Targets: One humanoid creature
Duration: 2d6 minutes
Saving Throw: Will negates

This spell charms the affected creature so that it regards the caster as a trusted ally and friend (NPC attitude of friendly). It does not, however, become subject to commands or wishes any more than a friend would. On the last round in which the creature is affected, its attitude changes to neutral (NPC attitude of indifferent). The creature becomes unfriendly or hostile following the expiration of the spell. If the creature is being threatened in any way, the spell automatically fails. Likewise, if the caster or another ally attacks the creature, the spell ends.

Material Component: Perfumed oil, mixed with silver dust.

Focus: Hood, worn over the caster's head. If the hood is removed, the spell is broken.

Casting Process: The caster smears the oil over his lips while casting the spell. Once the invocation is complete, he has 1

minute to trigger the actual effect, which is done by calling the creature's name. Thus, he may cast the spell in private before approaching the creature. If more than a minute passes, the spell energy dissipates and is wasted.

Deconstruct Into Chaos
Availability: Rare
Level: 6
Cooperative: Yes
Components: V, M, F
Strain: 6d4 nonlethal, 1d4 Wis damage, 1d4 Cha damage
Casting Time: 4 rounds
Range: Close
Target: One living creature
Duration: Permanent (D); see text
Saving Throw: Will negates

Armed with the flesh of a demon, the caster inflicts that chaotic essence upon a single living creature so that it collapses into a twisted mockery of itself. The casting of this spell also twists the caster's own mind to a degree, leaving him disoriented. If the spell is successfully cast, the creature deconstructs into a shapeless mass that bares only marginal resemblance to the original creature. Its Strength and Dexterity drop to 3 and its base land speed is reduced to 5 feet. It also suffers 1d6 permanent Wisdom drain and 1d6 permanent Charisma drain and cannot communicate or defend itself in any manner. The creature's possessions are unaffected by the spell. The only manner in which this spell can be dismissed is by casting the same spell upon the deconstructed creature, with slightly different incantations and components (see below). A creature restored as such never fully recovers – its Strength, Dexterity, and base land speed return to normal, but the Wisdom and Charisma drain are permanent.

Material Component: Flesh of a demon, obtained while the demon was disguised by *shapeshift*; container filled with acid. To reverse the spell, replace the acid with glue, and combine the demon's flesh with flesh from a creature of the same type as the victim (the victim's own deconstructed flesh cannot be used).

Casting Process: The flesh is combined with the acid so that it dissolves, or with the glue so that it is sealed shut. Once the reaction is complete, the container is dropped or thrown with enough force to smash it.

Deconstruct Into Spell Form

Availability: Legendary
Level: 6
Cooperative: Yes
Components: V, M, F
Strain: 6d4 nonlethal, 1d6 Str damage, 1d4 Wis damage
Casting Time: 30 seconds (5 rounds)
Range: Close
Target: One demon or one creature possessed by a demon
Duration: Instantaneous
Saving Throw: Will negates

In order to create a demonic item of power or to force the possession of a creature by a demon, a character must have access to a *deconstructed demon* spell – a spell that contains the actual essence of a demon, which has been deconstructed into base elements of magic. Only by casting *deconstruct into spell form* upon a demon can a character create such a thing. If the demon fails its Will save, its body and essence are torn apart, coded into the arcane formula of a unique spell which streams onto a designated medium (scroll, spellbook, tablet, etc). Casting the spell on a possessed creature extricates the demon from the creature while leaving the host body intact.

Casting the resulting *deconstructed demon* spell or destroying the medium on which it was coded reconstitutes the demon into its natural form. Only if it is properly cast, however, can the emerging demon be bound into an item in order to create a demonic item of power or into another creature in order to possess that creature. Failing to properly cast a deconstructed demon causes it to revert into its natural form, just as though the spell medium was destroyed.

The resulting *deconstructed demon* spell is a 6th-level spell that must be learned in the same way as any other newly discovered spell. It is cast in the same manner as *deconstruct into spell form*, except that no components are required beyond the deconstructed demon itself; once cast, the spell is destroyed. A deconstructed demon cannot be memorized, and transcribing one onto a second medium produces a dead spell with no power – successfully deciphering such a spell reveals it as a fake.

Material Component: A medium on which to store the resulting spell; 1,000 gp worth of diamonds; caster's blood.

Focus: A holy symbol dedicated to Azrae, constructed by the caster and worn close to his heart. The caster must consecrate the symbol in blood prior to using it each time he casts this spell.

Casting Process: The caster clutches the diamonds in his hands until the skin is broken. As the spell is invoked, the diamonds break down into dust. If the spell is successful, the demon's code is transposed onto the designated medium in the form of energy. By sprinkling the dust and blood onto this code, the caster cements it in place, at which point it becomes normal text.

Demonic Augmentation

Availability: Rare
Level: 2
Cooperative: No
Components: V, M
Strain: 2d4 nonlethal, 1 Wis damage, 1d3 Cha damage
Casting Time: 2 rounds
Range: Personal
Target: Caster
Duration: 6d10 minutes

The caster allows himself to become partially possessed by the demonic energy of the spell so as to augment part of his body (available augmentations are listed below). He always acquires some sort of visible demonic mutation for the duration of the spell, based on the desired effect; a bonus to strength might cause his arms to swell and scale over, while an increased movement rate might cause his legs to become deformed and his feet cloven-hoofed. Demons cannot cast this spell.

Claw Attack: One of the caster's hands is replaced with a demonic claw that deals 1d8 slashing damage. The caster is considered to be proficient with the claw and is treated as armed when making an attack with it. It is also considered to be a demonic weapon for purposes of overcoming damage resistance.

Darksight: The caster can see in any type of darkness, mundane or otherwise, with the same clarity and range as daytime vision.

Natural Armor: The caster gains a +2 natural armor bonus to Armor Class.

Physical Enhancement: The caster gains a +2 enhancement bonus to a single physical ability score of his choosing (Str, Dex, or Con).

Speed: The caster's base land speed increases by 10 feet.

Material Component: Portion of a demon's anatomy that is relevant to the desired augmentation, wrapped in parchment.

Casting Process: Portions of the spell formula directly related to the transformation must be transcribed onto the parchment in advance of casting the spell. During the casting, the component is crossed repeatedly over the caster's heart in the shape of a symbol of Azrae. When the spell is completed, the component is absorbed into his body and the augmentation proceeds.

Demonic Visage

[Fear, Mind-Affecting]
Availability: Uncommon
Level: 1
Cooperative: No
Components: V, M, F
Strain: 1d4 nonlethal, 1 Cha damage
Casting Time: 1 round
Range: Close
Target: One living, non-demonic creature
Duration: 1d4 rounds
Saving Throw: Will negates

The face and upper body of the caster contort into that of a hideous demon, whose attributes are tailored to the specific fears of a single victim. The creature must be able to see the caster. If it fails its Will save, it is shaken for the duration of the spell. A shaken creature takes a −2 penalty on attack rolls, saving throws, skill checks, and ability checks. Demonic creatures and hybrids are immune to this spell. Demons cannot cast this spell.

Material Component: Demon bones ground into fine dust.

Focus: An expertly crafted mask (worth at least 50 gp) resembling a demon head, which does not muffle the caster's voice.

Casting Process: The caster must wear the mask for the duration of the casting. He sprinkles the bone dust in front of his face on its completion, at which point the mask bonds with his head, contorting it into the desired shape. The mask detaches undamaged when the spell ends.

Despair
[Mind-Affecting]
Availability: Rare
Level: 5
Cooperative: No
Components: V, M
Strain: 5d4 nonlethal, 1d3 Cha damage
Casting Time: 1 hour
Range: Touch; see text
Target: One humanoid creature
Duration: Permanent; see text
Saving Throw: Will negates

This spell inflicts great sadness upon the victim, so that it becomes more despondent with each passing day, until it is left a miserable shadow of its former self. The creature suffers a cumulative −1 morale penalty on attack rolls, saving throws, skill checks, and ability checks, beginning at the end of each day after being touched (see below), up to a maximum penalty of −7 at the end of a week. If a priest does not disrupt the spell before the end of the week, the creature's affliction can never be cured, and it also suffers 1d3 points of permanent Charisma drain. The affected creature does not automati-

cally discern the reason for its sadness, or connect it to the caster's touch.

Material Component: The tears of a suffering humanoid creature, which is present at the time of casting.

Focus: A worn or wielded possession (clothing, jewelry, scabbard, weapon, etc) belonging to the victim.

Casting Process: In order to cast the spell, the caster must make an Intimidate check against the component creature so that it begins to cry (the equivalent of changing its behavior). The subsequent casting of the spell affects its tears, turning them black and oily, and forcing them to flow for the duration of the casting, usually into a bowl or other container. This creature suffers 1 point of permanent Constitution drain on the spell's completion, whether it succeeds or fails. While casting the spell, the caster uses the tears as ink, painting the demonic glyph for "despair" upon the victim's possession. On the successful completion of the spell, the glyph disappears. The possession remains effective for one hour, after which the magic dissipates. If it is placed on or given to the intended victim of the spell by anyone during that hour, the spell takes effect and the glyph reappears (it is normally painted on an inconspicuous portion of the possession or inside a pocket or other hidden crevice). Once activated, the spell's effect continues whether the victim continues to wear the possession or not.

Dismiss Demon
Availability: Rare
Level: 6
Cooperative: Yes
Components: V, M, F
Strain: 6d4 nonlethal, 1d6 Str damage, 1 Con damage
Casting Time: 3 rounds
Range: Close
Target: One demon or one creature possessed by a demon
Duration: Instantaneous
Saving Throw: Will negates

This spell represents the only hope that a non-priest has of sending a demon

back to the Abyss. It is often used out of desperation, after a plan to manipulate or deconstruct a demon has gone awry. When the spell is cast, reality tears open, temporarily creating a small, one-way conduit to the Abyss. If the demon fails its Will save, its body deconstructs into demonic energy, which is then sucked through the tear over 1d4 rounds. If targeting a possessing demon, the demon's essence appears as a blinding light, which is forcibly extracted from the eyes and mouth of the possessed creature into the conduit; regardless, if it goes unwilling, the demon's screams can be heard for miles around. All creatures within 30 feet of the opened conduit and with 5 or fewer HD must make a saving throw as though affected by the *abyssal window* spell; creatures are affected only as long as the conduit remains open.

Material Component: Caster's blood.

Focus: A priest's holy symbol.

Casting Process: The caster must grip the symbol tightly, so that it draws blood. While he casts the spell, blood gushes out of his hand, traveling up and over his body in countless long rivulets. When the spell completes, the streams buckle away from his body, intertwining into a single thick stream that surges against a designated point, tearing open the Abyssal conduit. In addition to the strain suffered by casting the spell, the caster is fatigued.

Explode Corpse
[Force]
Availability: Uncommon
Level: 3
Cooperative: No
Components: V, M
Strain: 3d4 nonlethal
Casting Time: 1 round
Range: See text
Area: 10 ft. radius spread
Duration: Instantaneous
Saving Throw: Reflex half

This spell leverages the latent energy that lingers in a recently dead body to produce a foul explosion of blood, gore, and demonic energy. The caster triggers the effect by invoking the spell upon a dead body, which he must touch on the spell's completion. Once touched, the corpse explodes in 1d3 rounds. The resulting explosion deals 2d6 points of damage (half force, half slashing) to all creatures and unattended objects within the area. For every size increment that the corpse is larger than Medium, the damage increases by an additional 1d6 and extends an additional 5 feet. A small corpse deals only 1d6 damage within 10 feet; anything smaller is ineffectual.

Material Component: A hollowed out egg, filled with tiny bones.

Casting Process: The egg must be placed in the mouth or another open orifice of the corpse (such as a wound). Once the spell completes, the caster touches the egg and the corpse is activated.

Eyes of the Grave
Availability: Rare
Level: 3
Cooperative: No
Components: V, M
Strain: 3d4 nonlethal
Casting Time: 1 minute
Range: Touch
Target: Dead creature touched
Duration: Permanent; see text
Saving Throw: None

The caster implants demonic energy into a corpse so that, by concentrating, he can spy through its dead eyes and ears. The spell lasts until the corpse is buried, burned, or decomposes beyond usefulness. The spying corpse appears as a normal corpse for all intents and purposes, though a DC 25 Search check reveals an unnatural glint of life left in its eyes where none should be. If this spell is cast on a second corpse, the connection to the first one is lost.

Material Component: A paste made of the urine of a newborn child, salt, and ash.

Casting Process: The caster must whisper the incantation into the dead ears of the corpse, alternating between them regularly. When the incantation is complete, he smears the paste over his thumbs and forefingers; the thumbs are pressed against the closed eyelids of the corpse and a forefinger is inserted in each of its ears. If the spell is successful, the corpse's eyes snap open and the communication channel is opened.

Flaying Despair
Availability: Rare
Level: 7
Cooperative: Yes
Components: V, M, F
Strain: 7d4 nonlethal, 1d4 Cha damage, 1 Wis drain, variable hit point damage (see text)
Casting Time: 10 minutes
Range: Touch
Target: One humanoid creature
Duration: Permanent (D)
Saving Throw: None; see text

This especially sadistic spell punishes the victim by flaying off a strip of its skin every time it partakes in an aggressive behavior. The creature inevitably becomes a recluse, hidden away from the world so that it might escape the vicious punishment it suffers for speaking up or taking action. There is no defense against this spell other than it being reversed (see below) or disrupted with the Voice. A creature cursed by this spell cannot take any active actions, whether as a response to another creature's action or of its own accord, without risking permanent injury. Such actions include making an attack, casting spells, using the Voice, etc. The creature is only safe when it remains passive, takes defensive actions, or runs away. Any time a creature takes a prohibited action, it must make a Will save against the spell. If it succeeds, there are no consequences for taking that action. If it fails its Will save, a strip of flesh is torn viciously from its body, inflicting 1d6 permanent hit points damage and 1 point of permanent Charisma drain. A creature reduced to 0 Charisma by this spell enters a catatonic state and dies the following day.

Material Component: Bodily fluid (tears, saliva, urine, etc) emitted during an episode of great suffering by a creature of the same type as the target. To reverse the spell, the fluids are substituted with those of someone that has found rest in a peaceful and recent death.

Focus: A tiny barbed whip.

Casting Process: The caster whips himself for the duration of the casting, inflicting grievous wounds into which he then rubs the fluids. If the spell succeeds, the wounds seal without consequence. If it fails, the caster takes 1d6 points of slashing damage. Upon the completion of the spell, the caster has 1 minute to touch the target creature with the whip (a melee touch attack), at which point the spell's effect is conferred.

Gibber
[Compulsion, Mind-Affecting]
Availability: Rare
Level: 2
Cooperative: No
Components: V, M, F
Strain: 2d4 nonlethal
Casting Time: 1 round
Range: Close
Target: One living creature
Duration: 2d4 rounds
Saving Throw: Will negates

This spell infests the language centers of a creature's brain, destroying its ability to speak. While under the effect of *gibber*, any attempts to speak result in babbled nonsense; the affected creature cannot sermonize, cast spells, or use the Voice. This spell does not affect the creature's ability to understand language.

Material Component: Caster's blood.

Focus: The tongue of a sentient creature, removed while the creature was still alive, sewn into a ball with barbed wire and boiled in vinegar.

Casting Process: The caster rolls the prepared tongue along the palm of his exposed hand so that it draws blood for the duration of the incantation. He suffers a −1 penalty to all attack rolls made with that hand for 24 hours after casting this spell.

Groping Hands

Availability: Uncommon
Level: 4
Cooperative: No
Components: V, M
Strain: 4d4 nonlethal
Casting Time: 3 rounds
Range: Medium
Area: 15 ft.-radius spread
Duration: 2d4 rounds
Saving Throw: None

Twisted, demonic hands with razor sharp fingernails explode from the ground to take hold of those that attempt to navigate past them. If the area around the hands is dug up, infinitely long arms seem to extend into the bowels of the earth. Every creature within the spell's area of effect must make a grapple check, opposed by the groping hands. The hands have a base attack bonus of +10, a Strength score of 18, and are immune to damage (new hands spring up to replace any that are severed). Once the hands grapple an opponent, they make a grapple check each round on the caster's turn to deal 1d6 + 4 points of slashing damage.

Material Component: A detached finger, the nail replaced with a slice of sharp metal.

Casting Process: The finger is planted into the ground, nail pointing up. It is sucked in on the completion of the casting.

Intellect Overload

Availability: Rare
Level: 4
Cooperative: No
Components: V, M
Strain: 4d4 nonlethal, 1 Wis damage
Casting Time: 1 minute
Range: Personal
Target: Caster
Duration: 1d4 days

By draining the life from the surrounding terrain, the caster gains a +1 to +4 enhancement bonus to Intelligence. The extent of the bonus depends on how healthy the terrain is (GM's discretion); a lush forest could provide 4 points while a barren desert might only provide 1 point. All soil and mundane plant and animal life within a 50-foot radius of the caster withers and dies, becoming permanently lifeless.

Material Component: Soil from the Saltstone Flats in the Deadlands; a complete literary or factual text of at least 100 pages; a fire source.

Casting Process: The caster scatters the soil in a circle around him. Once the circle has been formed, he lights the text on fire then rips it apart. The burning pages fall upon the drawn circle, then burst outward.

Listening Pool

Availability: Legendary
Level: 5
Cooperative: Yes
Components: V, M, F
Strain: 5d4 nonlethal
Casting Time: 1 hour
Range: Unlimited; see text
Target: One object; see text
Duration: 2d4 minutes
Saving Throw: None

This spell creates a communication network that two or more people can use to speak to each other over long distances. The network consists of multiple basins or bowls, all filled with liquid from the same source. The pool loses its connection to the network when the spell duration expires, or if the liquid in the pool is tipped out.

Material Component: Each pool requires a bundle of copper wire, two lips and two ears (all of which are drawn from a creature or creatures that can both speak and understand speech), and a pint of liquid that is identical amongst all the pools in the network (generally blood drawn from one source).

Casting Process: The basin is filled with liquid, then each component is dropped in as the spell is invoked. If the casting is successful, the pool resonates with a slight hum.

Living Effigy

Availability: Legendary
Level: 7
Cooperative: Yes
Components: V, M
Strain: 7d4 nonlethal
Casting Time: 30 seconds (5 rounds)
Range: Close
Target: One creature
Duration: Permanent (D)
Saving Throw: Will negates

This spell transforms one living creature and all its possessions (excluding items of power) into an inanimate form, made from a substance of the caster's choosing, which is present at the time of casting. Thus, a creature encountered upon frozen tundra can be turned to ice, while a creature encountered deep in a cave can be turned to stone. While transformed, a creature does not age and has no senses or awareness of its surroundings, but if the material from which it is formed takes damage, it is likewise damaged if restored to natural life. Thus, a creature turned to ice dies if the ice melts, and a creature turned to stone dies if the stone is shattered.

Material Component: A figurine crafted to appear bound, frozen, asleep, or otherwise incapacitated; vial of water.

Casting Process: The caster pours the water over the figurine while invoking the spell. As it becomes soaked, the figurine transforms into the desired substance but does not deteriorate as it normally would due to environmental conditions (such as if it was made of ice). Only by smashing the figurine can the spell be dismissed.

Locate

Availability: Rare
Level: 4
Cooperative: Yes
Components: V, M, F
Strain: 4d4 nonlethal
Casting Time: 10 minutes
Range: Long
Area: Circle, centered on the caster, with a radius of 400 ft. + 1d20 × 40 ft.
Duration: Instantaneous
Saving Throw: None

The caster can determine the approximate location of a specific creature by casting this spell upon one of its personal possessions. When the spell is cast, he senses the general location of the creature at that time. Thus, *locate* may reveal a person to be directly south of his position, or in the upper levels of a residential complex, but it will not reveal the specific room or level.

Material Component: Leather strap, long enough to be wrapped around the caster's arm.

Focus: Personal possession or substantial organic material (lock of hair, served limb, etc) belonging to the specific creature that is being sought.

Casting Process: The caster uses the strap to bind the possession to one of his arms, pulling it tighter as he casts the spell. When it completes, the strap bursts and the caster suffers a sharp jolt inside his head; he is dazed for 1d3 rounds after. If the spell was successful, the jolt is accompanied by knowledge of the creature's whereabouts.

Mark of the Pariah
Availability: Rare
Level: 5
Cooperative: Yes
Components: V, M, F
Strain: 5d4 nonlethal, 1d4 Cha damage
Casting Time: 30 seconds (5 rounds)
Range: Touch
Target: One humanoid creature
Duration: Permanent
Saving Throw: Will partial

This spell implants an invisible mark upon a person that causes others to shun him and view him as an enemy. If the target fails his Will save, he suffers a permanent −4 penalty to all Charisma-based skill checks. Additionally, NPCs have an attitude that is one step worse than normal when dealing with that person. If his Will save succeeds, he suffers a −2 penalty to Charisma-based skill checks for 1d4 hours.

Material Component: A portion of a dead pariah's body – someone that was burned, hung, or killed in some other manner as a consequence of hate or prejudice.

Focus: A swatch of cloth retrieved from the person of a diseased humanoid, living or dead.

Casting Process: The caster wraps the body part in the swatch of cloth, focusing on both while casting the spell. The body part is absorbed into the cloth on the completion of the spellcasting. The caster must then press the cloth to the bare forehead of his intended victim, at which point the mark of the pariah is transferred.

Memory Wipe
[Compulsion, Mind-Affecting]
Availability: Rare
Level: 4
Cooperative: No
Components: V, M
Strain: 4d4 nonlethal, 1 Int damage
Casting Time: 1 hour
Range: Touch
Target: One living creature
Duration: Instantaneous
Saving Throw: Will negates

By touching the victim, the caster wipes one memory permanently from its mind. The caster must have reasonably specific knowledge of the memory, by his personal account or through accurate third hand information.

Material Component: Abyssal tunnel worm. (This slippery, blue-green invertebrate is native to the Deadlands, where it can occasionally be found in the brains of deceased creatures after entering through the ear. There is a 20% chance of finding the worm in a corpse that has been dead for no more than 24 hours, decreasing by 1% for each additional hour.)

Casting Process: The caster holds the worm in his hand while casting the spell, focusing on the memory that he wishes to erase until it is imprinted. Once the spell is completed, he places the worm close to the creature's ear. It immediately tunnels into the creature's brain and removes the imprinted memory as well as the memory of the actual violation.

Night Terror
[Fear, Mind-Affecting]
Availability: Rare
Level: 3
Cooperative: Yes
Components: V, M, F
Strain: 3d4 nonlethal
Casting Time: 10 minutes
Range: 10 miles
Target: One humanoid creature
Duration: Instantaneous
Saving Throw: Will negates

The caster mentally shapes the summoned demonic energies of the spell into terrifying nightmares, which he then transfers to a sleeping creature. If the creature fails its Will save, it suffers night terrors throughout the evening that leave it fatigued the next day. A fatigued creature can neither run nor charge and takes a −2 penalty to Strength and Dexterity.

The spell only works if the creature is asleep, thus the caster must be within visual range or have access to an immediate report of the creature's state, such as by leveraging an active spying spell such as *vermin eyes*. If the creature is still awake when the spell is completed, the nightmares remain in the caster's unconscious mind instead, emerging that night; he must make a Will save to negate the spell's effects, just as though he was the intended target of the spell.

Material Component: Oil; fire source.

Focus: A fragment of bedding soaked with the sweat of a fitful sleep.

Casting Process: The caster places the cloth in a dish or bowl, to which he then adds oil until the cloth becomes soaked through. Proceeding to the portion of the spell where he shapes the nightmares, he ignites the cloth. The flames take the shape of visual elements of the nightmare (faces, events, etc), while the cloth remains intact. If the casting is successful, the cloth survives unharmed and can be used again; if the casting fails, the cloth is consumed and the caster must acquire a new focus before being able to cast the spell again.

Noxious Cloud

[Air]

Availability: Rare
Level: 6
Cooperative: Yes
Components: V, M
Strain: 6d4 nonlethal
Casting Time: 1 minute
Range: Medium
Effect: Cloud spreads in 20-ft. radius, 20 ft. high
Duration: 2d6 rounds
Saving Throw: Fortitude partial; see text

A bank of black noxious cloud billows out from the point the caster designates. The vapors automatically kill any living creature with 3 or fewer HD (no save). A living creature with 4 to 6 HD is killed if it fails its Fortitude save; if it succeeds, it takes 1d4 points of Constitution damage on the caster's turn for every round it ends in the cloud. A living creature with 6 or more HD that fails its Fortitude save takes 1d4 points of Constitution damage on the caster's turn for every round it ends in the cloud; if it succeeds, this damage is halved. Holding one's breath does not negate the effect, but creatures immune to pollutants (poison) are unaffected by the spell.

A moderate wind (11+ mph) disperses the fog in 4 rounds; a strong wind (21+ mph) disperses the fog in 1 round.

This spell does not function underwater.

Material Component: Sealed glass container, filled with black fog captured from the heart of Novdy Ottor.

Casting Process: While invoking the spell and shaking the container, the caster focuses on the spot from where he wishes the cloud to billow out. The container vibrates violently as the spell continues, until the top is finally blown off when it completes. If successful, the fog streams out to the designated point and forms the noxious cloud.

Plague Bearer

Availability: Lost
Level: 9
Cooperative: Yes
Components: V, M
Strain: 9d4 nonlethal, 1d6 Str drain, 1d6 Con drain, 1d3 Wis drain
Casting Time: At least 1 day; see text
Range: Personal
Area: See text
Duration: Instantaneous
Saving Throw: None; see text

The caster becomes a vessel for a highly infectious disease, the details and severity of which are up to the character. This disease affects only one type of humanoid creature, but the caster is immune regardless of whether it affects his race or not. Creatures affected by the disease must save against it as though they were resisting a conventional (though severe) disease (DC 20), rather than a magical effect. The consequences of this spell are far-reaching, potentially affecting the world at large. Thus, the GM determines the actual effect, components, and casting process.

Material Component: Determined by GM.

Casting Process: Determined by GM.

Prosthesis

Availability: Legendary
Level: 7
Cooperative: Yes
Components: V, M, F
Strain: 7d4 nonlethal, 1d4 Str damage
Casting Time: 1 hour
Range: Touch
Target: Living creature touched
Duration: Instantaneous
Saving Throw: Fortitude negates (harmless)

This spell restores a single severed appendage, replacing it with a matching part that is infused with demonic life. If the spell is successful, the new appendage functions identically to the lost one. Receiving such a blessing, however, brings with it the risk of corruption, due to the nature of the Abyssal energy that gives the appendage life. There is a 10% chance (rolled by the GM) that a restored appendage is corrupting, conferring 1 point of taint on the recipient per day that it remains attached. The GM secretly records this taint accrual, thus the recipient is unaware that it bears a corrupt appendage until actual consequences of the taint arise.

Material Component: A well-preserved appendage (hand, arm, foot, or leg) that matches the lost one, taken from a creature of the same type as the spell's recipient; a paste made from the brain of a demon.

Focus: Thread and needle fashioned from the flesh and bone of a hybrid.

Casting Process: Prior to casting the spell, the caster must sew on the new appendage by making a Heal check (DC 20). If the check fails, the replacement appendage is ruined. During the casting of the spell, the demon paste is rubbed into the fresh stitches until they disappear entirely on the spell's completion. The appendage is functional immediately following the spell's completion. If the spell was a success, the effects are permanent; if the spell completed but failed, the appendage ceases to function after 1d4 minutes, at which point it immediately begins to rot. The owner of a rotting appendage takes 1 point of temporary Constitution damage for each hour that it remains attached; severing it inflicts 1d4 points of Constituion damage.

Psyche Parasite

[Mind-Affecting]

Availability: Rare
Level: 3
Cooperative: No
Components: V, M
Strain: 3d4 nonlethal, 1d3 Int damage
Casting Time: 2 rounds
Range: Close
Target: One humanoid creature
Duration: 1d4 rounds; see text
Saving Throw: Will negates

This spell consumes a portion of the caster's own intellect, which is then used as a weapon against the mind of another living creature. If the victim's saving throw fails, it takes twice the amount of Intelligence damage suffered by the caster of the spell and is also confused for 1d4 rounds.

The actions of a creature confused by this spell are determined by rolling d% at the beginning of its turn: 01 – 10, attack caster with melee or ranged weapons (or close with caster if attacking is not possible); 11 – 20, act normally; 21 – 50, do nothing but babble incoherently; 51 – 70, flee from the caster at top possible speed; 71 – 100, attack nearest creature. A confused creature that can't carry out the indicated action does nothing but babble incoherently. Attackers are not at any special advantage when attacking a confused creature. Any confused creature that is attacked automatically attacks its attackers on its next turn, as long as it is still confused when its turn comes. A confused creature will not make attacks of opportunity against any other creature that it is not already devoted to attacking (either because of its most recent action or because it has just been attacked).

Material Component: An emulsion of alcohol, mercury, and the dried, powdered brain of a humanoid creature, stored within a glass container.

Casting Process: The caster swirls the ingredients throughout the casting of the spell. As the spell proceeds, the ingredients coalesce into the shape of a hideous demonic centipede. If the spell is successfully cast, the bug explodes from the container with great speed, passing through the armor and skin of the victim into its brain. If the spell fails, it dissolves into an inert paste.

Purification By Fire

[Fire]
Availability: Rare
Level: 6
Cooperative: No
Components: V, M
Strain: 6d4 nonlethal
Casting Time: 2 rounds
Range: Medium
Target: One corporeal creature
Duration: Concentration
Saving Throw: Fortitude partial; see text

With the casting of this spell, the caster causes one creature to be engulfed in flames until nothing is left but ash. For each round that the caster concen-trates, beginning on the round that the spell completes, the creature and all of its belongings take 2d12 points of fire damage. The effect is localized and does not spread beyond the affected target. The creature is allowed a Fortitude save each round; if two consecutive Fortitude saves succeed, the creature is unaffected by the spell on the latter round and the spell ends. While engulfed, the creature is overwhelmed with pain, and can take no actions other than wailing desperately and convulsing. Should the creature survive the ordeal, it suffers 1 point of permanent Charisma drain for every three rounds that it took fire damage up to a maximum drain of half its original Charisma score, as a result of severe scarring and disfigurement.

Material Component: Small cloth bag, previously soaked through with a demon's saliva, and filled with red phosphorus.

Casting Process: The caster holds the bag of phosphorous in his hands, which heats up as the spell continues. The phosphorous ignites on the spell's completion, engulfing the caster's hands in flames. If the spell is successful, the caster suffers no ill effect from the flame; if the spell fails, he takes 2d6 points of fire damage and suffers a −2 penalty to attack rolls and skill checks that require the use of his hands for a day, followed by a −1 penalty on the next day.

Sensory Multiplication

Availability: Uncommon
Level: 1
Cooperative: No
Components: V, M, F
Strain: 1d4 nonlethal
Casting Time: 1 round
Range: Personal
Target: Caster
Duration: 1d6 hours

The caster affixes new eyes and ears to his head, which make him nearly impossible to surprise. He gains a +4 bonus on Spot and Listen checks and a +2 bonus on Initiative checks for the duration of the spell.

Material Components: A fresh or preserved pair of eyes and ears from a creature of the same type as the caster.

Casting Process: The caster affixes the sensory organs to his head. If the spell is successfully cast, the organs attach, spawning nerve endings that connect directly to his brain. If the caster only has one component or the other, he can still cast the spell in order to gain a lesser benefit (+4 to either Spot or Listen checks and only a +1 bonus on Initiative checks).

Shapeshift

Availability: Legendary
Level: 4
Cooperative: No
Components: V, M, F
Strain: 4d4 nonlethal, 1 Wis damage, hit point damage; see text
Casting Time: 1 minute
Range: Personal
Target: Caster
Duration: 2d4 hours (D)

With this spell, the caster can transform himself into the form of any living creature that he has previously encountered, from Diminutive to one size larger than his natural form. His possessions do not transform with him. The caster cannot assume the form of a creature with more Hit Dice than he has levels. Upon altering his form, the caster acquires the Strength, Dexterity, and Constitution scores of the new form but retains his Intelligence, Wisdom, and Charisma scores. If the new form is of the same type as he is, he retains all of his own ability scores regardless of its appearance. He also acquires the new form's movement capabilities and other mundane physical qualities. Though he appears to be an exact duplicate of the creature, the caster does not gain any of its extraordinary, supernatural, or spell-like abilities or attacks. Thus, this spell is used mostly as a method of disguise rather than empowerment.

The process of undergoing a shapeshift is extremely hard on the caster's body. His skin, sinew, and bones tear and reform, pitching him into agony for what seems

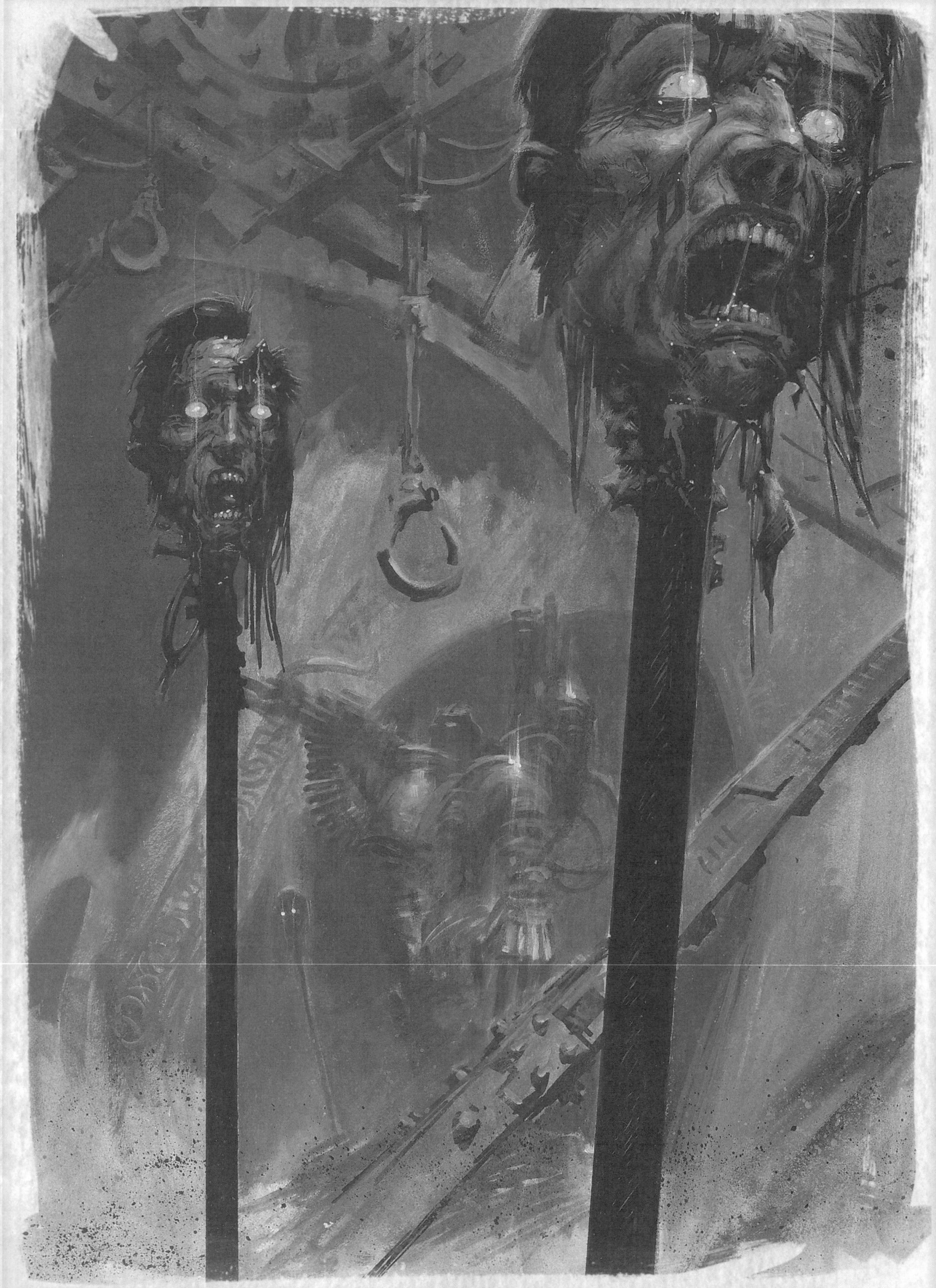

an eternity until the transformation is complete. This process inflicts 1d6 points of hit point damage per size category changed. Of the total damage incurred, 1 point is permanent – a side effect of the trauma to the caster's body. It takes one round per size category to transform. During this time, the character can take no other actions and loses his Dexterity bonus to AC. The damage and time required for *shapeshift* are repeated when the caster changes back to his natural form, voluntarily or otherwise. If the caster is transforming into a creature of the same size, the effects are determined as though he was still transforming by one size category.

Only by casting the spell a second time can the shapeshift effect be dismissed; otherwise, it ends after the specified duration. The spell also ends if the caster dies. If the spell is allowed to expire, the caster can sense his imminent reversion 1d6 rounds before it actually happens. A caster that transforms himself into a creature that cannot speak or handle components risks not being able to transform back into his natural form at a critical moment. Demons, able to cast this spell mentally as a spell-like ability, have the luxury of being able to transform as they please, regardless of the limitations of their current form.

Material Component: A bit of flesh from the type of creature the caster wishes to transform into.

Focus: A shard of broken glass.

Casting Process: While invoking the spell, the caster uses the glass shard to cut a line from his throat down to his groin. Once the wound has been drawn, he rubs the flesh component into it. If the spell is successful, the transformation process begins out of this wound, which then heals over. If the spell fails, the wound remains open and the caster instead suffers 1d6 points of slashing damage.

Shrieking Ward
Availability: Legendary
Level: 3
Cooperative: Yes
Components: V, M
Strain: 3d4 nonlethal
Casting Time: 30 minutes
Range: Touch
Target: One decapitated head
Duration: Permanent

This spell infuses a dead, decapitated head with a perverse sentience, allowing it to scream out a warning when a given condition is met. This condition may be based on a certain type of creature coming into visual range, a specific event occurring in the vicinity, hearing another ward within range scream out, etc. In the latter case, multiple heads can be set up as a perimeter alarm system. A *shrieking ward* cannot be reprogrammed once created. All wards have darksight and perfect hearing, regardless of the creature they originated from.

When triggered, a ward releases a horrifying scream that can be heard for 300 feet in any direction. The caster defines the duration, intervals, and pattern of the screaming at the time of casting the spell. A ward is incapable of carrying on a conversation, and has no mind or memory to speak of. If attacked, a ward has 1d8 hit points, DR 2/bludgeoning, and AC 10.

Material Component: The decapitated head; a demon's tongue.

Casting Process: The caster holds the tongue in one hand, close to the mouth of the head. As he casts the spell, the tongue begins to wriggle until it eventually slips free and attaches to the mouth. Once attached, the newborn ward waits for the caster's specified condition. Once this command is given, the ward's eyes ignite with demonic life, indicating that the command has been received and that it is activated.

Shuddering Bowel
Availability: Uncommon
Level: 2
Cooperative: No
Components: V, M
Strain: 2d4 nonlethal
Casting Time: 2 rounds
Range: Close
Target: One humanoid creature
Duration: 4d6 hours
Saving Throw: Fortitude negates

This spell twists the bowels of the victim, causing it to become sickened for the duration of the spell, during which it also defecates uncontrollably. A sickened creature takes a –2 penalty on all attack rolls, weapon damage rolls, saving throws, skill checks, and ability checks.

Material Component: A handful of spoiled food.

Casting Process: The caster must eat the spoiled food while casting the spell. If the spell is successfully cast, the spoilage is neutralized; otherwise the caster must make a Fortitude save as though he was the target of the spell or suffer the effect for 1 hour.

Skin Seal
Availability: Rare
Level: 4
Cooperative: No
Components: V, M
Strain: 4d4 nonlethal
Casting Time: 2 rounds
Range: Close
Target: One living creature
Duration: Permanent (D)
Saving Throw: Fortitude negates

The caster compels a creature's skin to shift and expand to the point where it seals up the creature's eyes, ears, or mouth. The resulting effect depends upon the selected organ: sealing the eyes blinds the creature, sealing the ears deafens it, and sealing its mouth renders it unable to speak.

If a knife or other mundane tool is used to tamper with the sealed skin, only muscle and bone are revealed. Attempting to undo the spell in this fashion inflicts 1 point of temporary Constitution damage and permanently destroys the sealed area. If the area is left unmolested, casting *skin seal* again with a slightly different component mix and words of reversal can restore it.

Material Component: An eyeball, ear, or lip (the component required depends upon the desired effect of the spell), cut from a sentient creature, and a container of glue that can be sealed and is large enough to contain the selected flesh. To reverse the effects of another caster's *skin seal*, replace the glue with acid.

Casting Process: The caster places the flesh component into the container of glue or acid then seals it. As the spell is invoked, the container folds in on itself until it disappears completely with the spell's completion.

Smothering Embrace

[Force]
Availability: Uncommon
Level: 2
Cooperative: No
Components: V, M, F
Strain: 2d4 nonlethal
Casting Time: 1 round
Range: Medium
Target: One living creature
Duration: 1d6 rounds
Saving Throw: Reflex negates

The energies released by this spell surge around the creature, crushing its body, smothering its mouth and nose until the creature loses consciousness. If the creature fails to dodge the effect with a Reflex save, it is held motionless for the spell's duration, unable to take any actions, and suffers 1d6 points of nonlethal damage per round.

Material Component: A short (less than 1 foot) length of rope.

Focus: An object that can serve as a surrogate head for the spell, such as a rag doll head, an actual decapitated head, a carving of a head, etc.

Casting Process: The caster wraps the rope around the surrogate head's mouth as he invokes the spell, pulling it tight as though to choke it. When the spell is complete, the rope combusts and is then possessed by demonic energy, lashing out at the target.

Soul Offering

Availability: Rare
Level: 6
Cooperative: No
Components: V, M, F
Strain: 6d4 nonlethal, 1d6 Str damage, 1d6 Con damage, 1 Wis drain
Casting Time: 1 hour
Range: Personal
Target: Caster
Duration: Instantaneous (see text)

The caster offers a portion of his soul as a sacrifice to the Abyss in exchange for a long-term bonus to any ability score, excluding Wisdom. If the spell is successfully cast, the caster is engulfed by a wash of demonic energy that painfully alters his body and mind to the desired effect. The transformation takes 1d6 rounds, during which the caster is helpless and experiences painful seizures. When the seizures end, he must make a Fortitude save (DC 12) or die from shock. If the save is successful, he gains an inherent +1 bonus to the ability score of his choosing for 12d6 months. If the spell fails, the seizures are not experienced and the Fortitude save need not be made.

Material Component: Caster's blood; perfumed oil.

Focus: Demonic dagger; holy idol representing Azrae.

Casting Process: The caster must anoint himself with oil and pray over the idol for 8 hours prior to the casting of the spell. He then invokes the spell, using the demonic dagger to inscribe glyphs onto his body that illustrate the desired empowerment. As his blood mingles with the oil, demonic energy begins to seep from the wounds until he is engulfed. If the spell is successfully cast, all of the inscribed glyphs heal except for one that is left as a permanent scar, its location randomly determined. If the spell fails, the caster suffers 2d4 points of slashing damage.

Spawn Umbilical Guardian

Availability: Uncommon
Level: 1
Cooperative: No

Components: V, M, F
Strain: 1d4 nonlethal
Casting Time: 1 round
Range: Personal
Target: Caster
Duration: 1d6 minutes

Upon casting this spell, 1d4 writhing tentacles created from the caster's own flesh erupt from his bellybutton, to serve as shields against projectile weapons. If the caster is wearing armor over his torso, the armor permanently loses 1 point of armor bonus per tentacle. If this damage reduces the armor to an AC of 0 or less, it is destroyed; otherwise it can be repaired. Each tentacle automatically intercepts a single arrow, bolt, or other projectile that scores a successful hit against the caster, at which point it falls off.

These tentacles can be targeted by attacks if desired; each has 6 hit points and an AC equal to the caster's AC minus any armor or shield bonus. All effects currently active on the caster also apply to his tentacles. Any surviving tentacles recede back into the caster's body when the spell ends.

Material Component: An umbilical cord, preserved in such a way that it remains pliant.

Focus: An arrowhead or bolt head coated with the caster's blood.

Casting Process: The caster winds the umbilical cord around the focus and then holds the point of the arrowhead or bolt against his bellybutton. The combination is promptly sucked in when the spell is successfully cast. The focus is ejected when the spell ends.

Spinal Decoder

Availability: Rare
Level: 1
Cooperative: No
Components: V, M, F
Strain: 1d4 nonlethal
Casting Time: 1 minute
Range: Personal
Target: Caster
Duration: 5d12 minutes

The caster summons a symbiotic demon, which grows out of the base of his neck then curls around his throat. The demon appears as a stubby, thick snake with a vaguely humanoid head and small nubs where arms and legs might otherwise be. While it is attached, the caster gains the ability to read, write, understand, and speak all mortal languages. His voice becomes grainy and hollow sounding while speaking a language with the demon's assistance. A high collar or similar clothing can effectively conceal the demon with a successful Sleight of Hand check (DC 15). If it is killed, however, the spell ends and the caster suffers system shock, taking 1d3 points of Constitution damage and 1d4 points of Intelligence damage. A symbiotic demon has 4 hp and the same AC as the caster, minus any armor bonus, shield bonus, or natural armor bonus.

Material Component: Saltwater.

Focus: Necklace fashioned from the spine of a reptilian animal or the body of a snake.

Casting Process: The caster coats the necklace with a liberal quantity of saltwater, and then dons the necklace, pressing it tight against his skin while casting the spell.

Steal Likeness

Availability: Legendary
Level: 5
Cooperative: No
Components: V, M, F
Strain: 5d4 nonlethal, 1d4 Wis damage, 1 Int drain
Casting Time: 1 hour
Range: Personal
Target: Caster
Duration: Instantaneous

With this spell, the caster transfers his essence into another creature that is the same type as he is, though it need not be the same sex. He gains the Strength, Dexterity, and Constitution scores of the new form as well as any specific physical attributes and qualities, but retains his own hit points, modified by the new Constitution score. For each minute that passes after the spell successfully completes, 1 point each of his Intelligence, Wisdom, and Charisma are transferred over to the new body. His old body withers and dies during the process.

There are serious consequences for the caster if the transfer process is interrupted. He must make a Fortitude save (DC 20) or die; if the save is successful, the transfer to the new body completes but only with the ability points that have been transferred to that point. Thus, a caster that makes his Fortitude save after being interrupted 8 minutes into the transfer comes out of the spell with Intelligence, Wisdom, and Charisma scores of 8. This effect is permanent and irreversible.

Material Component: The body of the creature whose form the caster wishes to steal, which can be dead for no longer than 24 hours.

Focus: Tiny double-sided mirrors, to be placed over the eyes of the corpse.

Casting Process: The caster invokes the spell while staring, unblinking, at the mirrors; for this reason, *steal likeness* can only be cast if it has been memorized. Once the spellcasting completes, the caster's essence begins to stream toward the mirrors, and is channeled through them into the new body. The process is interrupted if the mirrors are removed from the new body's eyes.

Torment Cage

Availability: Legendary
Level: 8
Cooperative: Yes
Components: V, M, F
Strain: 8d4 nonlethal, 1d6 Str damage, 1 Int drain
Casting Time: 8 hours
Range: See text
Target: One living creature
Duration: Permanent (D)
Saving Throw: None

This spell alters a small, localized environment such as a cage or cell, to serve as an inescapable prison that curses a single creature to eternal torment. The nature of the torment is up to the caster's imagination, but it is always based on some physical effect such as fire, spiked chains, drowning, etc. While trapped in the cage, a creature is consumed by unspeakable agony but it does not age, nor does it require food or water. Likewise, it cannot die or suffer from any external effect while caged, nor can it communicate verbally. For every week that a creature is trapped in a torment cage, it suffers 1 point of permanent drain to all ability scores, up to a maximum drain of half their original value. There is no saving throw against this spell, but the victim must be rendered helpless in order for it to take effect. A cage can only be neutralized by destroying the spell focus (see below) or if a priest with the Sanctity dominion disrupts it; it cannot be defeated by any conventional means, nor can it be transported. A creature that is freed from this spell suffers at least 1 point of drain to all ability scores even if released before a week has passed, is reduced to −1 hit points, and is exhausted upon regaining consciousness.

Material Component: A drop of the victim's blood; ink.

Focus: A gem worth at least 5,000 gp, bound in an ornate lead lattice.

Casting Process: The victim must be shackled, bound, or otherwise held fast within its cage. While the spell is invoked, glyphs of entrapment are scribed onto the cage, where they remain indefinitely. On the conclusion of the spell, a drop of the victim's blood is dripped onto the gem, triggering the effect. The cage immediately transforms into the desired vessel of torment.

Once the spell has been cast, the victim of the spell is permanently tied to the gem that was used as a focus. This gem cannot be used for a second casting of the spell. If the lattice is detached, the spell effect ends. However, if the gem is ever destroyed − even after the spell effect ends − the creature that was bound by it immediately dies. Likewise, if the creature dies, the gem crumbles.

Transference

Availability: Legendary
Level: 8
Cooperative: Yes
Components: V, M; see text
Strain: 8d4 nonlethal, 2d4 Str damage, 1d3 Wis drain
Casting Time: 1 hour per victim; see text
Range: Personal or one other living creature
Target: Caster or one creature touched
Duration: Instantaneous

This spell restores youth and vitality to a designated recipient or one of the casters involved in casting the spell. This restoration is accomplished by draining the life from one or more creatures that are of the same race as the recipient. He gains a number years equal to half the combined Constitution score of the creatures drained. If the recipient drops an age category in the process, he regains lost physical abilities, but he does not regain increases to mental abilities later as a result of reaching an age category that has been previously reached.

The drained creatures die upon the completion of the casting, whether the spell is successful or not. They are reduced to dry, emaciated husks, and their energy is transferred to the recipient. If the spell is interrupted before completion, each victim is instead reduced to −1 hit points and suffers 1d6 points of temporary damage to each ability score (rolled separately) excluding Constitution, to which they suffer permanent drain based on how far the spell proceeded. Thus, if the spell is interrupted halfway through, all victims suffer a 50% Constitution drain; round fractions up in this case. They are also aged a number of years equal to their Constitution loss.

Material Component: One or more living creatures that are of the same race as the recipient; one demon heart per creature.

Casting Process: The donors must be restrained or sedated, so that they are unable to move during the procedure. One demon heart is affixed to the chest of each victim's naked body. A network

of transfusion tubes is positioned so that each tube pierces one of these organs. An exit tube leads to the caster or to a designated recipient that is in physical contact with the caster, ready to be inserted into his mouth. The actual casting of the spell involves repetition of the same invocations over each victim, which draws that creature's energy away from its body and into the attached organ so that it beats with life. A final recitation compels the demonic organs to give up the life they have stolen. These organs explode with the conclusion of the spellcasting, whether successful or not. If the spell is successfully cast, the organs release their amassed energy in a violent gush through the transfusion network and down the recipient's throat. If the spell fails, the energy is channeled into the Abyss and consumed. Regardless of who gains the benefit of the spell, the caster of the spell is the one that suffers the casting strain.

Undead Proxy

Availability: Legendary
Level: 6
Cooperative: No
Components: V, M, F
Strain: 6d4 nonlethal, 1d4 Int damage, 1 Cha drain; see text
Casting Time: 12 hours
Range: Touch
Target: One humanoid corpse touched
Duration: Permanent (D)
Saving Throw: None

This spell animates a dead body, placing it under the caster's control and allowing him to experience the world through its demonically revived senses. The corpse does not decompose while controlled, thus it can appear for all intents and purposes as a living creature. The proxy begins its unlife as a shambling corpse, but as time passes, the caster can control it with greater refinement, to the point where it eventually becomes fully controllable as though it was the caster's own body. A caster can only ever have one proxy at a time.

As long as the caster concentrates, he can completely control the proxy's actions, speech (assuming its vocal

cords have not rotted away), and body language as though they were his own; he cannot take any other actions on the same round that the proxy does. If he loses concentration, the proxy freezes in place until the connection to the caster resumes. It has the physical qualities of the deceased (movement rate, sight, hearing, natural armor, etc), but uses the caster's base attack bonus and hit points. When first animated, the corpse has Strength and Dexterity scores of 1. For each day that passes, these ability scores increase by 1 point until they match what the caster's natural ability scores were at the time of the casting. Once the corpse is fully realized in this manner, the caster can use all of his skills, feats, and special physical abilities through it. The proxy cannot, however, use the Voice or cast a spell. An animated corpse is immune to mind-affecting spells and effects, and such effects do not feed back to the caster.

The caster gains experience when performing actions through the proxy just as he would by performing them himself. The attributes of a fully realized corpse increase parallel to those of the caster when his level increases. Thus, when such surrogates are used, they permit the caster to remain safe at home while adventuring through the borrowed body. However, for each year that the caster is connected to an undead proxy, he suffers an additional point of permanent Charisma drain.

Material Component: Blood taken from a living humanoid of the same type as the corpse, to be used as ink.

Focus: A diamond worth at least 1,000 gp.

Casting Process: In order to animate the proxy, the caster must have access to its brain so that he can implant the diamond directly into it, following which he replaces the skull's cap. Once the diamond is placed, he paints demonic runes of revival over the entire body using the blood ink while invoking the spell. On the successful completion of the spell, the skull seals shut and the runes disappear. Only the removal of the diamond, the severing of the corpse's head, or a priest's disrupting Voice can dismiss the spell's effect.

Vermin Eyes
Availability: Rare
Level: 2
Cooperative: No
Components: V, M
Strain: 2d4 nonlethal
Casting Time: 1 minute (10 rounds)
Range: 1 mile
Target: One Fine insect
Duration: 2d6 hours (D)
Saving Throw: None

The caster takes control of an insect, able to direct its movements and see through its eyes out to the spell's maximum range; the spell ends if it travels farther than 1 mile from the caster. The caster must concentrate to control the insect. If he does not concentrate, the insect remains immobile until he resumes concentration. The insect appears for all intents and purposes as a normal insect, but if the subject of its spying is expecting such a tactic, he can notice it with a Spot check (DC 20). If the insect is killed while under the control of the caster, the caster must make a Fortitude save (DC 12) or suffer 1d3 Constitution damage. As a standard action, the caster can voluntarily release his connection to the insect.

Material Component: A live insect; the preserved eyeball of a sentient creature, wrapped in copper wire.

Casting Process: The insect is placed into a jar or other sealable container with the wrapped eyeball. During the casting of the spell, the insect consumes the entire eyeball, eventually squeezing its way within the copper cage. On completion of casting, the copper is absorbed into the insect and the connection is established. The insect is released when the caster is ready to place it.

Vile Seduction
[Compulsion, Mind-Affecting]
Availability: Rare
Level: 3
Cooperative: No
Components: V, M, F
Strain: 3d4 nonlethal
Casting Time: 1 minute
Range: Medium
Target: One humanoid creature
Duration: Concentration + 1d3 rounds
Saving Throw: Will negates; see text

Upon the casting of this spell, the victim is enveloped by ethereal demonic tentacles that spring from the ground. If the creature fails its Will save, it perceives them as supremely desirable objects and is seduced for the duration of the spell. A creature distracted in this fashion is completely oblivious to the world around it, but it gains a new saving throw any time it would normally react to a situation, such as if threatened. The spell terminates if the creature is attacked or harmed in any way.

Material Component: Handful of beads.

Focus: A prostitute's undergarment or street wear.

Casting Process: The beads are wrapped in or affixed to the undergarment, which the caster must manipulate in a figure-eight pattern so that the beads brush against each other, all the while watching the target and invoking the spell. On its completion, a brief flare of flame consumes the beads.

Vitality Leech
Availability: Uncommon
Level: 2
Cooperative: No
Components: V, M
Strain: 2d4 nonlethal
Casting Time: 1 round
Range: Touch; see text
Target: Caster or one living creature
Duration: Instantaneous/1 hour; see text
Saving Throw: Fortitude half

On a successful melee touch attack, the caster drains the life force from another creature and applies it to himself or an ally of his choosing. If the attack is successful and the target creature fails its saving throw, the caster deals 4d4 hit points of damage to the target, which he can then immediately absorb or transfer to an ally with a second touch. If the target's saving throw is successful, only 2d4 points are drained. The caster can drain less than the rolled number of hit points if desired. The beneficiary of this spell cannot gain more hit points than it would take to kill the victim (remaining hit points +10 + victim's Constitution modifier). Any hit points gained in excess of the receiving character's normal maximum are applied as temporary hit points that last 1 hour.

In addition to gaining hit points, the recipient of the spell's benefit also experiences a temporary "buzz" for 6d10 minutes, during which he has artificially inflated confidence, followed by a period of depression that lasts 1d4 hours. While buzzed, the recipient gains a +1 morale bonus to ability checks, saving throws, and attack and damage rolls. When he slips into the depressive phase, this bonus is replaced with a −1 morale penalty. If a character gains hit points through *vitality leech* while still affected by a previous application of the spell, the cycle begins over again, but the buzz phase lasts 1d10 minutes less (minimum 1 minute) and the depressive phase lasts 1 hour more for each additional application. Thus, a character receiving a second application of *vitality leech* while still affected by the first will be buzzed for only 5d10 minutes, followed by 1d4 + 1 hours of depression. If that character receives a third application while still affected by the second, the cycle would begin again: 4d10 minutes of buzz followed by 1d4 + 2 hours of depression.

Material Component: Blood leech and an iron nail.

Casting Process: The caster impales the leech with the iron nail and then slaps the leech onto the intended target. The nail elongates to pierce the target's body, immediately feeding back vital energy from victim to caster.

Chapter 7: Grit & Consequences

"Each night, I hear their screams. We were brothers in arcanism, each trying to upstaging the other. The beginning of the end was the possession, when I saw the greatest of us overcome in an instant. The second to fall exploded in a fountain of gore. The rest… they tore into each other like beasts, their souls destroyed. Only I survive, but a shadow creeps upon me and voices whisper in my ear – their voices or the voices of demons, I cannot tell. But the shadow grows closer. If I could stop the magic, perhaps the voices would leave me. If I could stop the magic…"

\- Isish Trin, human arcanist

Dark Legacies is a world of consequences: be they the blatant, violent consequences of war that touches nearly every mortal life, or the insidious, self-inflicted consequences of touching the demonic soul through the science of arcanism. This chapter addresses these consequences: rules that emphasize the brutality of combat while also expanding on natural healing and death, and rules that reveal the effects and consequences of practicing dark magic.

Lethal Combat

The following rules make combat a more realistic and deadly experience. The rules for becoming clobbered and recovering from injury supplement the combat rules in the *Player's Handbook* while the new methods of calculating and applying massive damage, healing, and dying replace the standard rules.

The rules for becoming clobbered and massive damage apply only to single attacks that deal the requisite damage to produce an effect. If a character takes damage from multiple attacks, no one of which deals this amount, these rules do not apply. Creatures without Constitution scores are immune to these effects.

Clobbered: If a character takes hit point damage exceeding his current Constitution score, he must make a Fortitude save (DC = Damage Taken – Constitution Score) or become clobbered. When a character is clobbered, he can only take a standard action or move action on his next round. A character can only be clobbered once in a round.

Massive Damage: If a character takes hit point damage equal to or exceeding twice his current Constitution score, he must make a Fortitude save (DC = Damage Taken – Twice Constitution Score) or die instantly. Characters with the Diehard feat receive a +2 bonus to save against dying from massive damage.

Healing: The healing of damage in Dark Legacies is affected by a character's Constitution score just as the severity of his injuries is. With a full night's rest (8 hours of sleep or more in a day), a character recovers 1 hit point per character level plus a number of hit points equal to his Constitution modifier (if positive). If he undergoes complete bed rest for an entire day and night, the character recovers twice his character level in hit points plus a number of hit points equal to twice his Constitution modifier (if positive). If a character is successfully treated with long term care via the Heal skill, the base amount of healed damage is doubled but the additional amount granted by a high Constitution is not. If a character's Constitution score changes over the course of healing, the value used is the initial score when healing began. Thus, a 5th-level soldier with a Constitution score of 16 (+3 bonus) recovers 8 hp with a full night's rest, 16 hp with a full day's bed rest, 13 hp with a full night's rest plus long term care, or 26 hp with a full day's bed rest plus long term care.

Death & Dying: When a character's hit points drop to between –1 and a value equal to –10 minus his Constitution modi- fier (if positive), he is dying. A dying character immediately falls unconscious and can take no actions, losing an additional hit point every round until he dies or becomes stable. When his hit points equal or are reduced below this number, the character dies. Thus, a character with a Constitution score of 16 dies when his hit points reach –13, while a character with a Constitution score of 11 or less dies when his hit points reach –10.

Recovering from Injury: When a character is healed to 1 or more hit points from negative hit points, he requires some time before being able to fully rejoin combat, and thus is effectively clobbered for one round. A character that is healed to 1 or more hit points from 0 hit points is fully functional.

Taint

Magic is powerful but corrupting. Mortals invariably suffer a descent into chaos as they become enveloped in arcanism, the rapidity of which is governed only by the extent of their addiction. Demonic voices whisper in the ears of those that learn and cast spells, prodding them further down the dark road and skewing their disposition to commit unnatural acts. As this taint consumes them, they become increasingly detached – friend turns to foe, and demonic vengeance is unleashed upon any who would stand in the way of their practice.

Taint is an abstract measure of the extent to which a mortal has been corrupted by the use of magic. The effects are insidious, and may remain dormant until a critical moment. Because the GM adjudicates these effects, care must be taken not to use them as a weapon against player characters. Rather, taint is intended as a creative control on excessive magic use and a constant reminder as to magic's true demonic nature in Dark Legacies. For campaigns where a higher frequency of magic is desired or where role-playing is preferred for handling corruption, the effects described below can instead be used as a helpful guideline or ignored altogether. New taint effects can be added at the GM's discretion. Demons (and creatures that are a subtype of demon) are inherently corrupt and do not accrue or suffer from the effects of taint. Hybrids are humanoids despite their fiendish appearance and are as susceptible to the same depths of corruption as any other mortal race.

Becoming Tainted

A character accrues varying amounts of taint depending on the action taken. He gains 1 point any time he learns a spell, casts a spell (whether it is successful or not), or uses a demonic item's spell-like ability, regardless of the actual level of the spell in question. A character gains a quantity of taint equal to the number of qualities added to an item when creating a demonic item of power. A character that is possessed by a demon gains one point of taint per day that he is possessed. Certain other specific conditions may cause a character to accrue taint, such as corruption caused by the *prosthesis* spell, but taint cannot normally be inflicted upon another person.

An arcanist begins play with a quantity of taint equal to the number of spells he has learned (1 or 2).

Effects of Taint

Taint begins to affect a character when his total taint points compared to his current Wisdom score causes him to reach a taint threshold, as shown on Table 7-1: Taint Thresholds. Each time a character reaches a taint threshold, he gains a new taint effect by rolling against Table 7-2: Taint Effects and adding the threshold's effect modifier to the result (the higher the taint threshold, the greater the taint effect). If the effect can be acquired multiple times, as noted in its description, apply the greater effect as described; otherwise, reroll for a new effect.

If a character gains a new taint threshold (and therefore a new taint effect) as a result of a temporarily reduced Wisdom score, the associated effect disappears once his Wisdom is restored. His former threshold does, however, count against his highest taint threshold reached for purposes of determining recovery potential (see The Road To Recovery, below).

TABLE 7-1: TAINT THRESHOLDS

Taint Threshold	Total Taint Points	Effect Modifier	Taint Effect Save DC
1st	Wisdom × 2	0	12
2nd	Wisdom × 5	+1	13
3rd	Wisdom × 10	+2	14
4th	Wisdom × 15	+3	15
5th	Wisdom × 20	+4	16
6th	Wisdom × 30	+5	17

TABLE 7-2: TAINT EFFECTS

d20[1]	Failure Effect
1	None
2–4	Obsessive Behavior
5–6	Agitation
7–8	Paranoia
9–10	Reclusive
11–12	Depressive Addiction
13–14	Nightmares
15	Abyssal Slip
16	Component Fetish
17	Over-Protective
18	Slavering Dedication
19	Demonic Voices
20	Hunger For Knowledge
21	Careless Disregard
22	Hallucination
23+	Soul Drain

1 Add the threshold's effect modifier to this roll.

Most taint effects allow the character to make a Will save each time he would be affected; the save DC is dependant on the threshold in which the effect was acquired, as shown on Table 7-1: Taint Thresholds. When an effect manifests once

per day or several times per day, the GM should roll each time the trigger occurs (50% chance), to see if that is the occasion when it manifests. At the GM's discretion, a partial mood-setting effect may still occur if the save is successful. For instance, a save against the Component Fetish effect may result in lustful babbling over the potential components rather than their immediate retrieval, while a save against the Demonic Voices effect may result in the character hearing unintelligible whispers rather than clear dialogue.

Abyssal Slip

Once per day while speaking in a stressful situation, the character must make a Will save or inadvertently shout out a foul curse in the Abyssal tongue. The character slips once more per day each time this effect is acquired.

Agitation

The character becomes extremely agitated and obsessed with doing nothing but casting spells. He suffers a –5 penalty on all Concentration checks, except those made to cast a spell. If this effect is acquired twice, the penalty increases to –10. Reroll if it has already been acquired twice.

Careless Disregard

Once per day when in a combat situation, a character must make a Will save or succumb to the temptation of casting a spell that may have collateral damage effects upon his allies (such as *cascade of spikes* or *explode corpse*). This effect occurs once more per day each time it is acquired.

Component Fetish

Once per day, if the character encounters a situation where he might be able to retrieve a spell component (such as from a fallen enemy, an exotic plant, or as a result of a specific circumstance) he must make a Will save or immediately be compelled to retrieve the component, moving at maximum speed to the subject of his obsession. This effect occurs once more per day each time it is acquired.

Demonic Voices

Demonic voices whisper in the character's ears, casting doubt on what others say to him, and inciting him to behave erratically. Once per day when the character is in a tense situation, he must make a Will save or hear something that was not actually said. The GM should make a roll when the effect occurs, insinuating that an actual skill check had been made while actually rolling the character's Will save. For each additional time that this effect is acquired, the character is susceptible to hearing voices one more time per day. Demonic Voices may be combined with the Hallucination taint effect. The GM determines the exact nature of the voices and their effect on the game. Some examples of scenarios when voices may occur are described below.

Betrayal: The character is returning to the party campfire after gathering wood. The party is discussing the next day's plans, but the character instead hears them whispering about him in a conspiratorial tone.

Demonic Suggestion: A demonic entity is trapped or known to be hiding in a specific area. The character hears the voice of a child pleading to him from the same area, or whispered promises of power from the demon.

NPC Encounter: The character's party comes upon a group of soldiers, who speak to the party leader on the assumption that the party is law abiding and does not harbor any arcanists. The character instead hears the lead soldier accuse him of being a demon worshipper.

Depressive Addiction

The character succumbs to a deep depression that can only be alleviated through spellcasting. He suffers a −2 morale penalty on attack rolls, saving throws, ability checks, all skill checks except for Spellcraft, and weapon damage rolls. Each time he casts a spell, the depression recedes for 2d4 days from that point.

Hallucination

Demonic visions assail the character's eyes, betraying him as to what is real and what is not. Once per day when the character is in a tense situation, he must make a Will save or see something that does not actually exist. The GM should make a roll when the effect occurs, insinuating that an actual skill check had been made while actually rolling the character's Will save. For each additional time that this effect is acquired, the character is susceptible to experiencing hallucinations one more time per day. This effect may be combined with the Demonic Voices taint effect. The GM determines the exact nature of the hallucination and its effect on the game, but it is generally brief and related to magic or demons. Some examples of scenarios when hallucinations may occur are described below.

Back Alley Encounter: The character is making a deal with some smugglers for illicit demonic merchandise. As the deal nears to a close, the character "notices" a religious symbol on one of the rogues' daggers, identifying him as an ecclesiastic agent.

Treasure: The party comes upon a fork in a dark cavern and is undecided about which path to take. A demon is hiding down one path, pressed against the wall, but instead of spotting the demon, the character thinks he sees demonic glyphs marking a valuable spell.

Wilderness Path: The character is making his way down a wilderness path, from which he was specifically instructed not to veer. He spots an imaginary demon charging him from the distance, causing him to dash into the woods where real danger lurks.

Hunger For Knowledge

The character suffers a depressive effect similar to Depressive Addiction, except that the depression can only be alleviated through the learning of a new spell. While depressed, he suffers a −1 morale penalty on attack rolls, saving throws, ability checks, all skill checks except for Spellcraft, and weapon damage rolls. Each time he learns a new spell, the depression recedes for 1d4 weeks from that point.

Nightmares

The character is plagued by dark and twisted night terrors. Each night, he must make a Will save or be fatigued the next day. A fatigued character can neither run nor charge and takes a −2 penalty to Strength and Dexterity.

None

The character has miraculously managed to avert corruption.

Obsessive Behavior

The character develops some mundane obsessive-compulsive behavior or quirk related to magic. This may be innocuous, such as an eye twitch for a period following the casting of a spell, or disturbing, such as a need by the character to cut himself in order to concentrate while learning a spell.

Over-Protective

Any time someone makes a credible threat to confiscate or destroy magical materials belonging to the character (spellbooks, components, demonic items), he must make a Will save or immediately close to melee range and attack. He may make an additional Will save each round to regain control over his actions.

Paranoia

The character appears constantly agitated and afraid for his life. He suffers a −2 penalty on saves against fear effects.

Reclusive

The character shrinks away from society, abhorring the distraction of people and their petty lives. He suffers a −2 penalty to all Charisma-based skill checks. This penalty is increased by an additional −2 each time the effect is acquired.

Slavering Dedication

The character loses sight of any long-term goals he has except to advance as a spellcaster. He must select arcanist when he advances to the next level.

Soul Drain

The character suffers 1 point of permanent Wisdom drain, casting him deeper into the throes of corruption.

The Road to Recovery

If a character refrains from taking actions that would lead him farther down the road of corruption, he can achieve a moderate level of recovery, though the process is long and demanding. If he does not accrue any taint for an entire month, the character's taint total drops by 1 point. For each taint-free month thereafter, he loses one more point than the previous month. Thus, a character that does not accrue any taint for three months straight loses 6 points of taint: 1 point for the first month, 2 points for the second, and 3 for the third month. If he abstains for a full year, he recovers 78 points of taint. A character cannot recover more than 12 points of taint in any given month.

If a character's taint threshold drops as a result of recovery, the associated taint effect is eliminated. However, a character can never drop more than two taint thresholds beyond the maximum threshold he has reached, regardless of his current taint score. Thus, an active arcanist that reaches the 4th threshold of taint before deciding to quit his demonic obsession can never drop below the 2nd threshold, even if his current taint score would normally place him at a lower threshold. The effects of his 3rd and 4th threshold are negated but the effects of his 1st and 2nd threshold will remain with him until death. If he acquires enough taint to reach the 3rd or higher threshold again, he must roll for a new taint effect.

Taint Example

Petro Tillius is a capricious human arcanist, who, like many of his kind, finds security in the anonymity of megacity living. A job at a local factory provides him with enough money to eat, pay rent in a slum district, and guarantee membership dues to three distinct underground demon cults, where he leeches what secrets he can while paying lip service to Azrae. With a Wisdom score of 11 and a habit of experimenting on the homeless, he promptly accrues 22 points of taint and reaches the 1st taint threshold (Wisdom score of $11 \times 2 = 22$ points required). Petro's player rolls a 19 for the taint effect: Demonic Voices. Once per day, he must make a Will save (DC 12 for a 1st threshold effect) or succumb to presumably imaginary voices.

Several months and one more demon cult later, Petro reaches 55 points of taint, which is enough to take him to the 2nd taint threshold (Wisdom score of $11 \times 5 = 55$ points required). His player rolls a 14 for his second threshold effect; adding +1 for the 2nd threshold modifier gives a total of 15: Abyssal Slip. Petro is now subject to two taint effects per day: demonic voices from the 1st threshold (DC 12 to resist) and a strong urge to blurt out demonic curses from the 2nd threshold (DC 13 to resist).

By the end of the first year of his double life, Petro is still sitting at the 2nd taint threshold, but with a total of 90 points of taint after continuing his reckless spellcasting spree. After being tracked back to his seedy apartment by a crusader priest,

he successfully casts *deconstruct into chaos* against the intruder, reducing him to a gibbering mass. But in doing so, he suffers 3 points of temporary Wisdom damage from casting strain for a new Wisdom score of 8. Petro is now well over the taint total required to push him into the 3rd taint threshold (Wisdom score of $8 \times 10 = 80$ points required). His player rolls a 20 for his 3rd threshold effect; adding +2 for the 3rd threshold modifier gives a total of 22: Hallucination. Now, in addition to potentially hearing voices and spontaneously speaking Abyssal, he must make another Will save (DC 14 for a 3rd threshold effect) once per day or see things that are not really there.

Hustling from his compromised accommodations through a crowded market, Petro spots a religious procession coming his way through the crowd. He fails his Hallucination save and "sees" several members of the procession break off and run toward him. Failing to resist the Demonic Voices effect, he "hears" one of the priests speak his name to another of the priests. Convinced of the threat, Petro turns to run but instead plows into the midst of the deconstructed priest's party. Shocked, he fails his Will save against Abyssal Slip and blurts out an ugly curse in the demonic tongue. Though the party knows nothing of the horrid spell he recently used against their leader, the slip is enough to have Petro beaten, stripped, and sentenced to life in prison for crimes against the Faith.

One year later, removed from the tools of his trade, Petro's total taint drops to 13 (91 points – 78 points of recovery). Because his last spell pushed him into the 3rd taint threshold, however, he can never drop below the 1st threshold (two thresholds below the maximum reached) regardless of his actual taint total or Wisdom score. Thus, each day for the rest of the arcanist's miserable life inside a damp church dungeon, he must make a Will save (DC 12 for a 1st threshold effect) or hear demonic voices mocking his shivering, naked form from the shadows.

Possession

Though demons wear physical forms, these forms are only shells for a soul constructed of dark magical energy. When the shell is cracked, the demonic sentience within has the unique ability to possess another creature's body, consuming it entirely. The circumstances leading up to such possessions are rare and many demons would rather be delivered back to the Abyss than become trapped in a mortal body, but those that take pleasure from such opportunities are a horror upon the Earth. While constrained by the physical limitations of its host body, the demon is afforded considerable anonymity. This, combined with the ability to possess another creature once the host body dies, makes such demons extremely difficult to expose and to destroy.

Becoming Possessed

A demon can possess any living creature, excluding another demon or creature that is a subtype of demon. This can occur as a result of a particularly disastrous spellcasting failure, by way of an intentional binding of a deconstructed demon into a creature, or when a formerly possessing demon seeks a new host after being exorcized from its previous one or upon that host's death. In any case, the demon must be in a state of pure magical energy; a demon that exists in a physical state cannot possess a creature by any direct means. Likewise, a demon that is killed while in its natural physical form is destroyed completely. A demonic spirit that has not yet possessed a creature or that is in the process of attempting to possess a creature cannot affect the world in any palpable way and is likewise immune to all attacks, spells, and effects. It is invisible unless it wants to be seen, but there are often environmental consequences of its presence and associated ambient effects.

When a demon violates a creature's body in a possession attempt, a violent struggle for control over the creature's body ensues. The demon must spend 1d4 rounds in order to gain control. The intended host is effectively helpless for the duration, subject to seizures and barking out curses in the Abyssal tongue. At the end of this battle of wills, the GM makes a Will save for the creature (DC 10 + ½ demon's HD + demon's Cha modifier). If the Will save is successful or the host body is killed during the possession attempt, the demon is rebuffed and cast back into the Abyss. If the save fails, the creature is immediately possessed. The only physical indicator of possession is a brief transition, wherein the host creature's eyes grow dim as the soul within recedes, followed by a brief glow of demonic presence before returning to normal. Noticing this transition requires a successful DC 25 Spot check within 5 feet of the possessed creature. The GM may permit the character to continue acting normally for a time, only revealing the demon at a critical moment, at which point the possession takes effect.

Effects of Possession

Once a creature is possessed, it loses all control over its own actions; it becomes a silent observer, imprisoned within a body that now belongs to the demon. The demon acts as though it is the host in all regards during this time, but it uses its own Hit Dice and Will save when affected by a spell or effect that specifically attempts to extricate it from the host (such as exorcism or the *dismiss demon* spell). The type of the possessed creature effectively changes to demon, thus it does not experience spell failure effects and is affected by spells and effects that specifically target demons, rather than by those that target the host creature's type. The demon retains its demonic damage resistance and spell knowledge, and can also use its own spell-like abilities, during which the host body undergoes obviously unnatural effects, such as levitation, a flaming aura, glowing eyes, etc.

A measure of the demon's strength is also imparted onto the host, thus the demon averages its physical ability scores (Strength, Dexterity, and Constitution) with those of the host while retaining its own mental ability scores (Intelligence, Wisdom, and Charisma). It otherwise has all of the abilities of the host creature, including modes of movement and natural armor (if any). The demon not only has free reign over the creature's body, but it knows everything that the creature knows. It can recall facts and memories and can use any of the host's class features, skills, feats, spells, spell-like abilities, and supernatural abilities that are compatible with its ability scores.

Neither the demon nor the host gain experience points for the duration of the possession. While possessed, the host body ages at half its normal rate. However, in addition to accruing taint for any of the demon's actions that would generate taint if the creature performed them itself, a possessed creature accrues 1 additional point of taint per day that it is possessed and also gains 1 point of taint any time the demon uses one of its spell-like abilities. This taint only takes effect while the possessing demon is suppressed or after it is expelled completely. Thus, a creature that is freed from possession after being under the control of a demon for an extended period of time is never the same regardless of what their appearance may indicate. Such a creature may, in fact, be so disturbed that it still believes itself to be possessed, acting in all regards as though a demon controls its actions long after the demon is gone – the potential for dementia is limitless.

Terminating a Possession

Once bound into a mortal body, a demon cannot escape it except through the death of the host or by being forcibly removed by exorcism or magic, as described below.

If a possessing demon is dealt a killing blow with a holy weapon, its essence is destroyed utterly, just as though it was killed in its natural form. If the host body dies by any other means or if the demon is exorcized by a priest's censure effect (page 46), the demon is cast out from its host body but can attempt to possess another creature on its next turn. The new host must be no farther from the deceased host than 5 feet per HD of the demon. If this possession attempt fails or if the demon foregoes the attempt, it is pulled back into the Abyss. If the demon was expelled by a priest's censure, its effective Hit Dice is reduced by an amount equal to half the priest's level (to a minimum of 1 HD) for purposes of calculating the distance it can travel to make the attempt and the Will save DC for that attempt.

If a demon does manage to possess another creature after the first host body dies or after being exorcized, it does so in a weakened state – its hit points are only 10% of its normal total, before Constitution modifiers. This amount does not decrease further if the demon jumps from one dead host to the next, however, thus killing a demon's host is not always the most effective means of dealing with it; rather, forcing the demon to attempt (and hopefully fail) to possess a strong-willed character or pacification of the host for future exorcism or extraction via magic are generally a better strategy. Because a possessing demon is still affected by spells that target demons, it can be extricated by the casting of certain

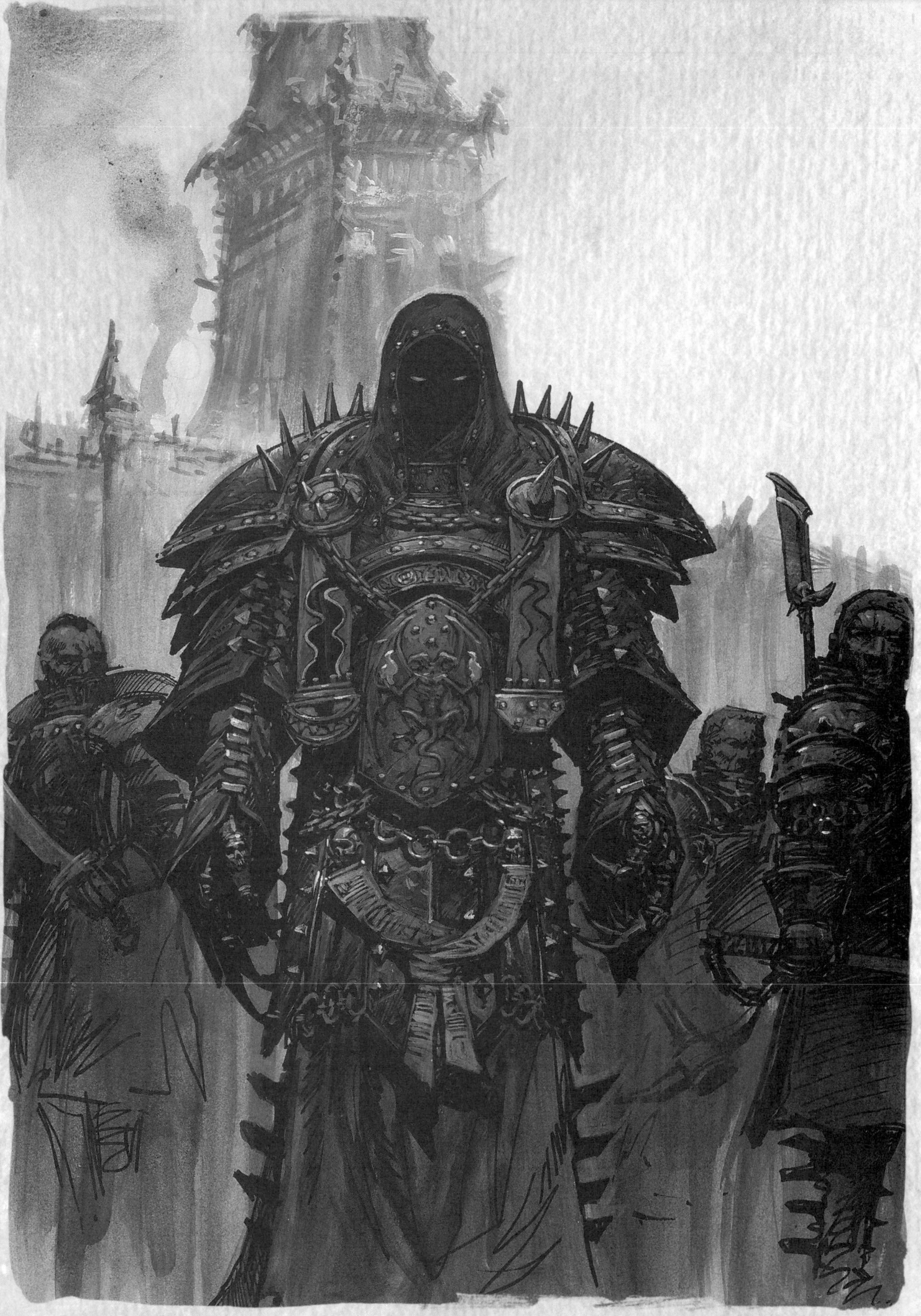

spells – *dismiss demon* (page 118) will rip the demon out of the host and cast it into the Abyss, while *deconstruct into spell form* (page 116) draws the demon out of the body and into the form of a spell.

A demon may also negotiate for voluntary release form a host body that it has tired of or that has grown old. Demons that spend an extended period of time in a mortal body may become enamored of mortal civilization, and thus wish to carry on in such a form rather than reverting to a demonic manifestation or returning to the Abyss. Killing its own host body is dangerous, as there is no guarantee for the demon that it will successfully possess another host. In order to be assured success, it is likely to jump from one demon cult to the next, seducing worshippers into voluntarily donating their body. The sacrifice of the old host body usually takes the form of a high ritual, rife with demonic trappings and dark incantations.

If the demon wishes to regain its natural physical form, its only option is to negotiate with an arcanist. By being deconstructed with *deconstruct into spell form*, then having the resulting *deconstructed demon* spell destroyed or cast, it manifests as a true demon. Regardless of what reward is promised, however, an arcanist is just as likely to break his promise and save the deconstructed demon for binding into a demonic item of power. Thus, a demon never enters into such a bargain without sufficient living or material collateral.

Possession Example

Sergi-Ishmane Gurkin, an infamous dwerof arcanist exiled from Dwer Zotha, has attracted the attention of the Under Matriarch in Nalterei, Sarlat, after corrupting a number of her priestesses. For the last two months, Dilectate Dielle Bask, a 16th-level priestess and Daughter of Beyella, has pursued him across the wilderness and from city to city. Initially amused, Sergi eventually grows tired of the game and decides to destroy the witchhunter. He retreats to a nondescript flat in the laborer district of Montrey, where he prepares to cast *creeping tumors* upon her.

Having previously acquired a vial of urine from her water closet by way of an enemy of Bask's within the priesthood, and already in possession of a beautiful jeweled skull and a preserved wedge of cancerous flesh, Sergi begins the incantation. His Spellcraft check result for the spell is 27, 19 short of the 6th-level spell's DC of 46. Despite the relative calm of his surroundings and his consummate preparation, the dwerof's invocations falter, tumbling into one mistake after another. As the spell completes, its energy surges out of control.

Sergi's player rolls a 96 for the spell failure effect, modified by the failure threshold of 19 (Spellcraft DC of 46 – Spellcraft check result of 27) for a final result of 115: possession. A deep chill enters the room, instantly casting a frost over the musty furniture and causing the apartment windows to explode outward. The dwerof feels a sentience emerge from the demonic energy coursing through his body, but before he can cry out in horror, the battle for his soul commences. Since Sergi was casting a 6th-level spell, the possessing demon has 12 HD, so he must make a Will save against DC 20 (DC 10 + half demon's HD + demon's Cha modifier of +4) or be possessed. Sergi's player rolls a 3 and is possessed; his eyes fade as the demon Vesellux takes control.

For the next month, Vesellux terrorizes the slums of Montrey, making no attempt to conceal its demonic nature. Following up on reports of brutal eviscerations and unchecked magic use, Dilectate Bask and a holy retinue of repeater-armed soldiers finally track the demon to the port city and corner it. Calling on the Voice, the priestess unleashes a resonating censure, invoking the name of Beyella against the possessing demon. Vesellux rolls a 12 on its Will save, failing against the Voice's save DC of 21 (10 + half priest's level + priest's Cha modifier of 3). An ungodly scream erupts from Sergi's mouth as the demon is ripped out.

On the demon's turn, it chooses to attempt to possess the very priest that exorcized it rather than concede defeat. The witchhunter suddenly breaks into violent convulsions, spewing out vile heresies against the Matriarch Beyella. But the censure reduced the demon's effective Hit Dice to 4 (original HD 12, minus half of priest's level of 16) so she must make a Will save against only DC 16 (10 + half demon's effective HD + demon's Cha modifier of 4) to resist the weakened demon. She rolls a 19 – Vesellux screeches, truly defeated, and is pulled back into the Abyss.

Meanwhile, the shuddering dwerof twitches erratically, his already corrupt mind suddenly bearing the brunt of a month's long possession. Dilectate Diella Bask, witchhunter of Beyella Divinity, points a shaky finger at her enemy, enraged by the chaos he has inflicted. As Sergi finally eeks out a word of awkward thanks, Bask commands her repeater squadron to fire...

Chapter 8: Adventuring

"I remember that night on the old road to Nowac Selna. You know, it could've been day, but who can tell when the air is choked with fog as black as a demon's heart. I was surrounded by creatures that were dead yet walked. Their eye sockets were empty, the sight of them stealing what was left of my breath. I remember the sound of my own screams and splashes of ice-cold blood on my face as I flailed about desperately with my spiker. The rest is a blur, days of running blending into one another until I had floundered my way back to the Crawl. Are there treasures to be had in the dark corners of the Earth? I'm sure of it. Just make sure you take an army with you when you go looking for them."

— Bradek Hirsh, ex-adventurer

With a reprieve from all out war and an uneasy calm before the new millennium, adventure and exploration are rampant upon the Earth. Clandestine wars are fought within civilized domains, as borders continue to shift and secret alliances are made. Parties of infinitely variable allegiances battle for possession of lost knowledge and artifacts, secreted away in each other's strongholds and in demon-infested lands. Races previously isolated from one another converge upon human megacities, each of which is a microcosm of politics and conflict. And brave men and women from all callings venture to the unknown edges of the world – the last frontier before the Abyss – to discover ancient secrets and unravel the mysteries of the past.

This chapter contains information and advice regarding adventuring in a DARK LEGACIES campaign, including hints on party allegiance and composition, traversing the contested and afflicted territories of post-Reversion Earth, and surviving encounters in a low-magic world.

Allegiances

The adventuring lifestyle attracts those who possess a strong sense of independence, enamored of a life free of commitment to an external interest. Still, for all the adventurers who claim such absolute freedom, there are as many whose very nature necessitates aligning with an organization or who find themselves pulled into one despite their best intentions. These allegiances invariably factor into a character's motivations, whether he explicitly acts to fulfill the mandates of his allied organization as a dedicated functionary or merely leverages it as a launch point for his own ambitions. They can also be a boon to adventurers in times of need or, at the very least, a valuable source of contacts and information. Though adventuring parties usually share a common cause, all party members need not defer to the same organizational authorities – former enemies can easily become allies with a single edict or recognition of similar goals between organizations, and the needs of the present regularly displace long-term agendas, if only for a short while. Typical organizations or affiliations with which an adventurer may align are described below.

Mercenary Companies

Mercenary companies are organizations of adventurers, managed by a central figure or committee that accepts contracts from employers on behalf of the company and delegates jobs to its members. Employers generally prefer mercenary companies to independent parties of adventurers, as the considerable resources of a company (i.e. a healthy supply of new adventurers should the previous parties fall) means that the employer can be given a reasonable guarantee of completion.

Mercenary companies are present in every major city, with the larger ones spread out across many cities or even extending into more than one country. Fighter guilds, escort services, exploratory specialists, and auxiliary militias are all types of mercenary companies, each with their own specialty and allegiance. While most mercenary companies are officially neutral, accepting contracts from anyone and everyone, their impartiality is as often a façade that conceals secret alliances with religious, demonic, or arcanist interests. Others are permanent extensions of one specific political or religious power – a trend that has grown since the end of the Kingdoms Wars, as governments seek to reinforce exhausted armies with sellswords.

By paying membership dues to a mercenary company – 10 gp to 100 gp per month, depending on the company's notoriety – an adventurer gains access to rumors, information, and opportunities to bid for specific jobs. Some companies also offer lodging and a measure of protection. When an adventurer and his party complete a job, they are generally paid a set fee, which in turn is a small percentage of the actual fee paid to the mercenary company. The party may also be a required to submit a portion of wealth or items acquired during the completion of an assigned task back to the company.

The extent to which a mercenary company enforces exclusive membership varies with the company itself. Small companies are usually understanding of their own regional limitations, and swap members constantly. Large companies with multiple branches often create elaborate contractual agreements with their members, restricting them from working for another company, and use branding and tattooing to ward them against courting from the competition. In the event of a violation, the disciplinary reach of these companies can be considerable, extending through other associated organizations and widely dispersed member networks to their mark.

Military Service

Soldiers and combat-savvy adventurers can spend their entire lives in military service, whether as part of a national army, a private militia, or as permanent employees of a mercenary company attached to a political body. The freedoms accorded to characters in military service are not as great as those to unaligned mercenaries or independents, but there are still numerous opportunities for adventure: large-scale wars have been replaced by small-scale skirmishes and clandestine missions, ideally suited to adventurers with diverse talents. While undertaking these missions, such characters can explore new and afflicted territories, encounter new races, and embark upon constant side-adventures while keeping in the service of king and country. Affiliation with a military institution usually means that an adventurer has a warm bed waiting for him when he returns home, assuming he does not neglect his responsibilities. If his personal ambitions drive him too far from these duties, he is more likely to be welcomed by far less inviting accommodations in a dungeon or upon the stand of a military tribunal.

Religious Affiliation

Religious institutions have the greatest reach of any organizations on Earth. They shape the will of the Corelands nations and court the souls of the Unbidden in the Eastern Ridge and beyond, where agents of the Faith act as missionaries and crusaders. All priests – and to a lesser extent, all lay functionaries of a church – are tightly bound to their respective denomination, and must abide by the regulations set forth therein. Paranoid high councils keep a tight leash on their priesthood, lest a member of the clergy fall from the path and weaken his institution in so doing. Regardless of these hierarchal controls, however, the considerable distance that most adventuring priests and church functionaries travel from their authorities grants a good measure of freedom. Additionally, the existence of countless disputing factions within their denomination permits a great deal of personal interpretation as regards the execution of their duties. A religious agent may operate within these gray areas or he may spend his life undertaking quests for his church, accepting salary and status as a reward. The extent to which he can ultimately leverage the support of his institution in times of need is generally commensurate with his own dedication to it.

Secret Societies

The world is riddled with secret societies, from the benign to the truly insidious: thieves' guilds, arcanist cabals, demon cults, political manipulators, and all manner of fringe groups fill the cracks of civilization. Regardless of whether allegiance to such a society is motivated by a genuine interest in its goals or simply as a means of fulfilling personal ambitions, a character that allies with shadowy institutions is both empowered and endangered by his membership. Most benefits of such a relationship arise out of the society's access to restricted information and goods, on account of their own criminal activity or associations. Danger arises when a character's allegiances are exposed, as secret societies invariably have many more enemies than they do friends and generally exist in violation of local or regional law. The discretion necessitated by membership in a secret society makes it more common for a single character rather than his entire party to have such an allegiance. This character may leverage his unique resources to the party's favor, diverting suspicion with eloquent bluffs and fronts provided by the society. In cases where he is specifically acting on behalf of his benefactors, a character may also use these resources as a means to manipulate the rest of his party to a higher goal.

Party Make-Up

In addition to the multitude of possible allegiances, an adventuring party is viewed and operates differently depending on its racial and class make-up. Suggestions on playing in both unified and diverse groups are detailed below.

Mixing Races

The majority of adventurers are human, pouring out from the Corelands and the Eastern Ridge to explore the mysteries of the world. There is no shortage, however, of nonhuman adventurers, breaking away from their isolationist homelands or, in the case of those races without a homeland, roving constantly in the absence of a meaningful existence. While most adventuring parties will consist entirely of humans, it is feasible for mixed races to find a common cause if not true fellowship. Most mixed parties can be created along geographic lines: a party consisting of briggs or novags likely originates in the east, while a party of dwerofs, eldrin, or even assar might originate in the western reaches of civilization.

Because bigotry is more common than tolerance in the realms of Dark Legacies, playing in a mixed race party poses both challenges and interesting opportunities for roleplaying. Incorporating a hybrid into a party, for instance, may have all the characters in that party branded as demon sympathizers in certain quarters, leading to a campaign of flight from inquisitors or other religious authorities. The internal party politics, as well, should not be ignored when mixing races, especially those that have a traditionally antagonistic view of one another. The friction created by these situations can create interesting scenarios that might be impossible within parties consisting of only humans.

Mixing Classes

Just as mixing races can prove interesting, mixing classes that might appear incompatible on the surface can produce great party dynamics. The most obvious example of this is the mixing of priests with arcanists, who by definition are sworn enemies. Though such combinations are unorthodox, factional variances within the priesthood, ties to secret organizations that override a character's official vows of allegiance, or special edicts enacted by a character's superior in unique circumstances can allow such pairings. The ultimate outcome depends on each character's conviction and the extent to which their fundamental values may inevitably clash.

Travel

Though Azrae's hordes have scattered and the world is not caught in the terrible throes of war, the Earth remains a dangerous place to explore. Its inhabitants crowd together in populous megacities, which in turn are surrounded by tight networks of farms, small towns, and well-traveled roads. Commoners generally keep to these locales, traveling only when necessary and rarely alone. Between and beyond these bastions of civilization are long stretches of wilderness, old highways, and dark rivers. These routes are plagued by demons, bandits, and the ungodly detritus of horrific wars, and are generally traveled only by adventurers, heavily armed trade caravans, and by political and religious envoys.

waiting in ambush near a well-traveled road than they are to pounce upon adventurers navigating wild terrain.

Still, venturing outside of an established route can be far more dangerous than risking exposure on proper roads, as it is in wild terrain where lurkers and far worse creatures lie in wait. With the dissolution of the demon horde following the Great War, each wild place has become a potential hunting ground for creatures of the Abyss, and once-natural creatures that have been tainted by their presence. This danger grows as adventurers explore beyond the borders of civilized lands.

Compounding all these hazards is the darkness itself; devoid of a moon to light the way, post-Reversion Earth becomes as black as coal once the sun sets. The infinite rows of lanterns that illuminate the streets of any given town or megacity are absent in the wilderness, making travel by night incredibly dangerous. Undertaking an adventure without a sufficient supply of light sources is suicide, as demons can see their prey just fine in the darkness.

Modes of Transportation

While many adventurers choose to travel by foot, traversing long distances is best accomplished by faster means. On land, horses and horse-driven carriages are still the most common mode of transport. Less common are steam-driven armored transports: gargantuan near-indestructible personnel carriers that crawl along the ground on steel wheels, belching thick smoke and the pained screeching of their motion. These transports exist only in the Corelands, and are used sparingly between major cities by those that can afford the considerable hiring and refueling costs. When a steam transport is dispatched, it is usually guarded by a retinue of soldiers and priests or by a dedicated escort company, and further accompanied by long caravans of commercial traffic that take advantage of the security offered. When such convoys are attacked, a battered but intact armored transport is usually the only vehicle to arrive at its destination. But even these wonders of technology are not immune from the dangers of the road – the rusting carcasses of destroyed transports can be found near the interior borders of the Corelands, torn open by incendiaries or powerful demons, and stained with the caked blood of their former occupants.

Hazards

There are a multitude of dangers awaiting adventurers that venture out of the safety of city walls. Even within the Corelands interior, home to the highest density of towns and cities, travel can be deadly. Most travelers coordinate with one another so that they can venture out in large groups for mutual protection, as it is not uncommon for small caravans to come under attack. Roads and charted rivers are the safest means of travel, since they are the most likely place to encounter likeminded souls and to trade for goods with merchant caravans. This same advantage can turn to a disadvantage, however, if a character or party wishes to evade notice, whether from authorities or competing parties. Likewise, bandits and roving gangs of barbarians are more likely to be

Numerous roads line the way between cities in the Corelands but they disappear as the human domain gives way. The most impressive of these roads are the unfinished branches of the Kingsroad, an ambitious highway system that was initiated during the reign of the Ilfernac Empire but ultimately abandoned. It was designed as an international route for armored transports, lined with refueling stations at regular intervals, but few of these outposts remain and the highway falls into disarray as it nears each country's border. Consequently, armored transports, which are dependent on the broad paved routes, are limited to travel within their own country. The only roads out of the central continent lead to Nowac Selna in damned Novdy Ottor, where constant trade traffic once traveled between human and novag territories. Roads leading from southern Ilfernac into Illgoth and those running from eastern Precaea south into Novdy Ottor are not man-made constructs at all. Rather, they are the permanent scars of Azrae's demon horde, which pounded the wide tracts into the Earth during the Great War.

In addition to travel on land, both conventional and steam-driven boats are commonly used by large trading companies and for military missions. Their speed is generally superior to any form of land travel but they also journey through wilder terrains and are less defensible. Many cities are located upon rivers, choked with traffic and sewage. Few boats, however, travel upon the ocean. The sight of the Abyss on the horizon is too much for most sailors to bear, as are the unnatural beasts that lurk in the dark waters on the edge of the world. The ancient hulls of the novag war fleet sit broken on the southern shores of Novdy Ottor, a reminder of the futility of trying to escape Earth's coastline.

Encounters

DARK LEGACIES can be a lethal campaign setting, on account of lower frequency of magic, less healing than is found in the d20 core rules, and supplemental rules that make combat a more dangerous experience. For these reasons, wading into battle is not always the best way of handling a situation, and can easily result in maiming or death. Stealth and discretion are key, even at higher levels, and especially when encountering demonic and other non-humanoid foes with supernatural powers. In a world where powerful demons can annihilate even the strongest party, meeting an adventure or campaign goal is most easily achieved through investigation and exploration rather than direct conflict.

Essential Skills

Most character classes in DARK LEGACIES have a large number of skill points. These should be applied not only to conventional skills that will help the character overcome physical barriers, but also to skills that can assist him with negotiation, investigation, and knowledge of one's adversaries. Bluff and Intimidation can be lifesavers, allowing a character to convince his enemies that he is a threat and thereby defeat them without needing to lift a finger; this is especially relevant in sensitive situations where a priest or arcanist wishes to leverage his abilities without actually using them. Diplomacy can be useful not only against the multitude of political and religious adversaries that will be encountered throughout a DARK LEGACIES campaign, but it may be a character's last hope of convincing demonic enemies to parlay rather than destroy him outright. The Gather Information skill should be used a great deal, as a means of acquiring valuable information indirectly before encroaching upon a hostile location where scouting or direct infiltration might be detected. Knowledge skills can provide valuable insight in a multitude of situations, from recognizing the symbol of a demonic cult to avoiding a catastrophic faux pas by addressing an aristocrat with his proper title. And lastly, the Sense Motive skill is an investigator's best friend in the absence of detection spells.

Combat Tactics

When combat is unavoidable, it should be approached carefully. DARK LEGACIES promotes consequences for every action in an effort to exhilarate players with tough challenges and real risk – and battle is no exception. Tactics are extremely important, especially when facing superior numbers. Rather than charging unsupported into combat, care should be taken to not allow yourself to become flanked.

If a combat situation offers no avenue of retreat, it is often better to avoid it altogether, as the likelihood of being healed during combat is rare, especially when cut off from the touch of a priest's Healing Voice or an arcanist's *vitality leech*. Running away is often the best strategy in DARK LEGACIES, as extremely powerful foes exist and they rarely permit weaker characters to encroach upon their territory unchecked. Most goals can be achieved through investigation and strategic avoidance of one's foes rather than direct confrontation.

Regardless of your character level, if you want to defeat an army in DARK LEGACIES, you're going to need an army of your own; at least one member of the party should obtain the Leadership feat as early as possible, so that cohorts and hirelings can be leveraged. More often than not, a party will have additional contacts in the form of a parish connected to the party priest, a powerful cult of which the party arcanist is a member, or a mercenary company that one or more of the party's combatants are allied – these contacts are as valuable a resource as the party's most exotic items.

OPEN GAME LICENSE Version 1.0a

The following text is the property of Wizards of the Coast, Inc. and is Copyright 2000 Wizards of the Coast, Inc ("Wizards"). All Rights Reserved.

1. Definitions: (a)"Contributors" means the copyright and/or trademark owners who have contributed Open Game Content; (b)"Derivative Material" means copyrighted material including derivative works and translations (including into other computer languages), potation, modification, correction, addition, extension, upgrade, improvement, compilation, abridgment or other form in which an existing work may be recast, transformed or adapted; (c) "Distribute" means to reproduce, license, rent, lease, sell, broadcast, publicly display, transmit or otherwise distribute; (d)"Open Game Content" means the game mechanic and includes the methods, procedures, processes and routines to the extent such content does not embody the Product Identity and is an enhancement over the prior art and any additional content clearly identified as Open Game Content by the Contributor, and means any work covered by this License, including translations and derivative works under copyright law, but specifically excludes Product Identity. (e) "Product Identity" means product and product line names, logos and identifying marks including trade dress; artifacts; creatures characters; stories, storylines, plots, thematic elements, dialogue, incidents, language, artwork, symbols, designs, depictions, likenesses, formats, poses, concepts, themes and graphic, photographic and other visual or audio representations; names and descriptions of characters, spells, enchantments, personalities, teams, personas, likenesses and special abilities; places, locations, environments, creatures, equipment, magical or supernatural abilities or effects, logos, symbols, or graphic designs; and any other trademark or registered trademark clearly identified as Product identity by the owner of the Product Identity, and which specifically excludes the Open Game Content; (f) "Trademark" means the logos, names, mark, sign, motto, designs that are used by a Contributor to identify itself or its products or the associated products contributed to the Open Game License by the Contributor (g) "Use", "Used" or "Using" means to use, Distribute, copy, edit, format, modify, translate and otherwise create Derivative Material of Open Game Content. (h) "You" or "Your" means the licensee in terms of this agreement.

2. The License: This License applies to any Open Game Content that contains a notice indicating that the Open Game Content may only be Used under and in terms of this License. You must affix such a notice to any Open Game Content that you Use. No terms may be added to or subtracted from this License except as described by the License itself. No other terms or conditions may be applied to any Open Game Content distributed using this License.

3. Offer and Acceptance: By Using the Open Game Content You indicate Your acceptance of the terms of this License.

4. Grant and Consideration: In consideration for agreeing to use this License, the Contributors grant You a perpetual, worldwide, royalty-free, non-exclusive license with the exact terms of this License to Use, the Open Game Content.

5. Representation of Authority to Contribute: If You are contributing original material as Open Game Content, You represent that Your Contributions are Your original creation and/or You have sufficient rights to grant the rights conveyed by this License.

6. Notice of License Copyright: You must update the COPYRIGHT NOTICE portion of this License to include the exact text of the COPYRIGHT NOTICE of any Open Game Content You are copying, modifying or distributing, and You must add the title, the copyright date, and the copyright holder's name to the COPYRIGHT NOTICE of any original Open Game Content you Distribute.

7. Use of Product Identity: You agree not to Use any Product Identity, including as an indication as to compatibility, except as expressly licensed in another, independent Agreement with the owner of each element of that Product Identity. You agree not to indicate compatibility or co-adaptability with any Trademark or Registered Trademark in conjunction with a work containing Open Game Content except as expressly licensed in another, independent Agreement with the owner of such Trademark or Registered Trademark. The use of any Product Identity in Open Game Content does not constitute a challenge to the ownership of that Product Identity. The owner of any Product Identity used in Open Game Content shall retain all rights, title and interest in and to that Product Identity.

8. Identification: If you distribute Open Game Content You must clearly indicate which portions of the work that you are distributing are Open Game Content.

9. Updating the License: Wizards or its designated Agents may publish updated versions of this License. You may use any authorized version of this License to copy, modify and distribute any Open Game Content originally distributed under any version of this License.

10. Copy of this License: You MUST include a copy of this License with every copy of the Open Game Content You Distribute.

11. Use of Contributor Credits: You may not market or advertise the Open Game Content using the name of any Contributor unless You have written permission from the Contributor to do so.

12. Inability to Comply: If it is impossible for You to comply with any of the terms of this License with respect to some or all of the Open Game Content due to statute, judicial order, or governmental regulation then You may not Use any Open Game Material so affected.

13. Termination: This License will terminate automatically if You fail to comply with all terms herein and fail to cure such breach within 30 days of becoming aware of the breach. All sublicenses shall survive the termination of this License.

14. Reformation: If any provision of this License is held to be unenforceable, such provision shall be reformed only to the extent necessary to make it enforceable.

15. COPYRIGHT NOTICE: Open Game License v 1.0 Copyright 2000, Wizards of the Coast, Inc.

System Reference Document, Copyright 2000, Wizards of the Coast, Inc.; Authors Jonathan Tweet, Monte Cook, Skip Williams, based on original material by E. Gary Gygax and Dave Arneson.

Dark Legacies: Player's Guide, Copyright 2004, Red Spire Press, Inc.; Author Yuval Kordov.

Product Identity: The following items are hereby designated as Product Identity, pursuant to section 1(e) of the Open Game License: the DARK LEGACIES name, logo, and trademark, the graphic design and trade dress of this book and all other products in the DARK LEGACIES line, illustrations, maps, and any elements of the game setting, including but not limited to symbols, capitalized names (excluding spell names, which are Open Content), spell components and casting processes, locations, characters, stories, descriptions, background, historic events, organizations, religious elements, and themes. The above Product Identity is copyright 2004 Red Spire Press, Inc., and is not Open Game Content.

Open Content: The following items are hereby designated as Open Content. All other items are designated as Product Identity and are copyright 2004 Red Spire Press, Inc.

Chapter 1: All race mechanics including the name of each race.

Chapter 2: All class mechanics including the name of each class, with the exception of the priest in its entirety, which is Product Identity.

Chapter 3: All skills and feats, excepting those that relate specifically to the priest class.

Chapter 4: All equipment mechanics including the name of each piece of equipment.

Chapter 6: All mechanics relating to the magic system in DARK LEGACIES and all spell mechanics and spell names.

Chapter 7: All new combat mechanics.

Please contact us if you have questions or special requests regarding the use of DARK LEGACIES open content or product identity.